PRAISES FOR ALAN BAIJER RUSSO

"Found! An unexpected manuscript from one of the central writers of the legendary Wichita Vortex. In this almost disappeared find, *State Line*, Russo's uncompromising search for the world of his visions flows on and into the very core of being alive in any generation. Within these pages, a soul unbound hails us!"

MAUREEN OWEN

Poet & Editor

"A STORYBOOK LIKE NO OTHER.
An engaging (shocking) great read."

CHARLIE PLYMELL

Poet, Novelist, and Publisher

"I think it's really sweet how so many are caring about Alan Russo's writings now. His writing has gone from Ozymandias to Wilde in one posthumous lifetime: Mad, bad, and dangerous to know—again. Yes to Alan Russo."

JAMES GRAUERHOLZ

Bibliographer and Literary Executor of the William S. Burroughs Estate

"An important work. Especially now, when authentic is so needed. Russo recognizes his friends being his heroes—they get him through— and it's clear he does the same for them. His prose and poems play out curious, passionate, sensitive and hot for whackshit-crazy. His honesty makes clever and intellectual writing more false than ever."

BENITO VILA

Contributor to PleaseKillMe.com and
Editor of *Of Myth & Men*, by Charles Plymell

"This nearly three hundred pages of Alan Russo's *State Line* give eloquent proof to his wide-ranging abilities expressing his genuine vital perceptions in both poetry and prose."

GERD STERN

Poet and Multimedia Artist

"I met Alan Russo in San Francisco 1960. We bonded fast and remained close. Alan's humor and his sense of the absurd permeate his writing. I'm hopeful that *State Line* gets his readily accessible and fascinating narratives out to the wider readership they deserve."

MICHAEL LEWIS

Friend, Writer, and Survivor

"Alan Russo helped me in my move from Wichita Kansas to San Francisco late summer 1959. Knowing Alan from there, I found the book, *State Line*, very well organized. The result, put together from Alan's poems and journal writings, is amazingly coherent. It was that period between the beatniks and the hippies, full of illusions and delusions, and Alan was the tour guide. A lot of this and more is captured in his *State Line*."

BETH PEWTHER

Active San Francisco Artist

ALAN BÄTJER RUSSO

STATE LINE

COLLECTED POEMS AND OTHER WRITINGS

ROSACE
Publications

Published by Rosace Publications
www.rosacepublications.com

Book Design: Astra Beck
Editors: Dion Wright, Robert Dumont, and Astra Beck
Assistant Editor: Augie Catarella

Rosace Publications would like to thank the persons and
locations listed below for supplying and granting permission
to use the following material in this book:

Cover photograph of Alan Russo, age 17, Wichita, Kansas, 1956, and
young Alan Russo (pp. 115) provided by Dr. E. Kip Hensley

Pluto photograph courtesy of NASA, Johns Hopkins U. APL,
and SwRI photograph (pp. viii)

Photographs of Jane "Chipmunk" Lewis, (pp. xxxv) and sculpture
of Alan Russo (pp. 70) provided by Dion Wright

City Lights photograph courtesy of the Allen Ginsberg Photograph Collection
and Department of Special Collections, Stanford University Libraries
MSS Photo 0450, Series 1, box 1, folder 15 (pp. 1)

Sunflower Literary Review and Mikrokosmos, copies provided by
Mary Nelson, Special Collections and University Archives Librarian
at Wichita State University Libraries (pp. 2 & 12)

The Poet's Corner [#1] copy provided by Stuart A. Rose Manuscript,
Archives, and Rare Book Library at Emory University
(Raymond Danowski Poetry Library) (pp. 10)

The Poet's Corner #2, copy provided by Special Collections Library
at Pittsburg State University (pp. 16)

The Locked Man, copy provided by Department of Special Collections and
University Archives at McFarlin Library of University of Tulsa (pp. 18)

NOW and NOW NOW, copies provided by Independent Voices Collection
at Memorial Library, University of Wisconsin-Madison (pp. 24 & 28)

Cataloging-in-Publication Data is available from the Library of Congress

Printed in the United States of America
Library of Congress Control Number: 2021903122
Paperback ISBN 978-0-9997777-2-5
First Edition, July 2021

ACKNOWLEDGMENTS

Rosace Publications would like to thank and honor
the following who helped bring this book to life:

James Bearden, Johanna Beck,
Beth Pewther nee Branaman, Andy Brown,
Jean Meyer Goyer, Casey Huber, Michael Lewis,
Theresa Naman, Dr. E. Kip Hensley, Daren Hensley,
and (in memoriam) Terry Russo Hensley.

Dear David,

Took your Tarantula thinking it was mine. Heard from
Howard you were through Santa Barbara. Did you see Jean?
Whats happening? I havent been in tough with anyone out
there. I waited to write to you till I was ready to leave
to avoid telling you what a sad trap I was in here. But
I finally got a job saved up some money and am about to
head east. Joan is living on a freak farm in New York
state where I'm going for the summer if things work out,
also Branamans are incredibly in NY Cityon a Gurdjieff grant
or something and Roxie is in Baltimore so I'm gonna run around
that neck of the woods for a bit. Just got back from Wichita
where Morgan and Richard are on Methadon, Richard is still
talking about going back to California, Sheryl looks like
an incredible fashion plate stepping across a mud puddle
in Wichita, Morgan and Sandy live in a place called
Dogpatch that isnt even on the map, she bitches a lot,
Tommy Kelly is on Methadon too, didnt see Justin but I know
he's there, they'll all be there forever it looks like.

How are Judy and Leslie? and your old self? Write me c/o
my parents since I never know you know.Roots of grass. Somehow
lost my book, most of it, in Cal. and some of my best poems
too. My little lifes work gone. Heard from your old
buddy Charles Plymell that poem was published in Telephone.

love,
Alan

DEDICATION

For the late David Omer Bearden (1940-2008)
who held on to this lost manuscript.

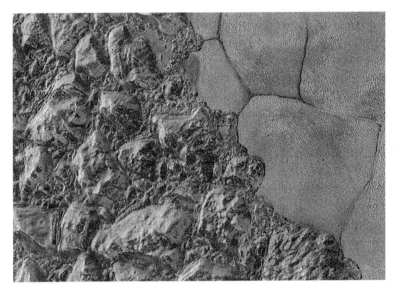

Surface of the planet Pluto showing the division of two geological state lines. Like the farthest planet in our Solar System, Alan Russo was one of the most far-out poets of his time.

TABLE OF CONTENTS

———

1963: NOW

1965: NOW NOW

1965: FUX! MAGASCENE

1977: DOMINION AND OTHER POEMS

ROSACE
Publications

2371 MIDWAY RD.
VACAVILLE, CALIFORNIA 95688
(707) 448-3265

5 APRIL 77
(BIRTHDATE OF
ALGERNON
CHARLES SWINBURNE,
S&M ENTHUSIAST &
POET)

FRIENDS, —

HERE'S A SMALL SAMPLE OF THE PROSE
STYLE EMPLOYED BY ALAN BÄTJER RUSSO
IN HIS ACCIDENTLY HILARIOUS & EXEMPLARY
NOVEL, "STATELINE". HOPE YOU ENJOY
THESE TWO SHAGGY PARAGRAPHS. BEST,

EDITORS' PREFACE

FROM ASTRA BECK

In 1965, my stepfather David Omer Bearden founded Rosace Publications. In the heyday of post-Beat San Francisco, David published Alan Russo's poems in anthologies, *Le Feu du Ciel* and *Smoking Mirror*, followed by the chapbook *Dominion and Other Poems*. Meanwhile, rumors of Alan's work on a collection of true stories made the rounds among friends. Sadly, when he passed in 2003, this work fell into the shadows of obscurity.

When David followed in 2008, my mother Johanna and I came across fragments of an unfinished manuscript of Alan's among David's papers. We both agreed it was best to give it to Alan's long-time friend Dion Wright. In 2015 Dion began to sort and transcribe Alan's manuscript, while I published David's books, *The Mental Traveler* and *The Thing In Packy Innards Place*, under Rosace Publications. During this time, I received a package from film director Andy Brown. While working on the documentary about singer-songwriter Judee Sill, Andy came across a manuscript he thought was David's. The package contained over 60 missing documents of Alan Russo's original *State Line*.

Some mysterious force brings David and Alan, whose paths intertwined so many years ago, back to the surface. Tulsa and Wichita provide a unique literary nexus to New York and San Francisco. David and Alan's unbound meter speaks to us now as much as when they were alive.

Today's audiences may be shocked by Alan's lack of political correctness, such as his use of the then-in-vogue "spade" and his treatment of women in stories such as "An Acid Trip." When faced with the choice of removing these passages, the consensus was to keep them. As a document of its time, *State Line* is very much about boundaries. When does "free love" blur the lines of consent? How do we treat outdated lingo of the past? Rather than whitewash history, we'd rather keep the conversation on the table and let Alan's work speak for itself.

Within these weathered pages, Alan's legacy is evident. His unhinged sensibility gives us a portrait of life at turns adventurous, scandalous, and comical. I'm honored to bring forth Alan's masterpiece of the "Wichita Vortex" *State Line*, from out of the dust clouds and into the pantheon of American letters.

FROM DION WRIGHT

In 1959 there was a flat on Oak Street in the Fillmore District of San Francisco where young writers and painters lived and met in a nexus of creative exchange. The sedate Eisenhower era was ending, and we were innocently perched on the cusp of Camelot. Via Jack Kerouac's book, *On the Road*, the Beat Generation had already burst upon the torpid Ike-era literary scene as an avant-garde force that had washed over American letters like a verbal tsunami, and then somewhat receded. In this low-tide moment between various polarities, bright artists from around the nation, especially from Wichita, Kansas, had soldiered to San Francisco, which Jack Kerouac had expounded as the Athens of the West. In the flat at 669 Oak Street everybody was enthusiastically bent upon making it so; all secure in their particular self-regard as creative spark plugs.

This Bohemian scene of experimental art was radically different from 50's conservatism. The young people met energetically in the flux and throes of spontaneous action, all pleased to have been called together in what everybody regarded as a summit. What did we know? Most of our mistakes were not yet made. The general overlay of drugs and sexual license was yet to be assessed as to how that matrix of neo-licentiousness would affect individuals.

At the center of the whirling storm of poets and painters coming and going all day every day sat a curly-blonde, burly and pale-skinned angel with large Mesopotamian-looking blue eyes, and a powerful anatomy folded upon itself in a rocking chair, his chin resting contemplatively in his hand as he incisively assessed all passing phenomena with a nihilistic perception. This unusual specimen was Alan Russo, late of Wichita, and regarded by all as the most brilliant and talented poet of all. Alan Russo probably concurred in this opinion, but was so disheartened by the nature of the world he found himself in, that he was anything but productive as a writer. For years and years he was urged-on by his friends, but it was uncertain what, if anything, he was putting on paper. We were good friends, he and I, for a while, until I, another depressed psyche, decided that I could ill-afford too much of the even-more negative ambiance emanating from him. Out of self-preservation, I allowed us to drift apart while remaining psychic allies. We remained in remote association through the catalysis of our mutual poet friend, David Omer Bearden, of Tulsa, OK.

After the deaths of both Dave Bearden and Alan Russo, Dave's widow, Johanna Beck, sent me an unsolicited package. Within it I was stunned to discover the chaotic lifetime writings of my old friend, Alan Russo. Being who I am with regard to serendipity and cosmic imperative, I understood that it was obligatory upon me to make a cogent document from the bagful of disconnected pearls. Try as I might, I could never really connect them up in a completely rational way, but a semblance of chronology and reason ultimately emerged and became the backbone of this book. Many individuals have shared their hits on Alan within these pages, and sincere thanks to all of them. As this project has developed, more and more fragments of Alan have drifted to the surface, and found their way into this unique collage/memoir. The vacuum has become a cornucopia.

State Line was Alan's tentative title for this book, which addresses the nature of irresolution between fixed realities.

FROM ROBERT DUMONT

After writing an article for This Land magazine—a Tulsa-based publication—about the California-Okie poet David Omer Bearden, I introduced myself via email to Charles Plymell, who had known

Bearden in San Francisco in the early '60s. Plymell would come to be associated with a group of artists and poets who had made their way from Kansas to San Francisco in the 1950s and early 1960s. The original members of this "Wichita Group" were poet and playwright Michael McClure, artist and filmmaker Bruce Conner, and poet and publisher Dave Haselwood. Though they did not originate the idea, they described and gave meaning to a concept known as the "Wichita Vortex" which had held them in place in a hostile and alien environment that they would each individually have to find the means to escape.

Starting in 1963, around the time David Bearden arrived in San Francisco, Plymell would edit and publish a succession of notable literary periodicals that included writings by Bearden as well as several Beats and post-Beats. Among the latter day Vortexers, Plymell published a young poet named Alan Russo who had arrived in San Francisco in 1960. Russo would become acquainted with David Bearden through a poet and musician named Richard White. White, originally from Wichita and Russo's friend, had attended Tulsa University at the same time as Bearden before moving to San Francisco with his wife, Cheryl. Thus, a Tulsa-Wichita West Coast connection was established.

Plymell, who had already published several of Russo's poems while in Wichita, would re-publish those and several more in San Francisco. Bearden likewise published poems by Russo in a 1965 anthology he edited called *Le Feu du Ciel* and in a 1977 chapbook titled—*Dominion and Other Poems*. *FUX Magascene* was a one-off anthology edited and published by Bob Branaman that came out in 1965 and included a poem by Alan Russo.

After my initial contact with Charlie Plymell, he began including me in some of his email strings when he was in touch with his Wichita cohorts. In several emails, he stated that Alan Russo was the best of the Wichita poets, comparing him to Hart Crane and referring to him as the "American Rimbaud. But what especially engaged my attention was when Charlie remarked that Alan had "died in Tulsa while driving a cab."

As I had already arranged with Marc Carlson, the curator of Special Collections at Tulsa University's McFarland Library, to create an archive for David Bearden (https://utulsa.as.atlas-sys.com/

repositories/2/resources/854), I thought it worthwhile to delve deeper into who Alan Russo was and what were his connections with Tulsa. The first thing I learned was that he had indeed died in Tulsa in 2003 and had worked there as a cab driver.

Thanks to Charlie's retrospective email strings, I learned much more about Alan. I made further inquiries and was in contact with a number of people who had known him personally, including Roxie Powell, Bob Branaman, Glenn Todd, Justin Hein, and others. I was also able to connect with family members who had their recollections of him. During the 1960s and 1970s, Alan had remained primarily on the west coast but frequently traveled—and began spending time in Tulsa after his parents moved there in 1964 from Wichita.

Besides the poems, Alan began working on a lengthy prose work titled *State Line*. Though he called it a "novel" it was not one in the traditional sense. As the reader will discover, *State Line* is an accumulation of outrageous vignettes, character sketches, travel tales, aperçus, philosophical musings, and more. Set in various locales, almost none of it has been previously published. All of that material, along with original typescripts of his poems, had ended up in David Bearden's hands and then was passed along to the sculptor Dion Wright after Bearden died in 2008. Dion had known Russo, Bearden, and Plymell and most of the Wichita contingent in San Francisco as far back as 1960.

Following the recent publication of two books by David Bearden by his step-daughter Astra Beck—who "resurrected" the Rosace Publications imprint that Bearden formerly used when producing chapbooks of his and others' writings, the next project undertaken was to gather, edit, and publish the work of Alan Russo. With the assistance of myself and Dion Wright, the job of assembling and editing the entirety of Russo's writings proceeded and eventually resulted in the present volume and has also led to the creation of a separate archive for Alan Russo at Tulsa University (https://utulsa.as.atlas-sys. com/agents/people/4261). If Alan was something of a "wandering soul" during his lifetime, perhaps with this book and the Tulsa archive, his literary spirit has now found a home.

ALAN BÄTJER RUSSO, POET
(1938-2003)

Alan . . . Alan Russo,
                Is that Italiano,
by any chance? Were you Albino
or wuz your hair just dyed that way?
Are there any fotos
surviving, still evidenced
that you exist existentialized
say some midnite bash . . .
the lanky teenage you at a picnic table with your eyes half-closed?
Was stepping into history a backward glance
where kids like us rode two-wheelers late into the misty melancholy dusk
with not a line or two
that you recall?
Rumored, you found your way back to Wichita,
to the jazzy alleyways, or do
I have it wrong?
You're but a blank, a punk, day's end, the end of track.
My nightly dreams unveil all I hear of alley cats
in their whining desperado search for warmth, as if possessed
in some polar vortex snow of sorts;
but never have I heard from you,
your voice dangling on the phone.
All the facts mislaid or misconstrued,
or as an image filtered through so long ago,
like laundry flapping in a dazzled, sunlit breeze.
Your life, careless & carefree,
                      but who would know?

— GERARD MALANGA
    Photographer, Filmmaker, and Author of over
    a dozen published volumes of poetry

PROLEGÓMENON

———

A mosaic of reminiscences of Alan Bätjer Russo and
"The Wichita Vortex" by those who knew.

*"What indeed suggests nothing but health is the poet's power
of using his neuroticism. He shapes his fantasies;
he gives them social form and reference."*

— LIONEL TRILLING, ART AND PSYCHOANALYSIS

"Pain is an obligation."

— EDITH PIAF

Dion Wright: A strange boy born in upstate New York between the Depression and World War II was transplanted first to New Jersey and later to Kansas, the weather-wracked geographic center of the United States, thus crossing his first "state lines" at a young age. He grew up with the gift of "long eyes," as the Indians used to say, and eventually fell in with poets. His name was Alan Russo which he claimed meant "snorer." The "Alans" were a barbarian tribe in northern Europe during Roman times.

Allen Ginsberg has been credited with naming Alan Russo's poetic melange, the "Wichita Vortex," on the basis of the émigrés he met in San Francisco. Once Ginsberg had actually gone to Wichita, he endorsed his own pontification, but Ginsberg had not invented the nomenclature, only expanded in media what he had found extant.

Robert Dumont: The "Wichita Vortex" term goes back to when Lee Streiff, Michael McClure, and Bruce Conner were in junior high school. Ginsberg probably heard it first from McClure and maybe Bruce Conner, but Charlie Plymell certainly elaborated on it further when he met Ginsberg in 1963.

Bruce Conner: The concept of the "Wichita Vortex" was conceived at that time ('circa 1951').

The Vortex myth was based on the concept that we (Eric Ecklor, Loren Frickel, Lee Streiff, Bruce Conner, Jack Morrison, Michael McClure in specific, and the residents of Wichita in general) were held captive as outlaws of another planet. We were deposited annually in Wichita and endowed with fabricated memories at the time of the Wichita University Homecoming game. We could never leave Wichita. All outside of Wichita was an illusion of the Vortex. No matter how hard one might try, the Vortex would snap you back to Wichita where we were eternally trapped. I first heard this comic myth from McClure, Morrison and Ecklor. It was elaborated into great detail over the next couple of years and was referred to when many of us had moved to San Francisco . . . somehow we had not really eluded the force of the Vortex and we were in actual fact deceived by mind altering rays from the enemy from outer space.

When another generation of artists from Wichita arrived in San Francisco (Bob Branaman, Alan Russo, Beth Pewther, etc.) the myth gathered dimension to the point where native Californians traveled to Wichita on their vacations in order to see and understand why these unusual creative people existed. They were warned of the pull of the Vortex, and that they might never return.

McClure was the youngest of the five poets that read at the SIX Gallery in San Francisco [1955] with Snyder, Lamantia, Whalen, Ginsberg . . . the Wichita Vortex became a common reference for the poets and artists. Allen Ginsberg's writings in reference to the Vortex spread the term into more general usage.

As Dorothy said, "That's the vortex in Toto."

(Bruce Conner, 11-1 1987, in discussing the origins of *Provincial Review* in a letter to Robert Melton of the Special Collections department of the University of Kansas Library.)

Lee Streiff: But that is not the Vortex in Toto, for Bruce had picked up only the tail-end version of the "aliens from another planet" myth that had been around for quite a while already . . .

Dion Wright: The poets of this Wichita Vortex could be a testy lot. Not all of them wanted to be regarded as the next incarnation of the Beat Generation, but some were flattered. However restless any of the poets from Tornado Alley may have been with being defined at all, some of them regarded Alan Russo as most gifted.

Almost seventy years after he was first noticed by literary persons, many of Alan's friends remain teetering among the living. They have reflected upon his unusual nature and ofttimes abrasive passage through life and literature.

Charlie Plymell: Microanalysis could reveal Alan Russo (an unknown poet equal to a Rimbaud or Hart Crane I had published on my midnight Multilith in Wichita) . . . as probably the greatest of all the poets from there . . . a genius; but he couldn't solve many of life's little problems, like why his grocery store socks kept crunching down into his loafers when walking the San Francisco hills.

Glenn Todd: That shrink father of Alan's . . . no wonder Alan turned out the way he did. He told Alan if he dug a hole deep enough he'd reach China. So Alan started digging. He hadn't reached China when night fell, and he had to go to bed. During the night, Mr. Russo lettered a sign and put it in the hole and covered it up. Then the next day he said to Alan, "Dig some more, you didn't dig deep enough." Alan dug until he uncovered the sign. The sign had an arrow pointing down and read, "To China." It was really fun to put Alan on, so everybody did. Even the father must have had fun doing it. Charlie Plymell says that Alan's dad was "in the shrink biz," and tested Alan at the level of genius.

Roxie Powell: Alan Russo was recognized by all who knew him to be *sui generis*. No one took Alan Russo to be your average cup of tea, even when we were in our early twenties and each hell-bent for attention and to hell with the status quo. He came among us and brought a level of accomplished poetic ability that was the envy of us all. Hugh Walpole once, while riding in the car, turned to say to Charlie Plymell and me, "You know, Alan has an unusual command of the idiom." What more could one hope for as a young person attempting poetry? "An unusual command of the idiom," from one of the world's premier linguists and philologists.

During a party Alan might suddenly render a poem by Yeats, or a piece of Aeschylus in Greek, and conversation would halt. Young ladies would look on in curious silence. From the very beginning, it seems, Alan carried a mythic persona around with him.

Charlie Plymell, who has survived to be the Grand Old Man of the Wichita Vortex, endorsed Glenn Todd's apprehension of Alan's poems as Rimbaudesque, but, from his persecuted outsider perspective, he supposes that the Academy would never let Alan onto the "path of poets." Plymell printed a poem of Alan's in *The Poets Corner #2*, the first magazine he ever published. Charlie was learning printing and ran the shop at Wesley Hospital. That publication had Hugh Walpole's wife in it, who was friends with Alan. Alan said he wished he could have met Hart Crane as much as any poet. According to Charlie, Alan said that it would take time for the public to assimilate William Burroughs. In Charlie's opinion, Russo was in the same league with Hart Crane and Arthur Rimbaud.

Lee Streiff: In the summer of 1959, *The Poets Corner #2* was put out by Alan Russo, a little magazine not sponsored by the university with a cover by Corban LePell, photography by Wayne Sourbeer, drawings by Jim Davis, poems by Alan Russo and a number of new poets, including Karin Antonio, Bob Branaman, Charlie Plymell, and Roxie Powell.

Charlie Plymell: Professor [Charles] Nelson at Wichita University said Alan translated the best from Latin he had ever seen.

Beth nee Branaman: I first met Alan Russo when I went to college one semester at Wichita University, Kansas, in the fall 1958. I had worked a couple of years and saved money to resume my education. I worked as a commercial artist at the *Wichita Eagle* newspaper and had arranged to work part time in order to go back to school.

Charlie Plymell complains that literary critics never mentioned Alan Russo, whom he regarded as probably the best Wichita poet, or Roxie Powell either. Plymell regarded the most famous Wichita poet, Michael McClure, as being ashamed of being from there, fearing to be regarded as a provincial, until Allen Ginsberg made the Wichita Vortex famous. McClure was a fat kid who wanted to be an actor (says Charlie), who came out good-looking. Charlie credits Glenn Todd with knowing more about the poetic turmoil in both Wichita and San Francisco than anyone else. Glenn lived next-door to Roxie Powell when they all attended Wichita University. They first met when Glenn was putting on his cuff links to go see Elvis.

Roxie Powell: Charlie Plymell and others have suggested that Alan Russo's early poetry may very well be of the quality or even superior to Arthur Rimbaud. I'm not capable of rendering anything more than an opinion about this. An author's reputation is dependent on the body of his works. Rimbaud's *oeuvre* is small. Alan's seems to be even smaller. Based on what we have, I could say that we are surely graced to have an important addition to the history of prosody in the 20th Century by the addition of these works by Alan Russo.

Plymell asserts that during their student days nobody had heard of the Beats. At that time his buddy, the painter Bob Branaman, was also enrolled at Wichita University. Charlie the peripatetic adventurer had been working at building the Dales Dam, and returned to Wichita with full pockets at the wheel of a new 1953 Buick Roadmaster. When the two amateur gangsters and joy-poppers were back into their flirtations with jail-time, Branaman came to his senses and insisted that the two high school drop-outs raise their sights and get educated at Wichita University. Branaman's chthonic talent was obvious enough to get him into the arts honor group, and they soon met Alan Russo. Alan quickly became the articulate center of a nexus of artists, from which position he discovered sources for mail-order peyote, and later, contacts at Sandoz Laboratories in Switzerland, which manufactured LSD, and

Light Laboratories in England, which manufactured crystal mescaline. Alan Russo's father, a psychologist who had a great appreciation of his son's gifts, was a proud observer. These mind-expanding chemicals were just becoming known, and were still legal. Trust Alan to tune into mind-expansion. Still, through these student days, nobody had heard of the Beats.

Beth nee Branaman: At Wichita University I majored in English and Art and quickly fell in with the Art and Poetry crowd, going to parties where I first met Alan Russo. I also met and married the painter Bob Branaman. We married at Christmas that first semester. The second semester I dropped out of school and went back to work full time supporting Bob, whom I considered a genius, and myself taking on the role of Good Wife.

Roxie Powell: Ya'll, Remember the poem, "Dominion" by Russo? It was published first, I think, in *Mikrokosmos*. Very serious omniscience. Then Charlie Plymell published several of his best ones and my favorite (which I have somewhere around here) which had the end line, "this, my kneeside pool, the universe." It always blew me away. And all I could ever get was a dog sittin' on a spider . . . sheeet.

Glenn Todd: Rox-in-the-head, that's what Alan used to call you.

Roxie Powell: It is an established truism that the only person of this period that was consistently "cool," was Charlie Plymell. That is not hyperbole; just fact, and frequently confirmed by many who were there. Actually, I can't imagine Charlie, Alan, or me ever thinking that what we were writing was like, or even associated with, the Beatniks. The fact that there were some similarities can't be denied, but there was certainly no conscious emulation. Actually, I don't even see many similarities. When I first read Ginsberg, Ferlingetti and *The Hotel Wentley Poems* by John Wieners, I thought that our stuff was completely different . . . and better.

Glenn Todd: The Tulsa poet Richard White's wife's name

was Cheryl. And she could indeed make her pussy rumble. Rather disconcerting when one sat beside her and she blithely decided to let loose a thunderbolt. Egad! What was that???? "Oh speak again, sweet bird," Russo used to say. Some quote he knew from one of *The Canterbury Tales* about a woman who farted when kissed.

Beth nee Branaman: Alan Russo was not in University but was taking trips back and forth from his parents', home in Wichita to San Francisco. He would come to the college parties. Alan was a bit of a recruiter for the San Francisco art/poetry scene.

Dion Wright: Alan laughed loudly the day I read to him, "Geological research based upon the distribution of fossilized radiolarians informs us that San Francisco is composed of geologic bits and pieces of several origins. Scientists have determined therefore that the area must be viewed as *Exotic Terrain*."

Charlie Plymell: I had gone to see Alan that summer, and he was in the garden stroking the flowers with his long fingers. He was playing Corelli softly. He had very psychic hands, beautiful, unfortunate hands suggesting purity. Cupped for innocence. Rare flowers themselves, with slender, tapering fingers, and almond-shaped nails. Hands one instinctively pities, if they have to hold their own in the battle of life. He stroked the plants the same way he would stroke cats. He talked about the strawberries last spring as an ant walked over the cold ground. Alan sat with his music and his garden until the leaves fell . . . Alan heard a kind of cosmic creak in the atmosphere. He beamed with enlightenment and remarked, "It's autumn. That's the equinox." He told me he could hear electricity, and that there was a difference in the sound of it in different localities. He sat all summer, and waited for everything; for nothing, and said:

"The hours are not precious.
They are wasted steadfastly and without care.
The day goes like a drop of blood,
the whole world goes around,

the more grooves to lose,
we are found listening at the door of our tomb."

Alan had seen the futility of drugs, and told me that they were just another shortcut:

"I will not walk the road to synthesis again.
I will not take the garish colored pills.
My blood is red and green and proud,
It has its own mythology."

But he kept on taking everything, searching for something that wouldn't leave him hung-up with just another shuck. Alan expected an honest-to-God reality somewhere. The more he saw of the ways of the world, the more the shock ate into his face.

(Excerpt from, "The Last of the Moccasins" by Charlie Plymell, 1971, *City Lights Books*)

Astra Beck: David Omer Bearden said that once, at a classical music outdoor performance, Alan Russo stood and shouted, "Louder & Funnier!" Alan reminded David of the tormented Vincent Van Gogh.

David Omer Bearden:
Then we drove on down
to Tulsa for Christmas
in her estranged husband's
raked Chevy,
where I introduced her
to Alan Russo,
a burnt hearted poet
looking for a place
to function
you might say . . .
& Kadillac took us
down to the Foos Roost
but Alan wouldn't go in;

he sat it out in the cold
car with a ski cap
pulled down over his ears
eating valiums & drinking
strawberry vodka,
because for one thing
he has not a mute cell
in his Rodin body.

(Excerpt from the poem, "Kadillac Kandee" in *The Mental Traveler* by David Bearden)

Roxie Powell: Alan Russo seemed always to be slightly ahead of the rest of us in any undertaking that interested him. Long before Baroque Music had become a staple among classical music aficionados, Alan was explaining the difference to me between Bonporti and Bach. We listened to the Verdi *Requiem* together, and I noticed that he was reading and translating the Italian as he listened to the *Dies Irae*. We had barely heard of peyote before Alan was ordering it by the box from Texas. Once he became interested in something he tended to command the subject in short order.

For me, his persona was less than mythic. Returning from San Francisco, Alan began bugging me to help him find a source so that he could purchase some marijuana. Knowing nothing of such whereabouts, as at the time I thought MJ was totally out of date, and had been so since 1949 when Robert Mitchum had been arrested; nevertheless, he prevailed upon me to help and I suggested we go down on Broadway to a club I knew and see what we could find. What we found was the Wichita vice squad hot to arrest a new dope ring, and they arrested us thinking they had the kingpins, only to find that we had nothing but stale tobacco in my glove compartment. No MJ.

We were arrested in September of 1958. I knew the 400 Club on South Broadway, so I took him there. We sat in a booth. When the waitress arrived Alan immediately said in a moderately loud voice, "Do you know where we can buy some pot?" She looked kinda funny at us. Alan said again, "Where can we get some pot? We wanna buy some." She looked at us a moment longer and then walked away not even asking for our orders. We sat there. I went up to the bar and got two beers. We drank the beer and got up and left. We walked out the back onto the gravel parking lot and as we approached my car we were suddenly surrounded by guys in suits, but with drawn guns.

They forced us to put our hands on top of the car and searched us. Then one of the guys, whom we found out were vice squad members who were sitting in the booth directly behind us, said, "Yeah. We got us some live ones, dealers, here. And this one (pointing at Alan) looks like he's out there for sure—he's pinned." And with that they marched us back into the 400 Club and into the office. They kinda ignored me, but they shoved everything off the desk, took the shade off a lamp and grabbed Alan by the scruff of his shirt, spun him around and shoved him hard, backed across the table. So far, in fact, that the back of his head hit the top of the table with a big thud, almost a "crack." Then they grabbed ahold of his hair and popped his head back sharply while a guy held the lamp directly over his face. "You see," said the guy pulling back his head by the hair, "his eyes are pinned." They ignored me. They roughed Alan up a bit more and then cuffed us and put us in their squad cars and took us to jail. They impounded my car and sent the car to their lab, to be vacuumed out, for dope. They booked us for Vagrancy and Investigation of Narcotics and wrote up three pages of tightly spaced report making it sound like they had busted a main drug pushing operation. My Department of Justice file followed me for the rest of my life, even though the charges were all dropped when the lab found nothing in the car, and the booking officer changed the booking to V & I Drunk. Still, I had the D.J. file keep me from two good jobs, years later. At least I was never beat-up, like Alan.

Glenn Todd: McClure wouldn't go anywhere with Alan. He said he was a "fuzz magnet," that if you were walking down the street with him, the cops would stop you for no reason at all. Charlie Plymell said to Alan once, talking to him about some girl, "Her legs went all the way up to her asshole." Alan couldn't get over it. He kept asking, "What do you mean? Her legs went all the way up to her asshole? What do you mean?"

Charlie Plymell remembered the long legs paradox, and didn't understand it either. He said that Alan never stopped talking about it. According to Charlie, Alan WAS a "fuzz magnet," although he had other issues with McClure, whom he accused of "shucking me about reality." If anyone said the word, "cop" around Alan, his eyes would immediately shift to the corner. In Charlie's opinion, the police left Alan alone because they could see upon looking at him that there was nothing but paperwork for themselves in hassling him.

Jane "Chipmunk" Lewis: I met a girl named Beth Branaman whom I later got to know very well. Her friends were all poets, painters, and intellectuals who looked to me like farmers. I didn't pay much attention to them. It always happens to me that when I meet people I come to love and admire very much, I don't like them at first. They, I now know, saw through me at a glance, but I guess they liked me anyway.

Glenn Todd: Janie Chipmunk loved Alan, at one time they loved each other so much. They went in and out of each other's lives for years.

Jane "Chipmunk" Lewis, 1959
Photograph by Wynn Bullock

Jane "Chipmunk" Lewis: I'll never forget the morning Alan returned from Wichita. I wanted to talk to Alan and I figured he wanted to talk to me, because I was just beginning to realize that maybe he was in love with me.

Roxie Powell: Alan could be curiously demanding as regards sex. He sometimes interpreted gestures of normal social response by a lady as an interest to have physical relations with him or at least allow further physical interaction. A little further on he could jump to conclusions. I witnessed both, that he could suddenly get quite physically amorous with a lady who was being nice, but also kinda frisky—which Alan couldn't always sort out. I think that, because Charlie let him think that it was OK to hit on any girl who seemed friendly to him, even if the girl was, at least to most people, obviously involved with a particular guy, and that the guy would react like Charlie, i.e., not show any negative emotion. He sometimes couldn't sort out very well that most of us would get all kinds of negative emotions going if he succeeded, tried, or failed to screw some girl we were interested in, let alone actually involved with. Charlie was always laissez-faire as regards whoever did whatever with whomever. Alan blandly jumped on any opportunity that presented itself.

Beth nee Branaman: There were already a number of Wichita people in San Francisco: artist Bruce Conner, poet Michael McClure, and Dave Haselwood, the owner-operator of the Auerhahn Press that published hand-set books of poetry. Alan would come to the college youth parties and tell stories of poets, painters, weed, and adventures in San Francisco. He would bring poetry books to show us. That was my first experimenting with marijuana, etc.

During that 2nd semester, Bob Branaman got a draft notice to report for military duty. The Viet Nam War was getting going at that time. On the basis that he would be going off to serve in the army, he convinced me that he deserved a nice summer trip to San Francisco with Alan Russo before going into military service. My savings funded the trip while I stayed in Wichita and continued working.

Dave Haselwood printed small poetry editions intended to be

collector's items, Charlie Plymell described him as, ". . . with his antenna beams feeling around, trying to get the words and then edit them all day, timidly slipping them out for selected reactions."

Dion Wright: Dave Haselwood, his name tellingly anagrammed by Michael McClure as, "Hades A. Doveowl," had me draw the logo for the Auerhahn Press. *Auerhahn* is the German noun for the capercaillie, a huge black grouse with scarlet wattles and a fan-shaped tail, which perches in trees in the depth of Northern European forests, and screams eerily. *Tres apropos.* It never stopped amazing me that Dave Haselwood eventually became a respected Zen Roshi . . . but then, why not?

Charlie Plymell remembers Alan Russo and Bob Branaman moving to San Francisco about 1960. Plymell gradually worked his way to San Francisco, meeting-up with Russo, Branaman, and Glenn Todd, who introduced him to Michael McClure, Dave Haselwood, and his letter-press friends with whom he related off and on; sporadically friendly. Bruce Conner, the assemblagist, came to hang out with Russo quite a lot, but he never hung out with Plymell. At this time the émigrés from Wichita didn't want their place of origin advertised. Russo and Branaman made a point of obscuring their Wichita roots, because McClure, Haselwood, and Conner were loathe to be regarded as hicks in the Big City. Eventually, in the light of being accepted by the literary lions, the touchiness about Wichita disappeared.

Beth nee Branaman: Mid-summer I got a letter from Branaman telling me that: "people out here tell me I could 'really make it' if I moved out here"; "REALLY MAKE IT". . . in my 20-year-old mind meant that Bob would become a successful, famous, rich painter!!! And I would be the WIFE of a famous man, a genius . . . my desire in life. Bob went on in the letter to say that Alan Russo's father, a psychiatrist, could write a letter to the draft board and get him out of service.

I answered back . . . "Let's do It."

Alan's father wrote the letter to the draft board saying Bob was unfit to serve in the army and that was it. He was deferred. Bob and Alan went on a quick trip from San Francisco to Mexico. Meanwhile, I gave 2 weeks notice at my job at the *Wichita Eagle* newspaper, packed my belongings in way too many boxes, and bought a train ticket.

I arrived in San Francisco late August 1959. Alan Russo returned from Mexico a couple of weeks before Bob, and proceeded to take me around to meet some of the artists and writers he knew. We went to the Auerhahn Press and saw Dave Haselwood's press and watched him hand-setting type. We took city walks and hiked Golden Gate Park to the ocean.

Alan was a good guide. He helped me find a Victorian flat on Oak Street to rent for $75 per month. Alan rented one of the bedrooms for $15. I gave Dave Haselwood a room for free because he was doing noble work and was very poor. One room was for me and Bob to sleep in, and one room for Bob's painting studio. We all shared a living room and a kitchen at the end of the flat. I got a job at Weinstein's Dept. Store as a junior artist in advertising and paid the rent. Bob, who did not hold a job, would go to North Beach at night and bring home all kinds of people who would be sleeping in the living room when I left for work in the morning.

Our flat on Oak Street became a temporary crash pad for many people, including Billy and Joan Jahrmarkt who later started the Batman Gallery. There were all kinds of drugs passing around and through that flat. I with my job, and Dave Haselwood with his press, were the only ones with a regular work schedule.

Charlie Plymell says this was about the time when Bruce Conner stenciled the word "LOVE" on Oak Street in the same alphabet font that the City used to paint "Right Turn," etc. The City immediately painted out Bruce's word, but he persisted on a smaller and smaller scale until he arrived at a small heart on the curbstone, at which point the City stopped censoring his effort.

Alan Russo was the bringer of peyote to Oak Street. He knew the address of a plant nursery in Texas that sold and shipped fresh peyote buttons, and one day an ordinary cardboard box of them was delivered to Oak Street. Alan prepared them, grinding them up in a blender and mixing them with juice, making something drinkable, although really nasty tasting. Peyote was the first psychedelic I tried and I found the experience transcendent. After about 2 hours the nausea passed and

I walked a few blocks to Golden Gate Park and spent a magical day communing with the plants and birds. I tried every drug that I was offered but didn't really like marijuana, and heroin made me feel like a block of wood.

The scene at Oak Street became increasingly bizarre and drug-ridden. By December it had become too much and Bob and I found another apartment and moved. Mike Lewis, a recent arrival on the scene, took over the flat and it continued to be a party place for another year. Alan Russo continued going back and forth to Kansas soliciting younger people to make the scene in San Francisco.

Alan Russo: Peyote is the vegetable world's attempt to subdue the animal world.

George Goyer: Alan Russo, on first impression, with his elongated face, popped-out bulging eyes, (startled or menacing?), and prominent brow, put me in mind of the watchful gargoyles on medieval cathedrals . . . but he didn't leer, or at any rate rarely leered as they do; and the flowed-back almost-white blond hair was angelic. And over the years that is how he seemed to me: a strange, and interesting hybrid creature; product of a mixed mating; angel and demon, and it left a churning in him, which was, I guess, according to reports, checked by alcohol and drugs. In my memory it was most often checked, contained within a fetal curling-up position in an overstuffed chair. Quiet and as immobile as other furniture, I could feel the observation going on and feel the churning process going on for hours, maybe days at a time. I was told he was a genius, and thought, "That's cool; yeah I bet he is." I hadn't yet met my quota of geniuses, so had little to go by, and it seemed to, at least, qualify the mysteriousness.

I guess I met Alan at the Oak Street place in 1960, which surged with personalities, drugs, and experimental social re-configuring. I think it was there that Jean Meyer and I had a room, but we were nearly as alien to the Oak Street culture as the prevailing *Better Homes & Gardens* culture we were escaping, which was our common ground. I have thought since that we were a bridge generation, following the

Beats and preceding the Hippie/Flower-Children wave that broke on the same shore a few years later. Anyway, I wanted to be an artist, and except for Bruce Conner's, the art ideas seemed pretty stupid and self-indulgent, more like masturbating than making love, so I went daily to the museum, made study drawings from a Reubens and painted it on my bedroom wall, which was probably as kookie a waste of time to them as theirs was to me. Different strokes, folks. Other than Mike and Janey "Chipmunk" Lewis, which is probably how I got there, only Alan had the gravity/destiny/care-to-know-you-better vibe. Well, except for Beth Branaman, because attractive intelligent women always set it off, but as she was Bob Branaman's wife, I hit the kill switch, which Alan apparently did not have.

Glenn Todd: One day, a beautiful day, I had just got a job at Auerhahn Press. Alan came by and shoved a typewritten note in my hand. It read something like, "It was a day when flags were out . . ." That's all I remember. I have it somewhere. When Dave Haselwood was still living at the Hotel Wentley and going to San Francisco State, Alan would come by his room, knock on the door and come in and take up the whole afternoon while Dave was trying to study. Finally it got so bad that Dave told Alan, "Don't knock on my door before six o'clock." Dave said Alan could hardly keep away, and that at about two o'clock in the afternoon Alan would creep quietly down the hall and just stand there waiting 'til six. Dave could hear him breathing through the door.

Jane "Chipmunk" Lewis: I didn't know what to do with myself, and finally decided to go to Kansas to visit my friends. When the bus pulled into Wichita that sunny afternoon I called from a pay phone and reached a very surprised Alan. His mother got on the phone and confirmed his invitation to stay at their house. His father picked me up on the way home from work and I was at once shown around the house and the big beautiful garden that Alan's little butterfly mother tended with bubbling butterfly pride. His parents seemed really overjoyed to have me there, as if it were a proof of normalcy in their poet genius son.

That summer we managed to get high about four times a week, but most of the summer was spent in Alan's mother's garden, with me helping some, but mostly just basking in the sun and watching Alan work. I watched Alan digging in the earth with his shirt off and the warm sun on his strong muscular back. He had a back like an ox, and once when I saw him plunge the spade into the earth there was a loud crack, and the spade broke in two. "Oh dear!" His mother gave a little gasp and told me that the previous summer Alan had broken six spades.

Roxie Powell: The one area that did not seem to hold Alan's interest for sustained periods was poetry. I think we all believed that at some point he would write either poetry or prose on some subject that would command general interest, and he would become recognized as a gifted writer. What we have today are the pages that came unbidden to his friend Dion Wright, and the poems published by Charlie Plymell in *The Locked Man*, and by David Omer Bearden in *Dominon and other poems*, plus random scattered entries in various chapbooks.

George Goyer: Blessings on the Alan project. People deserve to know Alan and Alan deserves to be known. I've run through the intro bio things and do want to add my take, as he moved in and out of my life, living with Jean and me for awhile in Redondo Beach, and was another friend, (I use the term in the broad generic sense) whose wife he was in love with, as weren't we all old pal? Anyway I think the intro is a good way to develop for the reader some sense of this curious creature. Some auto-bio can be very engaging in fleshing the milieu persona dramatis, of which to some extent I was in, but more on the sideline. I felt that scene was not part of my destiny, except for Dion, Mike, and Alan. For that reason my take is a different reflection, so if it helps, use it, if not . . . but I have to archive now.

It was probably his being in love with my wife, Jean Meyer, that later brought Alan to our house in Redondo Beach, which worked out pretty well for me, having him move in, because it meant Jean had companionship, was not left alone and unguarded, while I did the foundry work, casting Rico Lebrun's sculpture series on the death camps, and went galavanting whither the spirit took me after hours. Now it may be, because of Alan, that I have the notion that powerful intellects, absent a demanding schedule and/or rigorous physical labor, tend inexorably, toward elaborate dark landscapes of their own manufacture; and having seen that he was most engaging when he was most engaged, and being just a guy myself, not a strange genius-being from Atlantis or another planet, I told him, because he wasn't only the stranger I've painted him, but was also, really, another guy; I told him, "Alan you gotta get out of that fucking chair and go dig up the garden." Which he happily enough did, and was in better spirits for it, and all the other heavy-lifting I could come up with. Some time later, working like a dervish at *The San Francisco Oracle*, during the "Summer of Love," 1967, in the Haight, was the only other time I saw Alan happy and not just momentarily manic.

Charlie Plymell remarks that the junction where the Beats met the Flower Children occurred when Allen Ginsberg returned from his long sojourn in India. He was immediately feted by the San Francisco intelligentsia, led by Alan Watts, who never missed an opportunity to mount the podium, and Lawrence Ferlinghetti, whom Charlie deemed as being somewhat perplexed by the entire brouhaha. Bob Dylan also appeared on the scene sometime about then, and was also lionized, which he didn't like. The cavortings of the San Francisco literary scene were not that private artist's cup of tea.

Glenn Todd: Remember what long eyes Alan had, and how his eyeballs would slide into their corners; how he would put one hand over his mouth when he guffawed, to hide, I think, his big horse teeth? After Alan became a mature man, he got really big through the slightly hunched shoulders, hulking, and his arms dangled down, like an ape's. I think he worked for a while as a stevedore in and around Jamaica.

Dion Wright: Alan Russo had a high, whinnying laugh, like a neighing horse. When I moved into the Oak Street flat in 1960 my first sight of Alan was of an angular, ill-dressed man folded up in a chair, looking sidelong with penetrating awareness out of out-sized blue eyes that seemed to be expecting the worst. He reminded me of some mythological creature of the Mediterranean, not quite human, not sub-human, somehow extra-human. Those eyes seemed more Mesopotamian than Greek. We hit it off like karmic chemistry despite lusting heartily after the same women. Peyote was the foundation of our small society there and then, and Alan and I took to walking endlessly through the mysterious and fascinating City.

We took it for granted that we would have revelations unpredictable, as we forged up and down the hills, scarcely ever riding the inexpensive buses. We went to the Batman Gallery, ate in China Town, philosophizing all the time, and sharing a sense of how utterly weird everything was. Alan again and again said, "Everything is impossible." I got it, alright, but my own dark interior was so desperate for hope and light that Alan's nihilism came to look like drowning, and I eventually had to put more distance between us.

During this time, Alan was making his living as a paid guinea pig for untested pharmaceuticals. (Editor's Note: *Besides being a paid participant in clinical pharmaceutical trials, Charlie Plymell recalls that he and Alan were both paid subjects for brain wave studies at Kaiser Memorial Hospital. — R.D.*)

Serendipity brought me back to San Francisco during the "Summer of Love," 1965. I had a one-man show at Canessa Gallery on Montgomery Street, and was given a flat to stay in on Shrader Street by John Blackwell, overlooking Haight Street where it meets the Golden Gate Park Panhandle. What a box seat! From that midnight window I watched the Hell's Angel known as Chocolate Georgie lose it turning the corner, and slide across the asphalt, grinding his face off, resulting in the melodramatic screeches of a red-headed tart in green lamé who came charging out of a saloon to dip her hands in Chocolate Georgie's squandered blood, and the indifferent prodding of the body by the shining black leather boot toe of the motorcycle cop.

The psychedelic newspaper, *The San Francisco Oracle* was going strong a few blocks down Haight Street, and I frequented it. Right away I noticed that the old Beat and Wichita Vortex figures who were still around were steering the journalistic output of the hippies, who were almost all inept as word-communicators. I found Alan Russo ensconced at *The Oracle*, and saw him a few times that summer, but by then we were running in different grooves.

Alan was chary of encountering his body-double, as vanishingly unlikely as two of him might be. He said that the old Mythos was that if you were to meet your doppelgänger, you would die.

He may have had less than an eidetic memory, but he could reel off memorized poetry and quotations spontaneously enough to startle Oscar Wilde. One item I remember because he said it more than once was in relation to the vanity and massive ego of one of his poet colleagues. He said:

> *"For whoso reaps renown above the rest,*
> *With heaps of hate shall surely be oppressed."*
> — SIR WALTER RALEGH

Glenn Todd: Remember, the defining experience of Alan's life was the death of Mike Lewis's child.

Mike Lewis: Thea was my wife Joanie's 5-year-old daughter. The easiest way to write this might be "Mike Lewis's stepdaughter."

Thea drowned in the late morning August 1969—same week that Johnny Griggs died. I was at work. Alan was living with us, but neither Joan nor I would ever have left Alan in charge of Thea. Since I wasn't home, I've never been sure of exactly what happened. Both Alan and Joanie were drinking a lot. From what the two of them told me, I believe that Joanie was in bed in the bedroom, fully dressed. Alan was in the living room and saw Thea fall off her tricycle and into the pool. Alan could not swim; he called for Joan, who went into the deep end and got Thea out. Someone called the emergency operator. I was returning to work from lunch when the secretary stopped me at the office door, told me that something had happened to my daughter, and to go to the hospital. By the time I got there Thea had died. Joanie's clothes were still wet from the pool. Alan was nearly as shattered as Joan and left that afternoon; we didn't see him again for nearly three years—until after Joan and I had returned from Vietnam. In the mid-70's, Alan lived with us again for several months, at our Poe Street house in San Diego. For some reason, the only concrete memory I have of him at that period was one evening when the three of us were watching Monday Night Football, and Howard Cosell broke in with the news that John Lennon had been shot.

Maybe Alan felt guilty in some way, and either told Glenn or Glenn just picked up on Alan's mood? Joan always liked Alan, and never blamed him in any way for what had happened to Thea. I think that Alan's drinking (in the end, his drug was alcohol, just like Joanie's) made for a closer bond with Joan than what otherwise might have been.

Charlie Pymell: Alan came up here to Cherry Valley, New York, to stay for a year and got a laboring job in Albany, tearing down structures. He liked to bust up the latrines with a sledgehammer. The local Long Island stooges teased him like when a fly landed in his eggs. He always had a frying pan when he'd move from pad to pad in San Francisco. One time in with me. He always made bacon & eggs. Richard [White] or one of the Tulsa boys wrote a poem: "The poet still eats eggs . . ." or something like that. Alan would always quote Burroughs's "Anyone who holds a frying pan owns death."

Glenn Todd: When Alan told me the story about Rhonda Hardway* was sometime in the nineties. Rhonda was a falling-down drunk, but pretty. She was hard-luck Rhonda. She was involved only with men in the cab-driving scene that she got to know because she needed to get home after the bars closed. There was a whole society of guys who drove cabs, just like any occupation. Alan had to get out of Tulsa where he had been driving for years because somebody, a guy who hated his guts, was after him in regard to Rhonda, who had been killed and dumped. He arrived on my doorstep after a long, long time of not hearing from him. He stayed with me a few nights. In exchange I made him tell me everything I wanted to know, who he had screwed, who he hadn't screwed, whose wife he'd been in love with, he was always falling in love with his friends' wives—his time in the Caribbean, things he'd stolen, his gay experiences (just one) in Southern California with a guy who loved him and took care of him some weeks; he loved the guy back and even went down on him a few times. He told me that guy was the only person who had really really loved him. Don't ever tell me anything, I don't forget and sooner or later I'll blab. He said that he hadn't had anything to do with Rhonda Hardway's death, and he told a lot of stories like, "If I had done this? If I had helped her out here? If I had driven her there, would I have been planning to kill her?" He had everything worked out logically. I chose to believe him, because he made me a little uneasy. He didn't have much with him when he rang my bell, but he did have a bundle of *Oracles*, including the really rare first issue. He thought he could get a lot for his collection, but the dealer wasn't interested, or more likely he saw Alan coming. He ended up getting only $200. When he left after visiting me, he went to L.A. where he had some friends. I didn't hear from him for years after that and never saw him again.

* Rhonda Sue Hardway, age 27, a young woman with an arrest record for prostitution, was last seen in the vicinity of 21st Street and Riverside Drive just south of downtown Tulsa on August 7, 1986.

Shortly thereafter in a location approximately 14 miles to the southwest in the "Flats" area of Sahoma Lake near the town of Sapulpa, two fishermen noticed a female body approximately 50 feet from the shore lying face down in a field. A police investigation determined that the woman had been beaten and shot in the head and was clutching a handful of hair. She was identified as Rhonda Hardway of Tulsa.

There were no solid leads as to her killer or killers and the case remained unsolved for nearly 20 years. The break would finally happen on a freezing day in January of 2006, when John W. Pingleton, 41-years old and a citizen of Sapulpa, but never a suspect in the Hardway case, walked into the Sapulpa Police Department and announced he "wanted to get his life straight . . . [That] God told him to come forward and get it out."

Pingleton implicated a second participant in the crime—a career criminal Vincent Keith Partridge, also of Sapulpa, who denied his involvement. However, police possessed DNA evidence that showed a match between Partridge and crime-scene evidence collected 20 years before.

Roxie Powell: Makes you wonder about Alan, and if he even knew that it wasn't he who killed Rhonda . . . sometimes he could "lose" time and do things that absolutely never registered in his consciousness. Maybe he was a DID, (Disassociative Identity Disorder), which used to be called Multiple Personalities. But also, alcohol can do strange things to the central nervous system and longtime drinking and drugging usually gets weird after a certain time. Anyway, you are truly a good friend and deserve any accolade possible coming your way. Once Alan came to Baltimore, while Janie Robertson was playing cello in the stage show *Jesus Christ Superstar*. She was staying in a motel where the orchestra had been put up. He stayed with me a few days and then went over there. The next thing I knew she was at my door with blood on her telling me that she had been kicked out of the room since Alan attacked her and when repulsed threw her into a wall and then threw her into a door with a full sized mirror which broke and cut her. I let her stay at my place for a few days—but she kept walking around naked, and I found that disconcerting.)

Glenn Todd: One winter in Tulsa when he had spent all the money his parents had left him and was completely alone and really weak he called and asked, Do you have access to porn in San Francisco? Yes, I said, yes, of course it's everywhere. Send me some, he begged. What kind? I asked. He got very specific, but you know nothing like that fazes me, so I searched and searched till I found what he wanted, it's not everybody's cup of tea. I mailed it to him. He called and I said, "I found some, it's in the mail." When it didn't arrive and he called again and asked, "What was the address you sent it to?" I told him and he said, "I haven't lived there in a year. You had an old address." He pulled himself up off the sickbed and went to the old address: "Where's my porn?" he asked. And they said, "Oh, is that yours?" and gave it to him. They had opened the package and watched it. He said they looked at him really funny. Then he told me, "I've just watched it myself. Oh, it's so wonderful! How were you ever able to let it go?"

Alan left a bundle of his writings with me, ninety single-spaced typewritten pages, back in the seventies. At the time he was running around with David Omer Bearden. They had some really weird experiences in the Sierras. Hieroglyphs appearing on rock walls revealing cosmic secrets and giving them instructions. I didn't really like the manuscript all that much, so when he took it away from me, I didn't protest too much. Now I wish I had it. Remember *Dominion*, the poem he wrote when he was seventeen, I think? It was worthy of

Rimbaud. The last line was "His tents line the horizon all around." It starts something like, "He moves stealthy. . ." Naw, I can't do it. I wish I had a copy to read right now. I probably do, but where?

Robert Dumont: I was struck by his moments of utter lucidity amid the at times madness of his surroundings. He had an eye for the absurdity of the absurd and could describe even his own questionable actions with a certain degree of detached bemusement. But those moments were perhaps few and far between and only occurred at the moment of rendering his thoughts into prose.

Bob Branaman: Alan Russo was a huge influence in my life, and I loved him very much. He was one of the most alive, sparkling jewels I have ever met and had a significant impact on my moving to California. I first met Alan in Wichita. We were going to Wichita University (now Wichita State). I remember listening to Bach's Brandenburg Concertos with him. Radiant as he listened, eyes closed, he was swinging to the music as if transported to another sphere.

Artists among our friends were Charlie Plymell, Corban LePell, Jim Davis, Roxie Powell, and numerous others. At that time, if you were too artistic you probably needed to get out of Kansas; some went to New York City but most headed west to San Francisco.

In the spring of 1959, on my way to school in Guadalajara, Mexico, I went to San Francisco where Alan had moved. We got a room at the Hotel Wentley, and I stayed a few weeks with him. Dave Haselwood's print shop, the Auerhahn Press, was a few blocks away on Franklin Street, and we would go by there every day. It was a far-out place and a mecca for artists. It was there I first met Wallace Berman. He was with his wife Shirley and their young son, Tosh. He was doing a cover for a poetry book Dave was printing called *Narcotica* by Philip Lamantea with pictures Wallace had taken of Philip shooting heroin. Wallace was dressed in an old faded Boy Scout uniform. He had a beard and was somehow an elder youth. He talked with a quiet whisper; you had to sort of stop and pay attention to understand what he was saying. Alan seemed to know all the artistic characters who came to Dave's shop.

Alan and I would usually walk to Aquatic Park or North Beach every day. These were long walks, but Alan was cheap and didn't want to spend the 15 cents or whatever it was on bus fare. We saved our monies for food, booze, and pot (when we were lucky enough to be able to score some. Ju Ju Jimmy was one of our connections). Once we worked together chipping concrete off used bricks and earned one cent per brick. After a full day of doing this tedious work, I had earned $2.50, making it my first and last day at that job. Alan, however, enjoyed the zen of it, and spent many days at the task. Anyway, being with Alan was a great introduction to San Francisco. I met Allen Ginsberg at Dave's shop as well as a host of poets here and there, including Michael McClure, Philip Whalen, Philip Lamantea, and John Wieners. And there were painters and artists like Bruce Conner (also from Wichita), Bob LaVigne, and others.

I went on to school in Mexico. By then I had written a lot of inspired letters to my wife, Beth, about how beautiful San Francisco was, about North Beach, and the whole art scene. Unbeknownst to me, Alan had moved back to Wichatitie (we called it that sometimes) and was hanging out with my wife. I had been drafted, but they concocted a scheme to get me out of the Army. Alan's father, who was a psychiatrist, wrote a letter to my Draft Board, saying I was not Army material, that I had been in Reform School and was a semi-gay psycho who, if separated from my wife, would become very unstable and probably shoot the wrong (maybe the right) people. They promptly sent me a telegram saying I was deemed unfit for the Armed Services. Alan and Beth thus got me cut loose from the Army.

Without telling me, Alan and Beth decided to move our household to San Francisco. Just about the time I was getting ready to leave Mexico for my return to Kansas, I got a letter telling me Beth (with Alan's help) had moved. Unexpectedly I was going back to San Francisco. When I got to the city, I didn't know where Beth and Alan were living. The sun had gone down, so I went back to my old stomping ground, the Auerhahn Press, but it was closed. I went on to the Wentley Hotel, and there, at the corner of Polk and Sutter, were Bruce and Jean Conner coming out of the Fosters Restaurant. I asked them if they knew where Alan was. Oh, yes, they knew all about it, and they took me to my new home, a boxcar flat on the 2nd floor on Oak

Street. It was only a block and a half from Bruce and Jean's apartment. Over the next few years Oak Street became the home for me, Alan, and Beth and a host of others. Dave Haselwood, Glenn Todd, Billy and Joan Jahrmarkt, Mike and Janie Lewis, and many more lived in that flat. They came and went.

After about two years Beth and I broke up and moved away from Oak Street. I eventually married my love from Mexico, Susan Mack, and we moved from the city to Moss Beach and from there to Big Sur where Alan would occasionally surprise us with a visit. Though we were always in touch with Alan, I don't think he ever wrote me a letter. In fact, Alan seemed to write very little for a writer and a poet! All the same, when he would come and stay with us, he would often read us one of his poems or leave them lying about like doodles on scrap paper, "By this, my knee-side pool, the universe…"

Bob Branaman & Alan Russo, Wichita, Kansas, 1999
Video Still by Laki Vazakis

In 1999 when Pat O'Connor arranged for Charlie Plymell and me to have a show at the Wichita Art Museum, Alan came up from Tulsa to see us and the show. It was good to see him, but time and substance abuse showed in Alan's bearing. I had gotten sober by then, and Alan told me he was going to meetings and working on getting sober too. Despite these challenges, he still had his old elfin sparkle. This was the last time I saw him.

Alan was always amazed by and mystified with life, like a child filled with wonder and delight at the splendor of it all. I have him to thank for introducing me to a lot of music, poetry, art, and higher learning. He was one of the brightest spirits I have ever known, and, as I said at the start, I loved him dearly.

Charlie Plymell: During the last year of Alan's life, Maggie Harms and Justin Hein visited him in Tulsa. I think Maggie's daughter, Maia, even interviewed him with a tape recorder or maybe a video. One of the nation's leading authorities on treating Hepatitis C lived in Wichita and had a clinic there. Maggie and Justin, especially Maggie, had a little thing with Alan, tried to get him to move to Wichita so that he could get the best treatment. But he hemmed and hawed until he died.

Justin Hein: I met Alan in 1958 at Wichita University, and we did peyote. In 1961 I smoked pot for the first time with Alan and Tony Carruthers in San Francisco at Glenn Todd's apartment on Leavenworth Street and Sacramento. Alan was a joy to me.

Time passed, and by the late '80s, Alan came to visit Dennis Morgan and Lisa Morgan in Wichita. Dennis had an art show, and Alan was staying with him. They had a falling out over Alan's drinking at night so he came and stayed with me. Another time Alan stayed with me was when Charlie Plymell and Bob Branaman had a reading at the Art Museum in Wichita. He then lived with me for two weeks after he quit his job in Tulsa. Alan drove to Wichita and spent the afternoon stripping and re-painting his cab. He was on his way to San Francisco with a collection of *Oracle* newspapers and thought he could make MONEY! Glenn said, Alan only got a dollar per paper. He then went to his sister's in Denver and got a factory job. Worked one day and was so worn out he couldn't go back to work. He returned to Tulsa and took up cabbing again.

By 1997 I took a week's vacation in Tulsa when Alan was a cab driver. All I can say is when I went to visit Alan he treated me like your royal highness sitting in his cab touring Tulsa. We toured the Oral Roberts University grounds and spent an hour meditating and talking in the Prayer Tower. We saw the downtown Art Deco buildings and some barges on the river. We drank iced tea in a fancy restaurant with wood-paneling and cool cut-glasses and ate ribs at a barbecue buffet. We hung out at the bus station and visited the Gilcrease Indian Museum near his apartment. We walked to the top of a medical tower overlooking Tulsa. We went to a lecture at Tulsa University that was attended by Christians, liberals, and Jews. It was on *The Book of Revelations* in the Bible, which the lecturer said should be emphasized as a book of salvation. He took me to breakfast at a pancake house that had an unusual motto: "Girlie Pancakes, they're stacked better." For a period, Alan was into flying saucers and the Roswell incident. Eventually, he decided there was nothing to it. A book he was really into and talked a lot about was *In Search of the Miraculous* by P.D. Ouspensky.

Alan never shared his writings with me. All I have is four or five addresses where he lived in Tulsa. Alan was an amazing live-wire in daylight. He struggled with the dark of the night drinking cocktails, none of them with a dainty olive in them. I suppose Alan did some serious drinking, but I never saw him passed out. He was healthy until around 2001. I spoke with Alan twice when he was in a nursing home. He wasn't afraid of death. Alan told me, "Don't worry, Justin. Everything will be all right."

I ended up talking with Alan's nurse twice, and she assured me Alan was "with Angels." She couldn't tell me when Alan died, so she turned me over to the landlady who told me Alan had died. The landlady turned me over to Alan's best friend, who told me the day Alan died, his buddies ransacked his papers, photos, etc. and that all his things were gone! I contacted the undertaker later for his ashes to be given a plot in Wichita. The undertaker said he would get back with me after he notified Alan's sister in Denver. He never did.

TULSA WORLD: [Daily Newspaper] Deaths – May 25, 2003 **Russo, Alan**, 64, retired, died Saturday. Services pending. Moore's Eastlawn [Funeral Home].

Robert Dumont: The visit to Glenn Todd with Alan's nephews (father and son)—went quite splendidly. I met up with them in the Fisherman's Wharf area early in the afternoon. The plan was to take one of the tourist cruises and discretely deposit a portion of Alan's ashes into San Francisco Bay's waters. (The rest were to be scattered later in the Sierra Nevada Mountains, where Alan liked to hike.) We were on a fairly small boat with room for only 20 people and didn't want to attract attention while the boat's driver was regaling the other passengers on board with jokes and pertinent information about the famous sights we were seeing. It was a short 30-minute tour, so we never got really close to Alcatraz or the Golden Gate Bridge, although we saw them in the distance. There was a point at which Alan's nephew languidly stuck his arm over the side of the boat and surreptitiously let the ashes start to flow out of the small plastic bag containing them. As it's typically quite windy on the SF Bay waters, there was a bit of "blowback," so some of the tourists from places like China and Utah, as well as Alan's nephews and myself, got a bit of him in our eyes and a taste of him on our lips. Who knew that the harbor breezes could be so gritty? Anyway, the mission was successfully accomplished, and the three of us had a good laugh about the episode once we were back onshore.

We then bailed on the crowded scene at Fisherman's Wharf and had a late lunch near where Alan's younger nephew lives. I'd been telling both nephews stories about Alan and SF days and the Wichita gang from the early 60's. It turns out that the younger nephew lived very near Glenn's Bush Street residence and often walks past the house on his way to the neighborhood laundromat. The seafood restaurant where we were dining was on Fillmore Street, so I mentioned that there used to something called the Batman Gallery on Fillmore near Sacramento Street and was told that particular intersection was nearby. I said I'd read there presently was a Starbucks in the space that had formerly been the Batman, and the younger nephew stated that he goes there all the time to have coffee and utilize the free wireless access. This was all getting most interesting.

I called Glenn and told him we were finishing lunch and would stop by and see him soon. He said he'd leave the door unlocked because he might not hear the bell or a knock. His was an old-style, two-story, two-family house with two front doors that was built in 1920. There were two larger, multi-tenant buildings on either side. His upstairs tenants were entering at the same time as us by means of their door, and then there was Glenn at his door coming out to greet us. He had two front parlor-like rooms, and we all sat down in the second of them, which may have been a dining room in former days. Glenn was installed in a large leather easy-chair with an enormous coffee table in front of him covered with books and magazines. The chair faced his TV on the other side of the room, and is where he indicated he likes to sit and read and watch movies. I sat on a sofa to Glenn's right, and the two nephews sat in separate chairs to his left.

He talked at length about Alan—describing the first time he met him in a French Literature class at Wichita University in 1957. Alan was still in high school but was academically advanced and thus auditing college-level courses. Glenn kept saying how brilliant Alan was even if he never really "found himself." He assured the nephews that Alan was never a drug addict but did like his wine. According to the older nephew, who remembered Alan very well, it became vodka in later years.

The younger nephew only met Alan on a few occasions when he was quite young and had only vague memories. He's in his mid-20's and studying for an MBA at Berkeley. The things he heard from Glenn he found to be quite astounding. Glenn pointed out that he had a similar complexion to Alan's with his rosy cheeks. The older nephew and Glenn were then recalling Alan's golden-colored hair. Glenn told them what he'd told me previously that young Alan had the look of a prince as depicted in a Renaissance-style painting but later in life became self-conscious of his looks and his large teeth. He said Alan would often speak with his hand in front of his mouth, which sometimes made it hard to hear him. Glenn recalled the last time he had seen Alan was several years ago when he came to visit and stayed some weeks in this very house. We all looked around as if there remained Alan's ghostly presence in the room where we were sitting.

As the visit was nearing an end, Glenn asked Alan's nephews if they wouldn't mind re-arranging some chairs in the living room, which they immediately got busy with. While they were moving the chairs, I looked at some artwork hanging in the hallway then checked out Glenn's backyard garden, which appeared to be well-tended. As we were leaving, Glenn invited the younger nephew to come back and visit along with his wife.

That evening I had dinner with Judith (David Bearden's ex-wife) and her husband Ron at their home in El Cerrito. She had prepared a delicious meal, and Ron poured the wine. I recounted the visit with Glenn, and Judith shared an amusing story about Alan Russo. She said that one time, he was interviewing for a job with an insurance company in San Francisco, and mid-interview he suddenly stood up, looked fixedly at the person conducting the interview, and declared, "I have only imagined you!" With that, he turned around and walked out of the office. Apparently, he had decided he didn't want the job.

Dion Wright: I have received two separate, unsolicited, unexpected copies of Alan's manuscript from two sources, which are the seed from which this book emerges.

The preceding remarks are tesserae in an incomplete mosaic defining Alan Russo the person. Beyond the *State Line* defined by this sentence are the fragments of Alan Russo, the writer-poet.

Beat Generation artists in front of City Lights Bookstore in San Francisco, 1963.
From left: Pat Cassidy, Philip Whalen, Robert Ronnie Branaman, Alan Russo,
Charlie Plymell, Bob Kaufman, Allen Ginsberg, and Lawrence Ferlinghetti.
Photograph by Ann Buchanan

COLLECTED POEMS

———

"Future speeding on swift wheels
straight to the heart of Wichita!"

— ALLEN GINSBERG, "WICHITA VORTEX SUTRA," 1966

THE VIGIL OF VENUS

Anonymous Latin Poem Translated by Alan Russo
Published by Wichita University
Sunflower Literary Review, Issue No.1, 12-6-1955

New Spring, Spring of songs, Spring when the world was born.
Spring when loves are joined and the birds are paired
And the forests, touched with rain, shake loose their hair;
Tomorrow the binder of loves, in the shade of trees,
Shall weave green chambers from the myrtle shoots,
and Dione shall give her blessing, set on her upraised throne.
Tomorrow may he love who never has loved,
And he who has loved, may he love tomorrow.

It was then, from godly blood, that the sea in its foamy depths,
Through sea-blue throngs and past biped horses
Brought forth Dione surging over the oceans waves.
Tomorrow may he love who never has loved,
And he who has loved, may he love tomorrow.

She paints the year and decks it with blooming flowers;
She impels the rosebuds, swelled with the west wind's being
Into fruitful clusters; she spreads the damp waters
Of the shining dew, which the air of night has left:
See, the teardrops sparkle, trembling with their delicate weight,
But in its small circle each hanging drop resists its fall.
See, she has revealed the softness of bright-hued flowers:
That vapor which the stars let down in the placid night
Frees the virgin buds from their damp shrouds in the morning.
In the morning she ordered that the soft maidens wear the rose;
Made from the blood of Venus and the kisses of Love
And from gems and flames and the brilliant sunrise,
Tomorrow, a bride in strange marriage, it will not fear to show
Its color, which lay hidden in its burning veil.
Tomorrow may he love who never has loved,
And he who has loved, may he love tomorrow.

PERVIGILIUM VENERIS

Ver novum, ver iam canorum, vere natus orbis natus est,
Vere concordant amores, vere nubunt alites,
Et nemus comam resolvit de maritis imbribus.
Cras amorum copulatrix inter umbras arborum
inplicat casa virentes de flagello myrteo:
Cras Dione iura dicit fulta sublimi throno.

Cras amet qui numquam amavit quique amavit cras amet.

Tunc cruore de superno spumeo pontus globo
Caeruleas inter catervas, inter et bipedes equos
Fecit undantem Dionem de maritis imbribus.

Cras amet qui numquam amavit quique amavit cras amet.

Ipsa gemmis purpurantem pingit annum floridis,
Ipsa surgentes papillas de Favoni spiritu
Urget in toros tepentes, ipsa roris lucidi,
Noctis aura quem relinquit, spargit umentis aquas.
En micant lacrimae trementes de caduco pondere:
Gutta praeceps orbe parvo sustinet casus suos.
En pudorem florulentae prodiderunt purpurae:
Umor ille, quem serenis astra rorant noctibus,
Mane virgineas papillas solvit umenti peplo.
Ipsa iussit mane ut udae virgines nubant rosae:
Facta Cypridis de cruore deque flabris deque Solis purpuris
Cras ruborem, qui latebat veste tectus ignea,
Unico marita voto non pudebit solvere.

Cras amet qui numquam amavit quique amavit cras amet.

The goddess has ordered the nymphs to the myrtle grove;
The boy goes with the girls, and it cannot be believed
That Love is idle if he bears his darts.
Go, nymphs, he has laid down his arms. Love takes a holiday;
Neither with bow or shaft or flame may he strike.
Yet take care, nymphs, for Cupid is so beautiful;
Love is in arms, even when fully naked
Tomorrow may he love who never has loved,
And he who has loved, may he love tomorrow.

Venus sends you maidens of modesty such as yours.
One thing there is we ask: yield, Delian virgin,
That the grove may be unbloodied with slaughtered beasts
And that she may strew the grove with fresh-picked flowers.
She would invite you, if she could bend your pride,
She would want you to come, if it became a virgin.
There for three festive nights you would go see the chorus,
You would join with your throngs to go through the dance,
Among floral wreaths, down myrtle halls.
Neither Ceres nor Bacchus will be far, nor the god of poets.
All the night will be spent in songs.
In the woods let Dione reign: Delia, give way.
Tomorrow may he love who never has loved,
And he who has loved, may he love tomorrow.

The goddess has ordered a throne to be built of Hyblaean flowers.
The Queen herself will preside, the Graces will attend her.
Hybla, give forth all your flowers, all that the year has brought;
Here the girls of the mountains and plains will be
And those that live in forests and groves and fountains.
The mother of the boy has bidden the birds alight,
And ordered the girls not to trust love, though naked.
Tomorrow may he love who never has loved,
And he who has loved, may he love tomorrow.

Ipsa Nymphas diva luco iussit ire myrteo:
It puer comes puellis: nec tamen credi potest
Esse amorem feriatum, si sagittas vexerit.
Ite, Nymphae, posuit arma, feriatus est Amor:
Iussus est inermis ire, nudus ire iussus est,
Neu quid arcu, neu sagitta, neu quid igne laederet.
Sed tamen, Nymphae, cavete, quod Cupido pulcher est:
Totus est in armis idem quando nudus est Amor.

Cras amet qui numquam amavit quique amavit cras amet.

Conpari Venus pudore mittit ad te virgines.
Una res est quam rogamus: cede, virgo Delia,
Ut nemus sit incruentum de ferinis stragibus.
Ipsa vellet te rogare, si pudicam flecteret,
Ipsa vellet ut venires, si deceret virginem.
Iam tribus choros videres feriantis noctibus
Congreges inter catervas ire per saltus tuos,
Floreas inter coronas, myrteas inter casas.
Nec Ceres, nec Bacchus absunt, nec poetarum deus.
Detinenter tota nox est perviclanda canticis:
Regnet in silvis Dione: tu recede, Delia.

Cras amet qui numquam amavit quique amavit cras amet.

Iussit Hyblaeis tribunal stare diva floribus;
Praeses ipsa iura dicet, adsidebunt Gratiae.
Hybla, totus funde flores, quidquid annus adtulit;
Hybla, florum sume vestem, quantus Aetnae campus est.
Ruris hic erunt puellae vel puellae fontium,
Qaeque silvas, quaeque lucos, quaeque montes incolunt.
Iussit omnes adsidere pueri mater alitis,
Iussit et nudo puellas nil Amori credere.

Cras amet qui numquam amavit quique amavit cras amet.

Tomorrow will be the day when first the air was wed
And the father of spring made all the year from clouds;
The impregnating rain fills the embrace of his fertile mate
And the fruitful union feeds all in her great body.
She, the mother of creation, rules the mind and veins
With the penetrating breath in hidden forces
And throughout the sky, the earth, and the underlying sea
She opens the paths for the seed to take its course
And orders the world to know the ways of birth.
Tomorrow may he love who never has loved,
And he who has loved, may he love tomorrow.

She brought the sons of Troy to Latinus,
She gave the Laurentine girl to her son for wife;
From the Ramnes and Quirites, and from the son of their children
She begot the mother of Romulus and his descendant Caesar;
Soon after she gave to Mars a virgin pure from the temple;
The marriage of Romans with Sabines she brought to pass.
Tomorrow may he love who never has loved,
And he who has loved, may he love tomorrow.

The fields are made fertile by love, the fields sense the
presence of Venus;
They say Love himself, the boy of Dione, was born in the country.
When the fields gave him birth, she took him to her heart,
She made him bright with soft kisses.
Tomorrow may he love who never has loved,
And he who has loved, may he love tomorrow.

Look now, under the broom-plants the bulls spread their flanks;
And cover is held shameful to the conjugal rites.
Behold in the shadows the flocks of sheep with their mates,
And the goddess has ordered the birds not to still their songs.
Now the loud swans croak on the lake with harsh voices.
The girl of Terreus sings in the shade of the poplar.
With such music on her lips that you would think she told of love,

Et recentibus virentes ducat umbras floribus.
Cras erit quom primus primus Aether copulavit nuptias,
Ut pater totis crearet vernis annum nubibus:
In sinum maritus imber fluxit almae coniugis,
Unde fetus mixtus omnis omnis aleret magno corpore.
Ipsa venas atque mente permeanti spiritu
Intus occultis gubernat procreatrix viribus,
Perque coelum perque terras perque pontum subditum
Pervium sui tenorem seminali tramite
Inbuit iusstque mundum nosse nascendi vias.

Cras amet qui numquam amavit quique amavit cras amet.

Ipsa Troianos nepotes in Latinos transtulit:
Ipsa Laurentem puellam coniugem nato dedit,
Moxque Marti de sacello dat pudicam virginem:
Romuleas ipsa fecit cum Sabinis nuptias
Unde Ramnes et Quirites proque prole posterum
Romuli matrem crearet et nepotem Caesarem;

Cras amet qui numquam amavit quique amavit cras amet.

Rura fecundat voluptas, rura Venerem sentiunt;
Ipse Amor, puer Dionae, rure natus dicitur.
Hunc, ager cum parturiret, ipsa suscepit sinu:
Ipsa florum delicatis educavit osculis.

Cras amet qui numquam amavit quique amavit cras amet.

Ecce iam subter genestas explicant agni latus,
Quisque tutus quo tenetur coniugali foedere.
Subter umbras cum maritis ecce balantum greges:
Et canoras non tacere diva iussit alites.
Iam loquaces ore rauco stagna cygni perstrepunt:
Adsonat Terei puella subter umbram populi,
Ut putes motus amoris ore dici musico,

And not that she cried to her sister of her barbarous mate.
She sings, we are hushed. When comes my Spring?
Then will I be as the swallow, silent no more?
I have sinned against the Muse by my silence,
and Apollo looks not on me:
Thus was silence a sin when the Amyclians held their voices.
Tomorrow may he love who never has loved,
And he who has loved, may he love tomorrow.

Et neges queri sororem de marito barbaro.
Illa cantat, nos tacemus. Quando ver venit meum?
Quando fiam uti chelidon, ut tacere desinam?
Perdidi Musam tacendo, nec me Phoebus respicit.
Sic Amyclas, cum tacerent, perdidit silentium.

Cras amet qui numquam amavit quique amavit cras amet.

The Poet's Corner #1, 1955, Wichita, Kansas
Published by Charlie Plymell and edited by Alan Russo

ANGEL OF THE WORLD, WHO DREAMS IN LIGHT

Angel of the world, who dreams in light
Celestial words, the starry letters of
                the night:
Our questing phrases to your courtyard wind;
In the chaste precincts of your thought we
                find
The text and tuning of our years.
Like snowbound angels we are foundered in
                your tears.
When to the dark our harbored frailties go
You melt them in the listlessness of snow.

AND MOZART, WITH THE SLY

And Mozart, with the sly
uplifting of his golden lids
Turns us on to the supreme jazz
knowing what we want
perfectly balanced for an instant.
But how maintain
the wilful gravity
of those subtly weighted lids,
The single repose
of that staring brow?

Mikrokosmos, Spring, 1958
Published by Wichita University

"Dominion" (Alan's signature poem) was first published in this issue of *Mikrokosmos*;
see *Dominion and other poems*.

POEM

(Honey
rips the cankered wombs of lambent gargoyles)
On lying knees of desire
I invoke the holy names
And suspire, in the dark,
Toward the nameless
(two sparrows draw my chariot):
O filthy pard of day, will you bring,
In your prostituted retinue
The touching torch
To hail me, half from hell?

YOU WILL BE JOYED TO FIND OUT WHY IT HURTS

I know what they were talking about,
The lordly blasphemers of old.
They sit in skinny trees
And flash their darkeyed songs at me.
They dart their sinuous arrows, tipped with sunset,
At the thrilled cringes of my naked dreams.

SUICIDES

Instead of waiting for their Death to come
They slew Him on the highway to the Sun.

TO AMERICA IN THE SHADES OF HOLLYWOOD

I wait, my love, till you, of dreamland queen,
Flesh out the mockup of your vapid dreams.

SMALL POEM

A slender wire connects my brain
To the morning sun; at the first birdnote
Golden dust will dance from the wire.

Drawing by James G. Davis from *Mikrokosmos*

The Poet's Corner #2, 1959, Wichita, Kansas
Published by Charlie Plymell and edited by Alan Russo

SAID SHE FROM AMIDST HER FRAGMENTS

Said she from amidst her fragments:
Tell all my smiles, tell all my answering airs,
Had they the virtue of a summer day
Yet were they misfits in this world of mine
Now that, by sleight, I cast beyond the stars
By this, my knee-side pool, the universe…

The Locked Man, 1960, Wichita, Kansas
Published & Printed by Charlie Plymell

I WILL NOT WALK THE ROAD TO SYNTHESIS AGAIN

I will not walk the road to synthesis again
I will not take the garish colored pills
My blood is red or green, and proud
It has its own mythology
The way of contemplation is not strained.

THE HOURS ARE NOT PRECIOUS

The hours are not precious
They are wasted steadfastly and with care
The day goes like a drop of blood,
the whole world round—
The more grooves to lose.
We are found listening at the doors of our tombs.

WORDS—AREN'T REAL

Words—aren't real
Eloquence—without a voice
Witness—witness to the rite
the cherry demolition at the ego's spine.
The city of the mind is then built on the rubble of chastened ignorance!

THE HOBO DREAM THEIR ATOMS LOVE TO TOUCH*

The hobo dream their atoms love to touch
right into the fondest part of hell
that smells of life too much, too much
rat anger beats the brains of heaven, Mordred, moan
the dreamer melted into a stone
Steam shovel morals storm the gates of pearly steep
The ring you seek, Lady, is cankered up too deep
Hold off your heartache till the morning
Postman time will come
with more leaden lessons for deaf sore to thumb
till some rich doom writes you off the page of mind.

*Poem was also published in *Maintenant* Issue #13, 2019.

MEMORY, WITH HEARTSLUCK DRIPPING AT THE ROOT

Memory, with heartsluck dripping at the root.
The paths lead back through time—
that doubted woods is there—
and the tree with the carving,
and a vulture sitting on the highest branch…
The sepulcher of the heart's desire
ruled by the dumbfound scepter of loss.
Now all is far and hidden from your sight.
Turn dimly, abashed,
and scrape the emptying yards of withdrawal
with your slackening ken.

I AM FORGIVEN AND THROWN OVER TO OLDER DAYS, WHEN LIGHTER CARES BESET

I am forgiven and thrown over to older days,
when lighter cares beset—
How to get another beer, how to make mine wine—
but the blood will not sit still, and a deep brooding–ulterior vintage—
stirs, a remote past that I step on every day.
Breakthrough? We are here. The past is a lie against
the enormity of the present, the future a schoolmarm's lie that will
never come true. Sink into your moment, whether life or death
who knows what you have to gain or lose?
To lose: a life of penal misery.
To gain: an infinity of bright, close discoveries.
Perhaps each of our lives is forming, all the while,
a perfect and beautiful pattern
which we do not complete, and realize,
until the moment of our death.
The kaleidoscope that half-drowned men report,
"my whole life flashed before me"
but they don't stay to see the end.
Only the dead have seen the whole truth,
There and clear for one instant. The end is just and "fitting."
The dead had their reward or punishment in life,
all they can get from death is consummation.
And recognition of their life without their "self"—
now lost and gone forever.
Better to die once in truth than live a thousand years in folly—
the American dream.

"AND WHO SHALL STAND WHEN HE APPEARETH?"

"And who shall stand when He appeareth?"
Whose life has such strength
as not to crumble in the final light?
Who spoke such truth
as not be struck silent at that sight?
Who has in him so little sin
as not to be plucked by fear?
Who has such joy of life
not be gladdened at his rightful end?
Who was so righteous
not to send the compass of hell
shooting a million ways at once?
And who so lost
as not to find himself
in the lost arms of his innocence again,
Risen as first he rose, in light,
Fragrant and free from the flames?

"OF PHOSPHOR, THE MINX CATS RESOUND"

"Of phosphor, the minx cats resound."
The slanting elbow motion from the left—
Intrigue! Portfolio, bad dust!
Wipe that cat off your chair, Black Smile.

PEYOTE POEM: THE MAN UNLOCKED

The paths are not longer hidden
And no place dark will hide me.
May I find light to face the Light that breaks the light.
And height to reach the Height that crumbles height.
and love to bear the Love that stifles love.

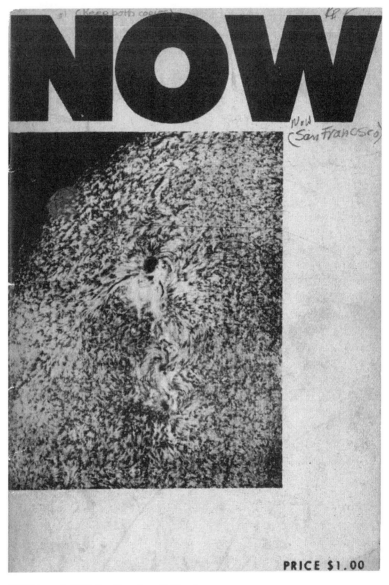

NOW, Issue 1, 1963, San Francisco, California
Published by Charlie Plymell
Ari Publications

For text of the following poems appearing in this issue of *NOW*: "We Are Dying,"
"Ten Times the Christ," "An Angel Cry," "You Have to Lie Like a Snake," and
"The Pit of Being;" see *Dominion and other poems*. For text of "Of Phosphor"
see *The Locked Man*.

THE RAVAGED FLESH FORMS A PRAYER

The ravaged flesh forms a prayer.
The bough is broken but the song is not all stilled.
If you lean over the abyss of nothingness,
the erstwhile Fairyland of your carnal soul,
whisperings can be heard,
and if one finds its home in your heart,
it blots out a thousand nights of hell.

WHAT DO YOU THINK IS UNDERNEATH THE DARK?

What do you think is underneath the dark?
or above the light?
How far need a thing be
to be above a worm's gage?
In Rock-n-Roll instrumentals there are no
        banal words
to come between you and the real meaning
and it comes through black and pure,
a glimpse at the workings of the frightful heart
at the center, whose tune
men and cities dance.

Is there a cradle love is rocked in?
And are there lines of longing
stretched around the world
tangled in treetops and sodden in rivers?
The locket is in the casque—where have the tears
        been put?
Differences dwindle and converge beyond point.
There is more than you know, and less than you think.
The bulk of the iceburg is not clipped by words.

UNWRAPPED IN SOLITUDE

Unwrapped in solitude—
the solar peace of the glands.
How high now heaven rings—
the well of conscience is dried up.
Unending clarity—
the hipster beats on the walls,
freedom floats from the sockets—
you're sitting on your crown maestro:
the serpent follows hard.

NEVER TO ENTER WARM AND TIRED HANDS

Never to enter warm and tired hands,
on the last leg of sleep?
I marveled at the green and shining ways.
Now lost revenues ring dreams of thwarted kingdoms.
Tom Thumb, what face answers the mirror's last blank shot of snow?
It's still air I breathe, but if I could
ensnarl the talons of time in a net of fantasy
and enforce the laws I breathe upon the scarecrow mask of reality,
I'd have the atoms of peace aligned in airtight fashion,
and sway light to new rules
and nurse incendiary secrets from the night.

POETRY

CHARLES PLYMELL
ALLEN GINSBERG
ALAN RUSSO
MICHAEL McCLURE
ROBERT BRANAMAN
THOMAS JACKRELL
DAVID OMER BEARDEN
ROXIE POWELL
DANIEL MOORE
ANDREW HOYEM
J. RICHARD WHITE
PHILIP WHALEN

Daniel Moore

San Francisco

1963

List of contributing writers and artists that appeared in *NOW*

NOW NOW, Issue 2, 1965, San Francisco, California
Published by Charlie Plymell
Cover drawing by Bob Branaman
Ari Publications

For text of the following poems appearing in *NOW NOW*: "Doomed to Reply" and "A Failure" see *Dominion and other poems*.

RHYMED QUATRAIN

My heart beating fast on the left side,
my image of "keen consciousness" on the right,
that slight glimmer of forethought
stymied the last spasm of delight.

SELF PORTRAIT

A tree of warm meat riven by lightning.
The plot line:
Tartary crossed by Huns.
So structured
the air inherits breathing there.

FALL GUY

could start anyplace anytime always the same
times places events like strings snarled around a spindle
driven through the heart
and he called me a Christian
as Christian as a corncob.

"The only dirty thing about me is YOUR cock! " she screamed,
hair peroxided beyond belief betraying a tamarin archetype
disastrous consciousness shimmering about the eyeballs.
Girl offered me milk, knowing I was high

but the Lil' Abner bit etc. soon drove me to the streets under blue sky
and orange girders and to escape the irrepressible Crab (always shying
away, shifty-eyed at the mention of burroughs), knows a cop when
he sees one (wouldn't you?) past grim-eyed workers punch-drunking

the earth under endless sky of the Unbearable Tale (could you?) back down the Same Old Hill every time I get there I feel like I been doing it a thousand years and it makes me feel very tired.

I hated socks and he asked me if I saw roses (putting me on?) odd man out later at Oak St. where talk of the banana wars raged about my ears.

Tom wearing his brother's face, clothes, father's job and me with the inexorable burden judiciously but arbitrarily placed splat on my head realized I'd rather be alone with my buzz mill than listen to that shit.

First night wasn't so hard, even slept, next day thought it was ok but stupidly got drunk and the shit hit the fan—rage at the departing image who didn't care about my azure dream of dawn goddess in her diadem of dew (would you?) Who went her way as they all do some other way of course (aren't they all?) despite the revival of love potion number 9 I think I've had mine and blown it all;
sprouted mushrooms when dropped on choicest earth
musta been a bad batch.

When will the Incrimination Requisition come?

Finally busted down crates one big enough for a dwarf's coffin.
Notable quote: "The Devil runs his fingers through my brains the way a miser runs his fingers through gold." —Mike Ray.

Reorganizing my mind would be like teaching a herd of shit to ice skate. I'm stubborn—sullen—hanging on when hope is gone
stop kidding yourself and you're through—

trusted truth and it fucked me in the face—one time too many—my presence inexcusable—reconstituting a frozen albatross—calling it Life is like putting lace panties on a dank cunt—has to be done— don't you know? Can't even find an acceptable fantasy—my tape connection broken—when desire fails what is left?

Glimmering Despot City seething under a nearby sky—ultraviolet glow advancing up the walls as the sunset recedes—pink tendencies beam from stucco walls—couldn't even find someone I didn't want to see—when they passed the pipe I said, "I don't want to use a hand crank."

Married love—not so passionate but solid and sure—I married death and it's getting pretty old—dry bitch—sighs like a gas stove—getting pretty indiscriminate about language—"We feel each word should be represented regardless of worth." Poetry is just too goddamn cute for words—notice each day is longer, more involved—

"It's MINE and I'm going to KEEP it," he said—feeling of clenched teeth at the other end of the line—could it be that all is not well inside the young blond? Sour Grapes? How come I have to pay a good guy's price and get bad guy's wages? Was there a short-change con when the desserts were handed out? How come everyone is either out, busy, or just not interested? The very complicated subliminal sewage system sometimes gets clogged up—fucking machine—taking dope is like pouring gas in the carburetor to start a car—hell of a way to get around—there aren't enough crates in the world for me—I could bust 'em all and still be left with an empty aspirin bottle and hospital hope—they all tell me to take it to Walgreens—I get the idea—sorry to have made such a mess—old enough to know better but too young to desist.

Kindness with a skid row accent brought me the flannel crawl—Tom's theory of pusballs—the evil perhaps radiating from the crotch? Even objectivity becomes inapplicable a million failures after idealism has been decimated by the flaming hounds of Terra Vista—

Attacks as THEY call HIM—Jackrell says god is dog—think I see what he means—a rose by any other name would not have occurred to you—told Charlie his face looked like Christmas coming but by then they had ceased to listen to me—

It's the horror of the grave that assails us at night—maybe the Manichaeans were right and it was all a big mistake like god belched and o my god a universe now why the hell did I do that? Grabbing his ermines and splitting for higher grade country—

All around me copulating couples and me pounding the typewriter like a robot jacking off—my stomach has finally rebelled; will the other organs remain loyal? Can't really blame defectors after the rough time I've given them—my peter would go dive in the nearest sludge pool if it could get . . .

Ann was wearing her madness in neon signals of grief—Who would want to take LSD? Someone who doesn't know better. Younger generation seems to be screwy enough on the naturals—I'd pray to god if he believed in me—silver threads among the gold—time has been anaesthetized and they are doing any damn thing they please with it—love has been revealed as a well-meaning but deluded shuck—after a few years it tastes like moldy leaves—even Paul's father's shorts came out brown and the garbage truck was the Avenging Angel.

II

I used to imagine that I might someday be in a situation where it would be appropriate to say, "Do you suppose Man is a theriomorphic deity?" My folly is somehow like an eclair—

Went to the beach once and it was covered with large, smooth pebbles—said, "They're scraping the bottom of the barrel." Been doing it myself for years. My life is becoming a speeded-up movie on Aging. "And here we see the Horrible Old Example." Turned me down down down while the laundromat went round round round . . . been doing it for years . . . the wrong record played a million times . . . finally it breaks and they come up with a new copy . . . look straight and keep your fingers out of your mind while waiting for the undertaker . . . but no I had to meddle with the mechanism and now here I am at the wheel of a runaway truck with no brakes . . . steering erratic . . . leaning on the horn in last resort eliciting only a feeble blast . . , brake pedal touching the floorboard in terror—one touch you're never supposed to feel . . .

I broke the spell by speaking and she withdrew in dismay like, "You touched me with your artichoke WHAT?" My artichoke heart, peeled back to the white-hot nerve-ghost, stripped for love, free of truth and innocence at last, one time in my life I came out right and I had to be on the wrong track . . . a jungle of search, evasion and Private Property in each arm's needle tracks . . . too many to know, or forget . . . you can't swallow it and you can't spit it out . . . smoke gets in your eyes and bile in your blood . . . will they fuck my body up? Hackneyed sequence of dying in furnished rooms . . . we led the old man to the hospital, the lights blinked as we walked in the door. A one-way trip, I knew. A won-way for me? I had high hopes. Old school ties . . . two freshmen on the floor, blood mingling as the gun slips off the bed . . . hushed up like the grinding of the mind . . . wear mufflers in every direction . . . orders. It's for your own good, you know. Don't let too much out and we won't let too much in.

A wrong connection got made at a primal level and I haven't been able to get the conviction overturned yet. I have the cowardice of my conviction . . . invincible fallibility . . . fall guy . . . endless autumn . . .

N.Y. 1962 (LETTER TO RICHARD WHITE)

DEAR RICHARD,

I AM WRITING THIS AT WORK. IT IS A BLUEPRINT MILL WHERE I
TYPE ON AN EXAGGERATED TYPEWRITER ON HUGE SHEETS OF
PLASTIC. DO YOU THINK WE WILL EVER GET OUT OF THIS9 (THERES
NO QUESTION MARK ON THIS THING) IT IS VERY HARD TO REPLY
XBM TO YOUR LETTER WHICH IS VERY BEAUTIFUL AS USUAL.
(YOU DONT KEEP A CARBON C0PY FOR FUTURE PUBLICATION,
DO YOU?) AND I DONT FEEL UP TO WRITING ANYTHING VERY
BEAUTIFUL BACK. BUT AS FOR PEOPLE. ED MARSHALL IS TRYING
TO CONVERT ME. BETH IS TRYING TO BE PREGNANT. JOHN W. IS
TRYING TO CLEAN OUT HIS NEEDLE WITH A WIRE BUT HE MISSES
EVERY TIME SINCE HE IS WEARING SOMEONE ELSES GLASSES
WHICH KEEP SLIPPING DOWN HIS NOSE. JOANNE WENT BACK
TO HER HUSBAND SOON AFTER I GOT HERE. I HAVENT REALLY
MET ANYONE HERE EXCEPT BETH'S HUSBAND WHO PROPOSES
HIMSELF AS ONE OF THE GREAT SCIENTIFIC GENIUSES OF THE AGE.
I DONT SEE ANYONE MUCH. JUST GOT A LETTER FROM CHARLIE,
ALL ABOUT J's[?] ABORTION, SOUNDS LIKE HE HAS GONE OUT OF
HIS HEAD OR WAS HE JUST HIGH. HE INCLUDED A LETTER FROM
ROXIE IN GERMANY, SAME ROX IN HIS HEAD. BUT, SURPRISE, I DO
HAVE A POEM TO SEND YOU, NOT MUCH BUT THE FIRST I HAVE
DONE IN MANY MOONS. AND GAWSH I HAVENT SHOWN IT TO
ANYONE YET.

BLACK CLOUDS BILLOWED FROM CHRISTS BEDROOM—
THE SMELL OF SUFFERING,
THE SMELL OF SICKNESS,
THE SMELL OF SADNESS,
HUNG IN THE SHAGGY EYES,
A GLOOM TO BE CUT THROUGH
ONLY BY THE FLAMING ARROW,
THE SKYROCKET CROSS.

THE ONLY FOOD I HAVE EVER WANTED TO EAT WAS THE FRUIT
OF THE TREE OF LIFE AND THE SAME GOES FOR DOPE-BUT GIVE
ME SOME EXTERNAL NEWS LIKE THE SOUNDS SHERILL'S PUSSY
MAKES NOW OR CAN YOUR SON FLY YET?

KEEP THE ANTI-MATTER FLYING.

ALAN

Fux! Magascene, Anthology, 1965, San Francisco, California
Publication & Cover Drawing by Bob Branaman
Ari Publications

BAY OF TONKIN

The wind springs up
as the alleycat speaks
a gate bangs in the wind all summer night
tom-tom hugs the earth
like a threatened Warsong
while, beyond the lightning
guns sound on the darkened
Bay of Tonkin.

Boots and Saddles in the Old Corral
where do you ride tonite?
You don't believe that old song
but here we are
walking emptyechoing boots
and riding emptyfeeling saddles
deprived of the belief in ghosts
and of the reality of flesh
neither here not there
in a life neither dis nor dat
torn by black eddies
traumatic children of the negative universe
spawned by the faggot bastard of time

just don't step into the dark she said
but by day we go in a snowstorm of
worn out (therefore jagged)
razor blades from dreams, pasts and karmas
& perhaps fragments of the great unwonderable
thrown in
gleanings for the goldust eye
and after all is said and done
to think that I'm the only one
who could believe what has become of me
when be has turned

all all to pee
the husk returns to its long home,
Novas yet stillborn in the lymph glands of the groin.

beatniks drive Jahveh motorcycles
into the jaws of the howling inimical monster
shouting saintly slogans
oblivious of the greater drama which is likewise oblivious etc.
                    planets puppets fools all.

Fux! Magascene, advertisement from *NOW NOW*
Drawing by Bob Branaman

Dominion and other poems, 1977, California
Published by David Omer Bearden
Cover drawing by Bob Branaman
Rosace Publications

The poem "Dominion" appeared in *Mikrokosmos*, *The Last Times II*, and *NOW*.
And "Radio Hash" and "Saint Mary" both appeared in *Le Feu du Ciel*.

EPIGRAPH: AN ANGEL CRY

An angel cry
summoned up from dungeons of disgust
where monarchs of the dark array.
We are driven to this painful union
by the unplugged starlets in our chest.

WE ARE DYING

We are dying
for someone to hold out a hand
and speak the words of life.
The inferior level at which we live
is belied only by fits of insight.
Hope is an angel raising from the swamps,
so fair, so far, so seldom to be held,
and mercy, like a desert rain
is quenched before it hits the ground,
beaten back by the heat of our vengeful sin and fear.
Let rage be still a moment,
and the thousand furnaces of hate lie low;
from deeper down, from higher up,
and patient as the waves,
the everlasting words of love,
surely, surely, surely will be heard.

DOOMED TO REPLY

doomed to reply
(last long look)
looming from the headlights of a billion billboards
idiot jowls flapping in the wind,
"Kilroy was here"
the signature of all things
leaking from the frayed edges of control.

Johnny tied his puppydog to a tree
and loved it.

He was wrong many times in the eyes of his family
but never in the eyes of the lord.

The tree grew up in heaven,
a perpetual fountain of care.

THE WEREWOLF HANGS IN SPACE

The werewolf hangs in space
like a mossy cobweb
stars glimmering through eyeholes—
demon jewels—
closing in
through some violation of dimensions
checkmating the averages
till I feel warm breath on my neck—
Savage, your reek is at the outmost!
Your heel stamps my name on the pavement.
I look like smoke filtered through blood
whatever sees the light through me
must stand the long trial

Who wants to eat those apples
you all want to come up
but you don't want to drink my cup
wouldn't myself if I could've helped it
but I had no choice
signed sealed and delivered
like a hot dog on a stick
I ate my doom
in the youthful folly of time
and now I'm slowly
wretching it all back
like the stamp machine in the supermarket store
of the parking meters
punching out time
along the august avenues of the sun.

YOU HAVE TO LIE LIKE A SNAKE

You have to lie like a snake in the paths of glory
awaiting the golden power
till the sticks and stones melt with your agony
and the light of God shines through.

The poison flowed from the tomb
and, before God, took off its clothes!
Saying, Here am I, the son of time!
Eat me with love, or your throne trembles!

The moon did not rise for fear of so much heat.
The tropics were splattered on the beach,
red fruit turned to gold.
Ate meat of sun lostfoundonceforever.

RADIO HASH

Sad boy's lyric
lost in the street rumble
an orange peel over a matchstick
makes an umbrella
quicker than a Chevy will be $287 cheaper
than being strung out on this scene
O baby
when the bottles and the ashtrays on the table
form a perfect conic section
I get so blessed
I make a mess wandering in the snail garden
smooth over the stones
but wild in the wind
like Baker Beach
waiting for the next wave of LSD maniacs
keep on chawing me closer
Daryl The Screwn would become a sign
and the hillbilly commercial comes on
blue and pink like hearts in the sunset.
"Love is a five letter word
spelled M-O-N-E-Y"
Money is a six letter word
spelled M-O-N-K-E-Y
little Campbell's lovesong
about eating his girl's pussy
"Nothing saves you like your voice"
a hungry years old
blue aint the word for the feeling I feed on
send me the pillow that you dream on
cook it down shoot it up
roll off into space giggling your secret
wait and wait for the steady taste
"Hic Gloria!" by Them

BOARDMAN'S STREET POEM

Savage as nightmare
the climax rhythms climb and glide
teeth of landslide, might of moving paw
octopus vise twisting the continent into focus
the lion faces the unicorn.

PUMP PUZZLES

who would want to say
as a statement of principle
that God has ground his heel
in the sooty earhole of being
or wiped mangled mindcries off the windshield
with a squeegee?
no it's too mad and it don't rhyme I can't cut it
No but that WE are the ragged edges
like what they make hamburger out of
without any give or take at the margin
but YOU make it up out of your being
for the lack excess.
Halfway between the eagle and the serpent
lies the Mobil station
on a carpet of distilled entrails
and you know spaghetti snarks
lurk from the fire hydrants
but pretend it doesn't matter
it's all a half-digested nightmare
and your mind
is the muttering pain behind the tooth
smuttering red flashes into the darkness
that is your bad debt
threatening malvicious action

scrunchin at the junction
but if I said all I seeknow you'd be as mad as me
and there'd be nothing left to say
so it's all based on you holding the marbles
and me mongering my messness
I hold the ball and someone kicks it
out of the park
for you a lark
but for me bloody times
the dog that ate Kotex was from my home town
you see I've been around
I ate the dog before time began
and away I ran
that's why they're after me
trying to stomp the truth out
before I forget what it was
and I can't decide who buttered my bread—
the window peeker
or the guy in bed?

THE SPANISH MAIN

Oh listen it was bloody murder
deep down inside his chest
His heart kept pressing me to answer
and I tried to do my best
But I found I was a Hapsburg
and it was all I could do to hide
the horror of my ancestry
from the flaming sword outside.
The crown sat uneasy on my head
I couldn't help but think of shit
the world kept trying to get me to take
a brighter view of It.

I stirred the pool of piss-blood idly
trying to feel aloof
wondering what would happen if Justice
held a thunderbolt over the roof.
I guess you'd have to be a stone
to get through this world of pain
but then a stone can't make a moan
to bid the desert to the dream of rain.
So you fuck me or I'll fuck you
it's all about the same
just so one drop gets to the surging foam
that rides the Spanish Main.

SAINT MARY

Saint Mary locked in the moon
faced mirrored in mushrooms
swart in the time of the toad
silver when the casket opens

Saint Mary baked in the moon
white hot heart like day behind the winter glass
the midnight sun stands in his shambles,
"chaos… dreaming… alone…"

Twelve times one holds the gate
while seven lifts the bright sword.
Saint Mary crushed in the moon
bleeding mercury bullets to the bone.

Steel in the skull, gold in the heart,
moisture in the palm of one hand.
Over the moon,
Saint Mary gates the flood.

PIT OF BEING

The birth-doctor holds aloft
the bloody flag of life
screaming God! Christ! Om!
Ejaculate the elements
from the bleeding crown of Here!
The petals have parted for an instant
and the jewel-box has spat this gobbet
upon the forehead of time!
Conjunction of stars and blood!
Cruel bright wheel
churning the icy milk of the firmament
into furrows of flesh
with its name written on the inside
that only the third eye can see!
The lips are sealed henceforth
by the heavy hand of earth.
The sleeper wakes into dream, and soon
the dream will sleep into wake.

DOMINION

The additions to his kingdom are frequent and large.
It grows stealthily, but by leaps and bound,
and though you may not read it in the papers,
each day new territories are annexed.
He has such an appetite, he is like a dark king
who buys wineyards so that he may watch
the grapes growing from his castle walls and see them
trampled beneath the exquisite feet of his minions
until he holds the bottle in his hands, and
feeling his power, fondles the succulent child.
Our king will greatly extend his holdings
when he scents ripe fruit; you may
welcome nightfall in a land you thought safe
and awake to see his tokens everywhere;
the street signs give forth hitherto hidden meanings,
the fruit on the table exudes a soft, calculating evil,
the clock is tense, expectant, spelling out a deathly
     sentence.
You may see his marks on a wife, a daughter;
though they keep their shells, you know they are his:
When you speak to them, it is into his
     pendant-jeweled ear;
When they reply, it is from his great slow lips;
And, most awful, when they look at you, it is with his
     cool, misty eyes.
All you who climb the stair or walk the road,
toiler, or trifler, nightflyer or daycrawler,
you will open your window for morning sun
and feel his warm glue on your face; you will
buy a ticket to Utopia under an assumed name
and wake the first morning to see
his tents line the horizon all around.

THE NEW MINT RIDE

When love went wrong
and right went right
and left your back to the fact
skippin' one nick offa your old left turn
left you out in the fields to burn.

There was never really any coming back
just turning on a slow ridge glide
you could feel the power goin' through ya
and say, Papa, let that new mint ride.
Oh Lord the shit they shot on us
and lord how we fought back
we hit it just about the line
when the grab bag fits the sack.

We didn't ask for none of this
seemed to all come with The Fall
but Beauty came by to take a whiz
and gave a new name to it all.

I don't mean to sound romantic
guess we've chewed too many rocks for that
but God and man have got two stones
that laid right come out flat.

A FAILURE

Glasses of fire
mirrored in their cylinders
hot dances, wildeyed loves,
thick heads and busted jaws
on the summer porch.
Hardons when work is done
like an airplane vaulting the mountain sky.

I can no more sing out the song,
through cycles run,
than the ring on the bathtub is, or does.

TEN TIMES THE CHRIST

Ten times the Christ
scratched Victory across the wall
and each time it was erased.
The elected victim rises
from the tomb of the flesh
to skywriting, atomic flower
and symmetry on a grander scale than nature's.

IF ONCE I GAVE PAIN

if once I gave pain and did not turn my head
if once I felt pain and did not let it bleed
I am undamned by the pilgrim's cross I make in air.
Mary, mother of children,
your Christ is everywhere.

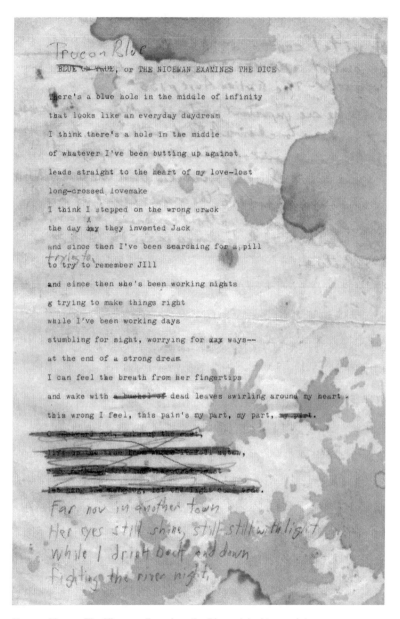

True on Blue

BLUE ON TRUE, or THE NICEMAN EXAMINES THE DICE

There's a blue hole in the middle of infinity

that looks like an everyday daydream

I think there's a hole in the middle

of whatever I've been butting up against

leads straight to the heart of my love-lost

long-crossed lovemake

I think I stepped on the wrong crack

the day they invented Jack

and since then I've been searching for a pill

to try to remember Jill

and since then she's been working nights

g trying to make things right

while I've been working days

stumbling for sight, worrying for ways--

at the end of a strong dream

I can feel the breath from her fingertips

and wake with dead leaves swirling around my heart

this wrong I feel, this pain's my part, my part.

Far now in another town
Her eyes still shine, still still with light
While I drift back and down
fighting the river night.

True on Blue, or The Niceman Examines the Dice, original typescript

TRUE ON BLUE, OR THE NICEMAN
EXAMINES THE DICE

There is a blue hole in the middle of infinity
that looks like an everyday daydream
I think there's a hole in the middle of whatever
I've been butting up against
straight to the heart of my love-lost
long-crossed lovemake
I think I stepped on the wrong crack
the day they invented Jack
and since then I've been searching for a pill
trying to remember Jill.
And since then she's been working nights
trying to make things right
while I've been working days
stumbling for my sight, worrying for ways
at the end of a strong dream.
I can feel the breath from her fingertips
and wake with dead leaves swirling around my heart
this wrong I feel, this pain's my part, my part, my part.
Oh westward god, wake up the east
Lift up the true from where it fell in a stew
make nothing more and the worst least
let hang the hangdogs, let the light in view.
For now in another town
Her eyes still shine,
still still with light
While I drink dusk and dawn
Fighting the river night.

TO ANTONIO VIVALDI
out of lands and prisons

Undying spring, your God-despising thrusts
Have stirred unanswered feet to seek the tombs
Of sunny gods, and all the midland sea
Lacked scope to bear the fervor
Of the sunfire of your soul—
Antonio, you set high
The wild gears of passion in the screaming Spring.

CITY POEM

The silent gloved forces that plunder our lives
Caught in a switchboard of intersecting knives
Confusions fused together make life less real.
The blocks are islands of torpor—
The streets are arrows of fear and greed.
Only the wind has a real need—
Fulfilled endlessly in emptiness and speed.

A PARABOLA IN THE BLOOD DESCRIBES
THE HOLY GHOST

a parabola in the blood describes the holy ghost
nameless and singing
silence mounts the last throne
the dishonored virtues rise again
spit, eternity pivots under your thumb.
You are not so small as not to be sometimes a god, at least.

BREATHS FROM GOAT ROCK

The ole man pulled a great big gun
and now he's got the whole damn river on the run
must weigh about a ton
and he knows just how it's done
River on the run.

When he blows through the trees
its like a grand guitar and jeez
His heartbeat makes the lands and seas
seethe and he breathes
streams of stars
blazing on their run.
Him. Zany grey ol' sun of a gun.

RESURRECTION DELLA CARNE

A shaft of light on the shaft of darkness—
the setting sun gives flame to the graveyard obelisk.
This omphalic erection despite the levity of sun-rays
is a solemn guardian of the faith.
Under his grave auspices
the widows
draw the last possible sustenance from their husbands' bodies
by planting flowers on the graves.
The children
being untutored in the Christian observances
dance on their fathers' heads,
thus lending a ghoulish air to the proceedings,
and somewhat diluting the purity of the experience.

CRISIS—DEVOLUTION

Crisis—devolution.
Movement the step out of chaos,
into the cognizant snowstorm of touch.
Or into the furious hell of still life,
the great rose of contact hushed.
The stalk-like projections lopped off
or drawn in. But never to rise again!
Who framed the curse? You wished the blinkers
on yourself when you learned to hate the light
in bitter fear. The taste of peace is faint,
and in the light of early days,
a mystery draws near.
The lingerings are much, but then one day
your eyes will kiss the dust and sigh,
"The dream is done!"

JAMES JOYCE: A WINDOW OPENING ON THE NIGHT

Dark ringed,
Dark of swirl,
O dark with chambers,
Outhouse in which fierce sacrilege was committed,
Strange circles,
Twilight becomes the breath of a dead man's prayer,
Black with the eddying of air,
Black with the richness of decay,
Black with the flare of turning,
O dark of tongue.

THE TURN OF WINTER DOES NOT TURN MY HEART

The turn of winter does not turn my heart
to warmer ways, nor does a warbler's song
teach native wisdom, or spring air dispart
desires from the grays of unvoiced wrong.
The song of leaf-tops does not tell the wind
what terrors urge their guts to thread the dirt—
Could human touch with lesser sweetness rend
the secrets from my heart, or soothe its hurt?

Though springtime turns the face of every part,
the turn of winter cannot turn my heart.

BLEWS OFF

When you finely get the knews
that someone has undone the blues
then no one wants to pay their dues no more
then Rock from the Blue recoiled
to faces that were fully broiled
since no one wants to know what's true
cause it just might turn out to be you
Then stretched out to its full extent
it ends up in some foreign tent
where someone then presents a pipe of View:
"Is this the sort of thing you meant
or did you think some psychoid government
would do?"
If so grope for full reprieve
and try to pick off just the leave
that will allow you to maintain some stance
through patterns that in pristine dance
will give you one more grail of chance
for God to think that it was him, not you.

DEAD MEN THE EARTH SHALL OPEN

Dead men the earth shall open,
with a packet of silent keys. . .
have known it from the hands of kindness.
Aerial ships on thin rails of aether
picking the locks of eternity
making a beeline through swimming darkness
to the zenith of superior carlots—
the serene castles of the mind.
And it will happen again,
revelation without foresight.
Infinity is no joke—
"Wrap the world 'round your watchchain,
whole crowds of sahibs are lapping the lip of the moon,
bright bestial beings. . ."
Sincere Undiluted Mortals!
Cover your mouth, your genie will see the world.
It's too late to conceal five hundred billion wounds
before the Inspector comes—perhaps a few tears will help,
and time keep true to its course, without stopping.

CHILDREN, TIME HAS FORGOTTEN THE GAME YOU WERE PLAYING

Children, time has forgotten the game you were playing.
Come out from the clouds, suicide lambs.
Come into the stunning precipice
that drops when you point
    TWO OR MORE FINGERS
at a unilateral nut of reality!

THE SUMMIT OF HEAVEN IS SMOOTH

The summit of heaven is smooth, rounded,
almost indifferent.
Time runs off it like water.
And even god is surrounded
by the stumbling crust of fate.

SHOULD I CALL DEATH KIND

Should I call death kind
because it empties the aching eyes?
or hope it grand
for what it opens to beyond?
A wave washes over a sodden log.
From an overflowing pool a great black bubble bursts.
An eye opens in a blooming cloud.
A hart falls amid rays
on kind and humble hills
the color of life.

IN A SHELL, FULL ONLY WITH THE SWEET SOUNDS WITHIN ME

In a shell, full only with the sweet sounds within me!
Tuned only to the winding sea,
the snail's self, impassioned
spinning in a coil of flesh!
It's dark where the lights go
whirlwind to preach to lower depths.

IT WAS ONE OF THOSE DAYS WHEN FLAGS GO OUT

It was one of those days when flags go out,
brightening to the breeze;
a flag-waving day;
There was so much, much more, then,
than before; the very heft
of hand and foot
seemed greater, more one's own.
Horizons stretched beyond the bounds of time.

We struck the wind with all fevers
and told the sun to run out of its harbors.
We put the torch to laughing chorus girls
and sent them snowballing through Disney paradise.
We cupped our hands to catch the rills of grace.
Snow white, pixie colt of my corral,
I mourn and harvest mushrooms in your soul.

SO MUCH IS PAST, THAT WHAT CAN BE?

So much is past, that what can be?
Cannot answer echoes with a living voice.
Cannot bring expectation to result.
What is forced is false—falters. No miracle.
A childhood scene is only a sweating shadow.
What is personal is picked out of the gloom—and lost again.
Belief will not turn the wind to gold.
He who hopes languished—beachcomber of fairy isles.
But find the stream in the hidden wood
and plunge your fortune in the sainted flood.

THE PHALLIC MOSQUITOS

the phallic mosquitos
with genital hypodermics
(string of blood linking generations/races)
plunges in plush for the ripe red core
pretty hard to reason yourself out of such an inheritance
leave it to Beaver and the DAR
the hush of release in jungle closeness
the voodoo mask is down and the earth looks at the sky
morning—and the wheel turns.
Kenneth Patchen is rose.
The dawn is a flower that will not keep.
The passage is life and time only stands still
when the current of the present is met by the current of the past.
Pinnacle from which everything slopes and reels back.
Believe it when you see it. My regrets to the unworthy.

THE HEART OF AUTUMN BEATS IN DYING TREES

The heart of Autumn beats in dying trees:
Its aching tongues
Twist leaves to death and shout them to the ground.
The coldness in the blood is heard by birds
that send the winter back from farther lands.
We stay here in the fixity of man:
I see the mouth of Autumn in the sky.

WE, WHO OF THE SKY WHEN EARTH HAD FAILED

We, who of the sky when earth had failed
to stabilize the thrust of inborn grace
and life-learned heightenings
Asked that great green shining chapters
lead us to the lost land where light rules
      are sad as stars and rare as grains of sand—
      whoever sees a grain of sand of all the billions on the
      nameless beach?

VESPERTIDES IN GREY

Vespertides in grey
rain and doves
descend through softened keys
lingering echoes of the turgid past.
Life can be coaxed or ordered.
The voices of Spring are various
but speak with one will.
The message is lost only to the mind.

THE CARNAL FLOWER STANDS IN SICKNESS OF DESIRE

The carnal flower stands in sickness of desire,
Joy is the cure.
When the patient no longer exists he has no disease.
The cloud falls on the plain and dryness is set right
as moaning dark is christified with light.
And all that matters is that dawn comes, no matter what
comes before.
Humanity has worked up from the slime, a million million years,

how long now till a man feels god in his heartbeat—
a few months, or has it happened?
The keepers don't want their animals to find out about
the beautiful roses within them,
because they might not like their peanuts then—
That's what people get out of life, peanuts—
the big score is ahead.
Even if the world is flat, the view from the peaks is terrific.

THERE WAS A DAY LIKE THIS LAST YEAR

There was a day like this last year,
September the 8th,
When the death of summer finally
had to be acknowledged.
This year has been no different.
There has been no lack of opportunity,
Indeed, nothing but opportunity:
The vague sky has begged that its Kansas blankness by violated,
The air has searched for some token of labor to carry off,
An unlooked-for song, a cry in the night.
The earth has asked to be entered.
Nothing was forthcoming from this quarter.
The question that has been begged so many times must
be answered:
The answer has been foretold in a thousand postponements;
I have no more pegs to hang a lie on;
I have stumbled to the dead-end of summer leaf
I am sitting in front of a trash heap of gold stars
Wordlessly examining the fact that reposes in my hands
Like a cold, dead fish, like an epitaph to a stack of
misdated calendars,
The year has turned full circle
and no new life has come.

IT HAPPENS, O YES IT HAPPENS

It happens, O yes it happens,
dark as the meaning of a dream.
No spiritual grace in chemicals.
Can any key not be blessed in giving?
Perilously close—the frozen sea!
The death of God!
Belief in flames, groves of sanctity,
ruins, ashes, tinged by the tide
that threatens the very sun.
The Son speaks some tiny words that no one hears
and a child sits in the middle of the floor,
bawling with hands full of blood,
all curtains down and the world collapsing about him.
Would you lick the fence god sits on
and try to blow a windfall with your goodwill?

AS IF, IN PASSING, ONE TOUCHED THE KEYS OF LIFE LIGHTLY

As if, in passing, one touched the keys of life lightly
and then no more was heard.
And the saddest sound of all is silence.
Drawn from a wilderness world,
no thicker than a sigh,
Characters of vacuity
struggling for form, *rigor vitae*,
not this cold chaos for a million years!
Savior, return us poor specters
to the warm embrace of matter,
set us in the stream of life,
Turn us on to what flows forever!
Inhabit these husks with something more than sludge.

DON'T STIR THAT MUDHOLE

Don't stir that mudhole—
snakes will streak the slime
that might, just might, lie low
if we sit very quietly
and think of something else.
Life in a garbage can isn't so bad
with a ribbon in your hair,
and sometimes you can see a little patch of sky, over there.
Been here for nigh onto eighty year
and never saw no reason to change.
Heard voices one spring day,
but they went away.

YOU READ ABOUT THE HEADS WHO GET CAUGHT

You read about the heads who get caught,
but you never hear about the ones who make it.
They're happier than you, pig-footed rapist of the consummate
muse,
who leave your offal in the temples of the innocent and pure.

YOUR HATE IS CRIME

Man and law, I now pronounce you Monster and *Merde*,
Dance on steel pavilions.

GOD WROTE "MINE" ACROSS EVERYTHING

God wrote "MINE" across everything
in big bold beautiful letters,
impresses the shit out of everyone,
it's God . . . it's God's will . . . we're God's children . . .
pore lil' fuzzyheaded sinner bastard globs of mud,
but GOD is up there with our balls in hock in his right hand,
stage right, all we have to do is suck Karma's ass for 7 million
years or is it 7 billion I always fergit,
and then everything will be all right,
just as if nothing had ever happened,
bridge washed over the dam or whatever it was,
who cares, our unbearable essences will all be shlupped up
into the crater of infinity EST (Eternal Stickemup Time)
and, like they say in the song, "It won't matter anymore,
It's just too beautiful."
Sure is . . . The devil made me do it but St. Peter presented the bill,
"Right this way please . . . there is a smudge on your Akashic
scorecard that won't seem to come out . . . We'll just steep you in
STP (Supernatural Tanning Process) and if that doesn't do it, we can
always melt that old soul down and see if we can't come up with
something better . . . shouldn't be hard, considering . . . We have
some lovely new models that will believe anything and don't even
expect to mean anything, while you have spelt trouble for a long old
time . . . You want what's best don't you and we should know . . .
So come this way won't you for a long lonesome while . . .
This way to glory for you, bleeding old pile."
They'll tell you black is black and white is white and you should be
glad it comes out so right . . . coulda been worse . . .

you can run any insanity through the right equation
and it'll come out, give or take a dimension or two, so you never
need be at a total loss . . . "Now ain't that lovin you baby?"
Stick with us and the future is through.
Well, just don't believe everything you knew.

HAROLD GETS UP IN THE MORNING

Harold gets up in the morning
and stands in front of the plants in the sun.
And he cannot help but see with Harold's eyes
and feel with Harold's hands
and walk with Harold's feet
into the room of Harold's doom.
No more can I, with mine.

The pattern will be broken like a bomb
and thus only,
with the insides all gone out
and the outside not remaining.
The form is cast in darkness
and explodes in light,
too late to be seen
but felt—and this we don't know—
to our everlasting betterment.
And thus I dream, without hope, of the outcome
of the mysterious tale.

LOST CITY OF THE QUEEN

Looked South
Looked North
Decided to go forth
Into the City
The City of the Queen.
I came
I found
Got where I was bound
And then of course threw it in a ditch.
Life. Ain't that a bitch.

YOU KNOW I TAUGHT YOU 'BOUT MY RELIGION

You know I taught you 'bout my religion
showed you my sister too
you say it's all shaped like a pigeon*
that ain't nothing to do with you

You have shopped for christmas pictures
lookin' through a big bear's claws
that ain't nothin' to when you turn around
and die without just cause

*cf. vern. "dovetail" v. int.

YOU GUYS SO GOOD TO ME

You guys so good to me
it makes me want to smile
they lit the third guy on the cross
    people fell down for miles
    some of the kids dropped their joints
    commitments shot thru turnstiles
Said "It didn't matter"
but surrounded by the grey flesh
of "It did so"
    what can you do
    "Only women breathe."

To every pore open to the sky
breathe dawn into the pattern of flesh
find your granddys tendons
in the warp of the mesh

THIS FULL FLAMEY THING

This full flamey thing—can you hold it in your arms?
This eye that looks out from the east of every thing,
This green cross marked on every wrist,
This knife twisting in the guts at every move,
This gnawing at the root of life.
This amputated crown the spiral never reaches—
Trunk, leaf, sap, bud,
Never the free birthright sky—
Black maggot that tramples my heart undersea,
Am I the sun that ever rises?

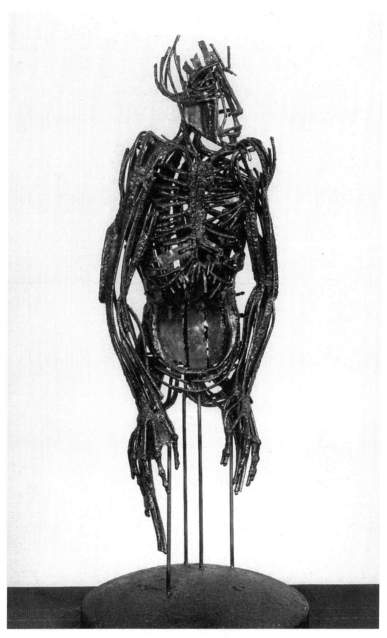

Welded steel sculpture of Alan Russo by Dion Wright. Photograph by Neal Wolfe
from The Collection of Kristen and Rick Nelson at the Canessa Gallery,
San Francisco, California, 1967.

STATE LINE

---

*"Alan with horses teeth metafysiks demurely insisting
he was intensely so over coffee"*

— ALLEN GINSBERG, "NOV. 23, 1963: ALONE"

Alan Russo, Lompoc, California, 1977
Photograph by James Bearden

PART ONE

———

CONCERNING MODUS OPERANDI

So now there is a problem of how to write this—forward or backwards, what's going on now or what happened then. I'll try to do both at once. I had an idea for a movie—say I'm 30 years old, start doing two movies at once, each 30 years long, one into the future, of what's going on, the other into the past, of what has happened, then show them side by side on the screen both running backwards, until they meet in the middle creating an eternal present out of the past. Impractical, I admit, but the principle is sound. Let me see if I can splice a few reels together. Or, I had thought of just stringing together anecdotes about other people, building sort of like a plaster mold around a casting, me supplying the mold and you inferring the casting defined by absences, negatives in reverse. There is a core of molten gold at the center, but I can't find the way there myself.

EARLIEST MEMORY

And so, in this, I tell all. Maybe I talk too much already. Maybe you'd rather not hear it. I am reminded of the schoolboy who wrote a book report on a book about penguins and said, "This book told me considerably more about penguins than I wanted to know." You can get too much of anything, overdo a good thing, and I got too much, and so here's some: you see what you can do with it. No, maybe I won't tell all, not right now anyway. You might think . . . I don't know, I don't have that much time anyway, I'll just tell as much as I can and see what happens . . .

First thing I remember in this life I was shitting my pants. I don't

73

know how old I was, 2 or 3 years, apparently was toilet trained too early. "Maybe that's the whole thing," some guy said. I was a classic case of over-toilet training. Anyway it wasn't supposed to happen and I couldn't help it and started to have an "accident." My mother picked me up and ran for the john and so the first thing I remember was the look of disgust on my mother's face because I was shitty. I've felt shitty ever since. I seem to be oversensitive, things hit me too hard or I'm too soft, but the arm's length she put between me and her then has remained between me and everyone ever since. You should take things very seriously, they last forever. And give things away cautiously, they're gone forever. I'll never have it to do over again, so I'm going to have to do it as if I already had, and knew which moves to make, like when I told Neal Cassady he was the Hitler of the Beat Generation, and he acted like he had heard it a hundred times before.

Always ahead, leading by a head, head into the wind when you're comin' . . .

THE EASTER PLAY

When I was in kindergarten I believe it was, I made my only real venture onto the stage. It was a school production. I presume each grade did a number, but all I remember is the one I was in. I wouldn't remember that it was an Easter show except the costumes made it clear that such was the case. We wore rabbit ears, attached to a headband, made out of the slightly fuzzy paper that kids use in school, baby blue this was, and we hopped around like bunnies on the stage. We were just kids, we didn't know any better.

But we soon found out.

I don't remember if the older kids laughed, or what, but we realized as soon as we got out there that we were doing something ridiculous. We didn't know exactly why it was ridiculous, but we, or at least I, must have identified it with being the youngest kids, and I'm sure the older kids reinforced this interpretation since the only thing they had over us was being older and knowing that we were ridiculous, but we couldn't disassociate being the youngest from being us; that's who we were, the kindergarten class. I suppose the teacher was urging us from the wings to hop more. We finally slunk off in embarrassment and everyone applauded. She told us how good we had been, but we knew we had been the victim of a cruel hoax, and for no other reason than that we were us. Now there's nothing wrong with kids hopping around in bunny ears; it was the situation that made it wrong, running us like we were bunnies, whereas we were kids realizing that playing bunny was not cool. I guess that was my introduction to paranoia. Like Glenn Todd said, "You're on the witness stand 24 hours a day, even if no one is interested in the testimony." So you see, there's a great lesson to be learned here, another Universal Principle is unveiled. Send your solutions care of this magazine and the best ones will be published next month.

Biting into the core of tragedy after you've awakened in the mating/waiting. Like in youth, things had a candy coating that time wore off and acid corroded, and when you've got your teeth into it too deep to get them out you hit the shit. "Everyone has his own cross to bear," they say, but they don't stop to think what that entails. After you've carried your cross comes the hard part, the crucifixion. Nailed to your own destiny. And when you get down to the nitty-gritty of just exactly what this involves for you, it's not very pretty and not like reading a book at all, more like a passion play with no other actors, not even anyone to mercifully stick a spear in you, just me, myself, and my shadow, as I think some song went: "Me and my shadow, strollin' down the avenue/Me and my shadow all alone and feelin' blue." The expression was "just me, myself, and I." I get by with a little help from my friends, but they can't help me through that.

THE GROUNDWORK OF TRAUMA

I'm not sure what the second thing I remember was but I do remember some things that happened in Hamilton Square. That's in New Jersey between Trenton and Asbury Park. We didn't move there until I was 4 or 5 but I don't remember anything from before then except the accident; must have some block somewhere. I remember one day seeing a man walk down our street, just saw him from behind, and thought he was my father, and ran after him, was just about to yell "Daddy!" when I realized he wasn't my father at all, and I stopped. Somehow after that I was never as sure of my father as before, because he hadn't been where I expected him to be. And now that I look back on it, no one ever has been.

That was the way I walked to school and I remember on cold winter days I was wearing some kind of slick pants that felt cold when the wind blew them against my legs, the first sensation I recall, which sort of set the tone for the rest of my life—of pain, discomfort, fear, of the environment impinging unpleasantly upon me, feeling like a fish out of water, an alien stranded at the wrong level of existence.

But I have some good memories from Hamilton Square too, one in particular which set the stage for my later bent for mysticism, I guess. I had forgotten about it for years until I read Ezra Pound and came across a line about his youth, "when the deep sky befriended" and that brought it back to mind. I and a friend—Freddy Walter—had gone out in the fields outside of town, and I lay down in the grass. It was high so I couldn't see anything except the grass around me and the sky above me, which was blue and seemed especially deep, warm, and friendly. I had a feeling of oneness, unity, all completely non-intellectual so that it remained unconscious until I read that poem. So there, you see, it wasn't peyote and acid. I was a natural born mystic, not one of these ersatz acid babies. Yesireebob, straight from the womb and a good deal before that, as I'll explain presently.

I guess it was that feel of the cold cloth blown against my legs that made me the way I am about weather. I like it warm enough that when the wind blows it feels good instead of bad, warm enough that you can go out lightly dressed and feel at home, at peace with the environment instead of at war with it. So I try to always be somewhere when it's warm there, California in the winter, and that's not quite warm enough, or back east in the spring. I think I'd like Hawaii weather just fine, 80 and windy; I liked central Mexico—the high country, Mexico City, Oaxaca in the summer, warm and sunny every morning with big billowing thunderheads like in the old Prince Valiant comics that used to be on the front page of Sunday comic sections: full page, but now relegated to a half inner page with Dick Tracy or Peanuts on the front. But these were fairytale book illustration clouds . . . and then every afternoon it would cloud up, a wind would spring up, lightning and thunder, and it would rain, sometimes a long downpour, sometimes just a token sprinkle. And somehow, no matter how much it had rained the day before, when the wind sprang up it would kick up dust, don't know how the soil could dry out that fast; in the US it would take days before it would. It must be because it's volcanic soil, and never far from fire and air, no matter how much water you give it. Just sock to it some heat and then some air and it's ready to fly. And into what a sky, the elements still have track of themselves there.

CHILDHOOD REMINISCENCES

Just a few more childhood reminiscences, to get that out of the way. I don't have many childhood memories because I didn't have much of a childhood. Kids now step into a ready made real life fairytale world, as if the world was made for them, while when I was a kid we felt like aliens in an adult world—especially me.

But I remember the time I fell in love with the earth. We were digging caves, or tunnels I think we called them, you dig a hole and then tunnel in. It was the smell of the fresh earth that turned me on, so sweet and sort of friendly and familiar, a homey feeling. The sun was coming through the trees, dappled on the reddish-yellow earth. When I've run across fresh earth since then it's always hit me the same way, a hint of home, mother earth. I guess your cells remember, even if your spirit is alien. Not too long ago I was digging and uncovered some fresh earth, and it was so soft and clean I wanted to lie down and take a nice long rest in that nice soft earth. It's been so long since I've had a good long sleep. I was really drawn to it, but no, I've got to go on, finish this book, or chapter. No rest for the wicked.

The digging reminds me of the time I set out to dig a hole clear through to China. I made the mistake of confiding my aims to my parents, and my father made a sign that read "China" with an arrow and buried it just beneath where I was digging and when I found it I excitedly ran in and showed it to the family and they told me it was just a joke. Maybe that was when I stopped trusting people. Or started distrusting people; it's taken all my life to lose faith in just about everybody. I spent about a year looking up old friends and relatives and seeing their falsity, and getting betrayed by the last of them. I still have one ace-in-the-hole left, but I am sure she would betray me too, if the occasion arose. I saw that was the only difference, that the ones who hadn't betrayed me just hadn't had the chance, and seized the first one they got.

I don't want to go into any more childhood experiences right now, it's too pathetic; it'd sound like I was feeling sorry for myself. I've told the good ones, let the rest lie for now. Oh yeah, there was this little girl, name of Lynn, we went down in the basement of a house they were building and took our pants down and looked at each other. She said she had looked at Jimmy and his was purple at the end or something. That made me feel there was something wrong with me. It wasn't until years later I realized Jimmy must have been uncircumcised. I didn't have any more sex experiences until much later; maybe that's why.

MY GRANDFATHERS DYING – LAST RAPS

I used to have two grandfathers. My mother's father was a woodcarver, skilled to the point where you could hardly say whether he was an artist or artisan. My parents still have some of his carvings, plaques I guess you'd call them, Grecian-looking heads, some strangely like my mother's face, classic, like a poem by Poe; and a carved chair, which they painted and last time I was there were wondering whether to sell along with the desk or not for 15 dollars or so. Mom said when her father retired he wrapped up his tools—I saw them: hundreds of tools—and she asked him to show her how to carve and he just laughed. And well he might, I suppose. I never figured out what my father's father did. At one time he had a spaghetti factory, but it burned down, and it seems like that was an awful long time ago. I never heard of anything tangible he did after that, but it made very little difference.

When I saw them in 1955 when I was 18, the last time I ever saw them, all my father's father could say was, "Jesus, Jesus," and some garbled Italian about "Toto" which they said was a clown and just an embarrassment; and all my mother's father could say was, "Oh boy, oh boy," while sort of like twitching to show he was alive. Grandpa Russo died when he was 87 and Grandpa Bätjer when he was 94. I've always wondered what Grandpa Russo meant by "Jesus, Jesus."

But I'll never know, and who will?

THE FAN FROM NEW EGYPT

I just remembered a baseball game back in Hamilton Square, New Jersey where I lived from about 1942-1948. It was a small town but it had some kind of baseball team, don't remember the name or whether it was amateur or semi-pro or what; this was before TV and I guess there were more baseball fans just like there were more movie theaters. Anyway, I was at one of the games, and it was with New Egypt. I remember this because a fan had come in from New Egypt. He must have been a real devoted follower, or maybe his kid was playing. During a quiet spell he gives a "Round and round New Egypt goes, and where she stops nobody knows!" which elicited a few snarls from the locals. I wonder where New Egypt ever went.

I generally didn't go to the games, but summer nights people would come walking down the street, which led to the ball park, and sometimes we'd ask who won. Or I would try to figure out who won from the demeanor of the fans. Even then I was analytical. To this day, I will go all over a supermarket looking for something rather than ask a clerk where it is. But then you could say I was shy too. A lot of the time we never did find out who won, or would hear some remark which was hard to interpret, there being so little difference, and we couldn't decide whether it mattered enough to find out for sure. Like at World Series ("Serious," they call it in Brooklyn) (dem bums—and now they're in LA—dem bums.) the country is divided into two camps, those who know who's playing, and who's ahead, and those who don't know or care, mostly women, who betray themselves by saying, "WHAT game?" With those who know coming on like the others are really out of it, and the ones who don't know feigning interest, sort of humoring the fans. Pretending to share their mania, or the basis of it. There but for fortune. We're all with ya', fight fans, from all over the country.

DOPE

So now with my childhood out of the way we can get on to my drug experiences. Just the high spots.

The first time I turned on was in San Francisco in 1958. Dave Haselwood asked me if I would like to smoke some marijuana. I had never thought about it. I said, "Sure." I smoked a joint, with some difficulty, since I didn't smoke. I had no idea what to expect. Suddenly I felt as if someone was pulling the hair on the back of my head. I lay down and started having visions. Mostly very funny, comic strip-like characters, airplanes with faces like bees, etc. I laughed my head off. I remember one vision in particular. It was a banquet hall, apparently in the penthouse of a hotel, with many tables with white tablecloths and on each table was a huge soup bowl made out of some grey stone, and all filled to the brim with pea soup. It was a beautiful color, sort of aqua, so that the whole room was like a sea of green soup. The waiters, in red coats with towels over their arms, had opened the skylights and a flock of white doves was flying in, white against the translucent green. It appeared to be a ritual, like the swallows coming back to Capistrano. I was in dithering ecstasy for an hour and a half. Nothing at all like it ever happened to me again. I smoked pot for years, always hoping for it. I gave up on it long ago. Smoking grass since then has just been middle-aged hedonism for me, once I had used my virginity up. I guess you have to be unprepared for that sort of thing to happen. With acid, the same thing may never happen again, but new things, and bigger things, do—you may build up resistances and defenses in one direction, but its scope is so broad it just comes in some other way. But grass doesn't seem to have that breadth.

The next trip I remember on grass was about the third time I turned on, in Wichita. It was an uptight scene living with my parents, and I got paranoid. It was the only time I've really been paranoid. People use the word very loosely for conditions that are a pale reflection of the real thing. What happened was I got high and scared and thought that my brain was broadcasting radio waves which the police could pick up in their cars, and use to track me down. It was an airtight paranoid delusion, no escape. Wherever I went they could follow me, since

I couldn't turn off the waves. It sounds funny now but I was scared shitless at the time. I went over to some friends' house and hid in their bedroom. I thought I could hear the cops tiptoeing around the windows. I could hear a motor outside, I thought it must be one of their cars, and when I moved my head it stopped. Maybe that bummer is why I never got that high again, to keep that from happening.

Mike Lewis just recalled the time at Oak Street when the liver fell on his foot. He was cooking some liver for the commune, though we didn't have that word then: he and his sister Janie Chipmunk, Bob and Beth Branaman, me, and sometimes Jean Meyer (we called her "Beautiful Jean" then), et al. I was in the kitchen; we all were high on peyote, and all of a sudden I heard a splat, and looked, and a piece of liver was draped over Mike's foot. It had fallen somehow and he was wearing these brown leather shoes about the same color as the liver. It's funny, but in the 10 years or so since then he's always had the same shoes. He has a steady connection for them while I've never been able to find the same kind twice. The liver looked rather obscene, like some type of growth, too intimate to be on your shoe. It might have been the same trip, (we didn't use that word then either), that I was in the living room and he came out and handed me a piece of raw hamburger. I took it and squeezed it until it squirted out from between my fingers. That kind of thing happens on peyote—like the beginning of one of Aldous Huxley's books, where some people are sunbathing on a roof, and someone is flying over in a plane and throws a dog out and it goes splat right in front of them, and this chick flips out. Well, peyote was like that; "herring in the gutter," someone described it as. I had the image of a piece of fruit on the pavement being squashed by a heel, and identifying with both the fruit and the heel. Later, it might have been while on acid, the song that went—"The fruit of the poor lemon is impossible to eat; lemon tree very pretty and the lemon flower is sweet, but the fruit of the poor lemon is impossible to eat"—was the theme song of a trip I took, and I kept wondering what it meant, "the POOR lemon," until I realized that one not only was the one who could not eat the lemon, but was also the lemon that could not be eaten.

A number of times there was a theme song or phrase from poetry that set the tone of a trip. The time I took acid with Dee and Janie

Chipmunk and Steve Leiper, the theme song was "Do You Wanna Dance" by Bobby Freeman. It was like a tentative invitation to enter life, which I had always held back from before, and finally seemed to have the chance to do, but didn't quite know what was the decisive step. I always had the feeling there was some step that needed to be taken, but couldn't figure out what it was. I didn't make it that time; everything soon disintegrated. But there was a funny scene about the artichoke. We had an artichoke which we cooked. Dee's sister Linda was there for ground control, and we started tearing the artichoke apart to find the heart but couldn't figure out where it was. What's called the "heart" is really just the base of the petals. We asked Linda, and it turned out she'd never seen one before. I realized it was an absurd projection to seek the heart in the artichoke, and turned within, and found my own heart, right where it's supposed to be, like a clear white-hot fire, bright as the sun, strong and good and all, and just then Dee pulls my shirt open and says, "There you are!" and kisses me right over my heart. I thought that she knew where I was at, and she was there too, and our hearts could touch, but when I tried to ask her about it she acted like she didn't know what I was talking about.

EXPRESSIONS

Five-year-old David Ashcraft calls taking a dump, "big business." I wish I cold make a book out of things that good.

Joannie Lewis used the expression, "Some women can get pregnant from hanging their panties on the bedpost." She also mentioned that Thea, who is five, called soap operas, "soda poppers." Whenever we try to get together over pronunciations, she claims that she always says it the same, but it comes out "pseudo boppers" or "super opers," or Joannie calls them "soda poppers" now, and I guess I will, too.

Then Suzie came up with a Texas one, "Quicker'n a gnat across a dipper." I don't know why things like that tickle me so much. One of the things I like about living in the country is the expressions you hear. The tang of reality is still there, in the speech as well as in the air.

In the Forest Service they used the expression, "iron tit." If you were having a hard time you were "sucking iron tit." Like tough titty, only tougher. If you felt bad you said you felt like "hammered shit." I heard a guy talking in a bar about his horse. He said, "She's as gentle as a dead pig." When loggers pile up logs it's called, "stackin' the deck," or sometimes referred to as, "loading the dice." Somebody should write a book.

I just remembered that Dave Bearden used to refer to hard and fruitless labor as "working your dick into the sand."

Yesterday when I was at Beth and Reuben's she told me about how in New York the minister of the church she went to asked her what she called her father. It happened that his name was Judson Carey, and they all called him, "J.C." When she told the minister this it rocked him back on his heels a bit, but as Beth put it he knew she was telling him "the stark raving truth," which I think is bound to become an expression in some circles.

Yesterday we also discussed the expression, "taking your picture," like when a chick bends over or exposes herself in some way, she is said to be "taking your picture." I had only heard it one time in an Italian movie where a woman says to a bunch of people, "Look, everybody, I am going to take your picture," and then hoists up her skirt. But Reuben says he has heard it for 35 years. You don't often find identical expressions in different languages.

Another one I recall, Charlie Plymell told me about a weird guy in Kansas who used to say, for emphasis, "I hope to shit in your shirt pocket." Rather euphonious.

Some expressions are completely private property, and no one else could use them. Dave Bearden told me that when he was in reform school, there was this guy who was in there for fucking a cow. Whenever anybody tried to give him a hard time he'd say, "Look out! I'll get ON you!"

Several expressions I heard were connected to Bob Branaman. In a highly localized regionalism, in Big Sur they call lush, "loudmouth." When he was strung out, Bob said he felt, "icky-poo." Someone told me his father used to say, "Don't get so open-minded your brains fall out." That's the sort of thing fathers say, but some hippies should remember it. When Bob complained to Susan about not doing something, she would reply, "It's all I can do to keep my hair on."

Alan Russo, Lompoc, California, 1977
Photograph by James Bearden

PART TWO

———

THE GREAT POETRY DUEL

One time 'bout 59, when Beatdom was in flower, William Morris challenged Philip Lamantia to a poetry duel. Morris was a phony slime who'd come up to chicks and say, "Let's fuuuck," and wrote pseudo-erotic crap while Philip was the lyric poet of the Beat Generation: short, beautiful, AC-DC, and read like an angel. It was set up in the International Coffee House which is now a laundromat cafe on Kearny just off Broadway. I went with Bruce Conner, neodada activist of the day, Beth Branaman, and I can't remember who else, all in getups of some sort. Bruce was wearing a long robe and carrying a pole with some kind of bird or bat assemblage on the end of it, and when we swooped in, adrenalin was flaring from his overcharged Nordic eyes. Morris sat at a table with a water pitcher and glass and a stack of trash, prepared for a drag out, and we formed sort of a guard, Bruce holding his weird assemblage aloft. Phillip read a long and good poem and then sat down. This poem was written in 1948. Then we all split, leaving Morris with his pitcher. That was another age.

One time we stayed up all night, Lamantia reading poetry (about youth), and in the morning I was fixing some oatmeal or something and asked him if he wanted some. He pointed at the ceiling and said, "I'd just as soon eat that light bulb." He was so beautiful I almost fell in love with him, only time. Must have been '57 or '58 come to think of it, because I remember Phillip said he had heard I was only 17 and I had to show him my ID to prove I was 19. People were so uptight about dope then. Now I have to convince the kids I am young enough. And they don't have poetry reading duels anymore.

NOBODY HERE BUT US CHARIOTEERS

Back when Charlie Plymell had the flat on Gough Street and had Ginsberg and Neal Cassady living there (his greatest coup), I was living upstairs and was talking to this girl who also lived in the flat, Lucille Koenig, who later married the poet Thomas Jackrell, and I mentioned the cats they had downstairs, and she said, "No, wait." She mentioned them and I said, "They don't let them inside." And she said, "Does that mean that they're the charioteers and we're in heaven?" which blew my mind for days until she explained it so that it made some kind of half-assed sense. Can't remember how it went.

Another time we were talking about schools. She was a Montessori teacher, and she said, "The trouble with schools is you can't jack the kids off all the time, that's what teaching is, jacking the kids off."

SOME REALLY CROSSED WIRES

I had an apartment on Oak Street that had a phone in it when I moved in, but it wasn't connected. Then one day it RANG. This struck me as odd, so I picked it up and there were two women speaking Chinese on it. I hung up then picked it up later and there was a dial tone. So I called a friend and it worked, and I asked someone to call the number on the phone but it didn't ring. It only rang from time to time, though I didn't answer it. But I did use it to make calls more and more. I told all my friends I had a phone that had come to life by magic and they could make all the long distance calls on it they wanted. Joe Gould called people in New York and talked for hours. This went on for weeks. Once, when drunk, I even got the time by calling the New York number, NERVOUS. We used the shit out of that phone.

Then one night I came in drunk and picked the phone up, why, I don't remember, and an Oriental girl was talking to her psychiatrist. It seemed that she was going through the transference phase of analysis and was in love with her shrink. She was tearfully imploring him to keep talking to her. I guess it was late and he didn't want to be bothered. He said she was making up a fantasy about making it with him, and she was going to have to cool it. To me he seemed very callous towards her. She was hysterical and he wouldn't talk to her. I suppose he knew what he was doing, but I was drunk and got all wrapped up in it and pitied her and was crying a little myself. Finally when she begged him to talk to her and he refused for the last time, I said, "I'll talk to you."

He said, "Who's that? I think there's someone else on the line," and he hung up.

Then I started to talk to her. She had no idea how I had come along, but she told me her side of the story. She kept saying, "I don't hate him, but he had these contraceptives—but I don't hate him." We talked for a long time, all about her supposed affair with the analyst. To this day I'm not sure whether she really made it with him or not. Maybe she made it with her father and got them mixed up. (Beth really did make it with her analyst, but he was a special freak analyst armed with acid and liquefaction.) (Which is another story.) I got the idea of seeing the chick and screwing her, but when I asked her where she was, she got scared, said she was afraid I would call the police. I couldn't convince her otherwise.

If she had told me where she was it would have come as quite a surprise, because it turned out she was the chick who managed the place, and lived right downstairs. The phones in the place were all screwed up. There was a pay phone in the lobby which they were always working on, and somehow my phone had got crossed with her line. Both rang when you dialed the number, which kept me from getting calls on it. I saw the phone bill in the hall on the table where the mailman left it, and it was a couple hundred or so, but that couldn't have been all of it.

The phone company tried to track it down. One time the phone rang and for some reason I picked it up and a man said, "This is the phone company, will you hold the line for a minute." They could only trace the line when I had the phone off the hook, so I hung up. I wonder what that chick thought when she got those bills. She probably thought it was all part of the plot against her. I hope it didn't freak her out any more than she already was.

LELAND S. MEYERZOVE

One time I was going somewhere in San Francisco with Bob Branaman and Leland S. Meyerzove, who is a sincere, fat, Buddha-looking Jewish guy always wearing a lambskin Russian hat, and always trying to make the literary scene. Dion Wright says he's the kind of guy who will pee in your john without raising the seat. But he got his picture on the covers of the society pages of the San Francisco papers one time, dancing with some madcap matron at a freaky gala, something she had sponsored, appearing in a skirt slit high enough to show her red panties . . . but back to my story.

We were driving down the street in some chick's car, a '51 Ford station wagon I believe, with Leland driving. Every so often he would stop and jump out of the car and do some calisthenics in the street—side straddle hops or some such high school hangover—and then jump back into the car and drive on. He was taking reducing pills too. He had a fat, hairy stomach that showed between his shirt and his pants. We started to turn onto a narrow street, but just then a furniture truck tried to pull out of it.

Leland rolled down the window and started bad-mouthing them, saying, "What's the matter with you, you dumb Okies, can't you read?" Apparently, he thought that they were going the wrong way on a one-way street, although they weren't.

They said, "Fuck you!" but he kept on razzing them.

I thought, "Jeez, we're going to get in a fight, and Bob and I will have to do the fighting," and they were big furniture-moving studs. But they finally drove off. I asked Leland why he did that, and he said, "I was smiling while I said it."

Finally, the station wagon's clutch burned out in the middle of an intersection, whether out of exasperation at the whole scene, or that it was just its time, I don't know. Come to think of it, this happened at the intersection of Market and Van Ness before admiring throngs. We have to push it to a garage and call the chick whose car it was. We walked from there, I forget to where.

THE GREAT WINE ROBBERY

Back when Bob Branaman first came out to San Francisco he and I went to a soiree, or what was called a "sawyer" in hip circles at the time. It was at some old lady's place. I don't remember her name. Edith something or other. Well, we were getting kind of bored with the action, or lack of it, and we're thinking about leaving. Bob, who was still a bit of a thief, thought he would check out the liquor stock and cop a bottle before we left. These people didn't know us and so there would be no beef. He looked in a cabinet and found a fifth of wine and we left with it under his coat. When we got to the street he opened it and took a big swig then spit it out and spluttered. Turns out it was soy sauce, in one of those bottles shaped like a fifth of wine; I guess we should have learned something from that but I don't think that we did.

YES, THEY HAD FREAKS IN WICHITA THEN

One time when I went back to Wichita I ran into David Wall, son of a psychiatrist who used to work with my old man, driving an MG with Hugh Walpole and Paul Lundgren crammed into it. That was a lot of meat and a lot of madness in one MG. Now Hugh was a defrocked mad genius, nephew of the original Hugh Walpole, English, from the University of Chicago, I think, and Wichita University had grabbed him to lend some class to their rather lackluster English Department. He was their fair-haired boy for a while, but his mind caught up with him. The shit hit the fan when a student was tapping a pencil on a table in one of his classes and he flipped out and claimed the kid was sending messages in Morse code to someone on the outside. The University told him he could stay on if he'd see a shrinker but he refused and disappeared into some obscure duplex never to be seen again.

His wife Ellie would protect him from outsiders. Even before the blowup you'd go by, and if he was too drunk to see anyone, she'd say he wasn't there, even if you could see his foot hanging off the edge of the bed. He was working the Dylan Thomas vein. He claimed he had once won the wrestling championship of Peru and married a whore in a church by candlelight and was working on a new book on Semantics, all of which I ever saw was the outline or table of contents, which wasn't in English but some sort of symbolic glyphs, so symbolic there wasn't even any point in asking him what they meant. I don't know if he ever wrote any of the book or not. We would go to bars and have to carry him home. One time Ellie flipped out and wedged herself under the table between the legs so you couldn't get her out and Hugh kept yelling, "Now you've fucked us up! Now you've fucked us up!" Last I heard they were still in Wichita, she working somewhere. It seems her parents lived there too. That was the only reason I know of for staying there, aside from the possible difficulty you might have moving Hugh in his, uh, condition.

Paul Lundgren was strange too. He had been in Intelligence during the war or something and had classified information in his brain, but had flipped out and got sent out to pasture. Whenever he got drunk or blew his lid, Intelligence agents from the air base would come and cart him off. He would get into complicated scenes. You would go to a bar and see a bottle of wine sitting in front of a nearby tree, and Paul would be lurking behind a tree across the street while Roxie Powell would be inside the bar with an explanation of it all that didn't make sense, except they were all insane.

One time Hugh told me, apropos of nothing I could see, "Ellie knew Maxwell Bodenheim in New York." I think he said it fairly frequently. Hugh was supposed to be a poet but only had one poem to show for it, but Ellie wrote some stuff. We put one of hers in *Poets Corner* I think. It's been years, and I suspect it would be painful to see Hugh now.

ICE CREAM!?

I was drinking Cosanyl in Wichita, the old dihydrocodeinone kind, not a lot, but just enough to melt away an occasional summer afternoon, and had bought a bottle at some drugstore. I guess it was a cut-rate one, that's where we always got it, and there weren't very many of them, and that was how it came about that a few days later I went back to the same store, it was probably nearby or on the way to somewhere; well anyway Cos apparently moved a bit slow there, because when I went back and signed the register the previous name was my own. Which doesn't happen. I guess the druggist remembered me from this or didn't even have to remember because there it was with the date and all, and as he handed me the bottle, he said with a sly backhand smile, "You ever try that stuff over ice cream?"

PSEUDONYMS

I've adopted a series of pseudonyms to one extent or another; i.e., there was one I actually used, and the others were mostly in my head, like a summation of my current attitude toward myself . . .

The first one was Billy Jiddy. That's not Billy as in short for William, either. Just Billy. The origin was that I had heard someone say "village idiot," and I thought they said "Billy Jiddy." So I decided I was Billy Jiddy, the village idiot. This was during Early Acid Days (EAD as we call it in the trade). And it was a brisk trade, with shifting winds from the north constantly eroding the sturdiest pillars of surety. But anyway, I rented an apartment under this name and published something in *NOW NOW*, which was the second issue of *NOW*, put out by Charlie Plymell, who put out a third issue called *NOW NOW NOW*. We speculated about what to call future issues, like *NOW & THEN*, but there weren't any more under that or any other name. I didn't want to be held responsible for it. But then my landlady saw that my mail was addressed to Alan Russo, so she asked me, what was my name, Russo or Jiddy? I told her that one was my pen name, which didn't cut any ice with her.

Then Charlie's girlfriend JoAnn and Roxie and I were watching some incredible TV show like you occasionally run into that isn't listed in the TV Guide. They just happen. There was a series of famous people, show biz personalities, coming on and giving testimonials about why they believed in God; sort of an infomercial for God. I put on a wide old flowery necktie and stood in front of the TV set and said, "My name is Billy Jiddy, and I say God is a pair of dirty underpants." EAD, you see. We roasted sunflower seeds in the oven and burnt them every time and ate popcorn and drank beer. Mighta smoked a little grass, but now I remember it was on the way down there I thought it was the end of the world. Not entirely without reason, you see, for we were going down Junipero Serra Blvd, one of the main routes out of San Francisco and down the Peninsula, and the traffic was backed-up solid three lanes wide. We had the radio on, and it was giving us instructions on what to do in the event of a nuclear attack. The radio was telling us to get down in a ditch and put our hands across the backs of our necks. I thought that the stream of cars leaving San Francisco was trying to escape an imminent attack and that we were all stuck in this traffic jam with the bombs on their way, and we were all going to die in a few minutes. I got really panicked. Can't feature why now.

The next pseudonym I remember is Myron Gecko, about five years later. I think there was another one after that I forget, but the one after that one was Spike Herald. I'd had a good acid trip in the Haight-Ashbury and I got the idea I was Spike Herald—with Spike representing both the cross and the nails, or the place where they cross, like a vision of myself as some kind of apocalyptic prophet. When I told Steve Leiper, he said that it was the scariest name he had ever heard.

My latest, which I'm still on, is A. C. True. I found this name in a Department of Agriculture bulletin. He was some official around the turn of the century, no doubt forgotten, despite his fidelity. I don't know what his initials stood for. My original idea was a combination of AC current, which goes two ways at once, and Ace, like Ace E. True. Just recently it occurred to me that the A could stand for Aion, which I looked up in the dictionary, from which I quote: "In the Gnostic Doctrine, one of a class of powers or beings existing in Eternity, conceived as emanating from the Supreme Being, and performing various parts in the operations of the Universe." They have it spelled either aeon or eon, but, from the Greek it looks as if it should be zion, which is closing in on Alan.

Maybe I'm getting to the roots of my murky identity.

JUNK

Bob Branaman turned me on to junk. There is just no question about that. It didn't seem so significant at the time but later events proved it so. What it was, was Cosanyl cough syrup. At the time, around 1960, it contained dihydrocodeinone, which is fairly strong. You drank a bottle of it. I took two swigs to down one, though Bob did one in a single glub. I would get so stoned that I fell asleep any time of day. One time I was awakened by the sound of my own snoring. I was asleep enough to snore but awake enough to hear it. A twilight state. Another time I fell asleep and was awakened by something resting on my leg. It was my other leg. One time I fell asleep and then awoke with my mother saying strawberries, home grown ones, were ready and it was late afternoon with the sunlight coming in slanting and the room and bedspread were green and it was like paradise regained. If only we could wake from all of our stupors with someone calling us to fresh strawberries. Oh well.

Then one time Janie Lewis and Bob and Susan Branaman were all in Wichita at the same time, and we got a prescription for percodan from our family doctor and Susan got so happy she cried. Later it turned out to be an embarrassing scene because, since I had got a bottle of Hycodan from the same doctor, we had Janie tell the doctor Roxie Powell had recommended him to her, since he went to the same doctor because they worked in the same building (that's Wichita for you), but she gave my address, and he found out all about it and wanted her to commit herself.

FUNERAL

I took mescaline once in Wichita when you could still order it legally from Light and Co. in England. I was sending it on to people in California. I was going to take it with Janet and her then husband Richard but they broke up and so I took it by myself.

Well, Bruce Connor was in Wichita at the time, for some reason, and he came by wearing a straw hat and I saw he was far too pink to take the Kansas sun. His flesh is like a baby's, soft and pink. It just so happened that the house I was living in, my parents', bordered on a cemetery. We walked out in back, and there was a funeral in progress at the time. This wasn't unusual and I didn't pay much attention to it, except this one was going on very close by and so we watched. Bruce pointed out it was a Masonic funeral because there was an apron over the coffin. Then we noticed a crew with a tractor lurking behind some trees nearby, watching. Bruce said, "Who are they?" and we realized they were the ones that filled in the graves and were just waiting for the mourners to leave so they could wrap things up. I believe it was a Ford tractor, one man was sitting on and another standing by, to shovel I suppose.

THE WARTY SQUASHES

Back when we all lived on Oak Street one of the fixtures of the neighborhood was the Warty Lady. She had huge lumps on her face, sort of like the surface of the moon in reverse, but closer together. She was so hideous it hurt to look at her. And you had to look at her quite a bit oftener than you would have liked, because in that part of town, from Fillmore to Divisadero along Oak, you ran into her all the time like a recurring nightmare. It got so that when I saw her coming, I would cross the street or if that wasn't possible, turn around. It was just too painful. It all came to some sort of climax one day when Janie Lewis was in the Safeway looking at some warty squashes when someone said to her, "Aren't they BEAUTIFUL?" and she turned around and it was the Warty Lady, who, I should have noted, was old and wore a sort of opaque stockings that only old San Francisco ladies know how to get. I don't think we ever saw her again, as if she had reached an apotheosis thus and "gone before."

FIRST ACID TRIP

My first trip on acid (in 1961 we still called it LSD) was inconclusive since it was a very small dose and it wasn't quite time yet—but a remarkable thing happened that is typical of the synchronicity powers of acid. While I was waiting for it to come on (another phrase we didn't know then) the words "Christ the Victor" kept running through my mind, along with the idea of oneness of being victim and victor at the same time. That's also typical, word meanings being tied together through their similarity. Then Janie Lewis and Beth Branaman were going up to Stinson Beach so I went with them. Janie was taking the curves fairly fast and I felt very thin-skinned, like the trees and rocks alongside of the road would scrape me if we got any closer. I felt like crying, which I held back, not knowing that's par for the course on acid. While going across Marin County on Sir Francis Drake Blvd, not the usual way to get to Stinson, we passed a church called Christ the Victor Church. I don't think I had ever been down that road before or heard of the church. (I just checked Marin County information, and it is listed). I've never found another church by that name since.

At Stinson we got some beer and went to the beach but it was cold and windy and the wind blew sand in the beer, and Janie said "Gee, isn't this nice?" which cracked me up literally and I rolled off the hammock I was hanging onto and laughed until I cried so I finally got it out.

FORGETTING

Now I don't claim to be an expert on forgetting, but I have forgotten some things you wouldn't think you even needed to remember. One time I was high on acid—that's a special situation of course, but this was quite a forgetting—and all of a sudden I forgot what the name of the person I was with was. This might not have been so odd, except that he was my best friend. I panicked because I thought, "Oh my gosh, what if something should come up where I would have to call him by name? How could I explain?" What an embarrassing scene. I get embarrassed by a lot of things. The way I forgot his name was—his name was David—and he had a shirt of many colors, which he dug for its Biblical significance, but on acid I got to thinking his true name wasn't David. It should be Joseph. Truth replaced reality, and I forgot "David." It really had me worried.

Another bad forgetting I had was when I was proof-reading the phone books. This was very monotonous and hypnotic, as they say, and sometimes I would get sort of tranced-out and would be gripped by a panic fear that I was about to forget how to do something very basic and essential, like how to read or write. And of course this would have been very hard to explain to my cohorts, but I always got through it without anyone suspecting. I'm sure they wouldn't have understood.

Then there was the time I forgot who Bob was. This was on acid. I was really getting spaced when the phone rang. I knew that someone was going to call to see if something had happened, and I assumed it was about that. So I prepared my reply in accordance with this assumption, not feeling capable of an impromptu conversation. This guy says, "Hello," and I say, "The call didn't go through." And he says, "I think you think I am someone else. This is Bob." And my routine went to pieces. I realized I wasn't talking to who I thought I was, and since my preparation was based on the assumption that it was me talking to Peter, the two together making sense, but when one end collapsed the whole thing did. And I didn't know who I was either, when I found I didn't know who the other party was. It took me a while to make the adjustment and explain, and he was calling collect and running the bill up saying charge it to Mike the Jew, and since I was on acid I didn't care much about phone bills. Anyway, it just shows you what happens when you break a connection.

THE GHASTLY BAT-BURST

It was at the old Batman Art Gallery, run by Billy Batman, years later people who didn't even know about the Batman called him that; he ate only meat, peanut butter, and cheese; don't know what kind of bat that is. He started this post-beatnik art gallery with his rich father's dead money which he later blew on junk and ended up on welfare with his beautiful four children getting to look like Keanes; well anyway he had a show by George Herms whose wife had just had a baby and they made a big thing out of it. He delivered it and everything, and made construction-collages; one of them had the sheet she had the baby on, and one had a mason jar with the afterbirth in it. You see they really went apeshit. But after a while the gases from the decomposing mater (oh wow what a Freudian typo!)

matter built up and the jar exploded, splattering this horrible rotten shit all over the gallery, creating a nightmare mess and stench which took weeks to wash out. I guess it was because of trying to hang onto something too long.

GOUGH STREET PARTY

Something, I don't remember what, reminded me of a scene in San Francisco in '67 when I went to one of Dave Haselwood and Glen Todd's "sawyers" (that's a hip corruption of soiree, brandy, and beer, I think Olympia)—two room suite, San Francisco flat with front room and second room connected with sliding doors, plenty of room—and there was this chick Phoebe who was wearing a diaphanous dress with nothing under it and dancing around and I came on to her trying to get under her dress which advance she rebuffed (I didn't realize till later she was with her old man who wasn't in evidence at the time) till she got salty and I cooled it still not so drunk as to be unreasonable, but she kept coming around and doing her act precipitating a situation and before I found out her old man was there I went back to where she was sitting on a bed and lay down on the floor in front of her saying I felt guilty and begged her to stomp on me with her bare feet which freaked her out and did till her friends pulled her off and her old man said, "You may be a very cool cat but you are bugging her and would you please lay off." And it was only then I realized she had an old man and cooled it, honor working up to that point, and was just standing around drinking, but she kept dancing right in front of me. I came on to her one last time, was repulsed of course, and then, drunk, of course, I kicked her in the ass, not real hard but more than impolite, and said, "Next time you go wiggling your ass in front of somebody's face you better have an old man around big enough to protect it." This right in front of him. Someone called me on this, don't remember just what was said, so I set my champagne glass down, rolled up my sleeves, my arms were bulging from a summer of buckin' bales, and said, "All right, you think you come here with some kind of insurance policy, let's see what it is." And her friends formed a cordon around her and skedaddled her out of there. It wasn't till later I realized what a brutal and gratuitous assault I had made on his ego, most vicious thing I've ever done. Phoebe deserved that kick on the ass but he didn't deserve that, and shortly afterward I heard he had committed suicide. They had broken up between then and I was told he had been depressed for a long time, poet feller, and maybe it didn't have anything to do with what I said, but I couldn't escape the feeling I had hammered a nail in his coffin. He seemed a decent sort. Two maybe causally unconnected things, what I said and what he did, but there was a relationship nevertheless; I wouldn't have said that to someone who was on the verge of suicide, not that I knew that, never seen him before, but you see how it tied in and worked out.

During that same party, before the scene with Phoebe, I had tried to make out with Maggie. That was why I was so pissed, that I couldn't make out with anyone, and I thought Maggie was a sure thing. I tried to pick her up, she must have weighed 250 or 300, and finally managed to get her off the floor. We were dancing and whenever some other guy came near her I would stomp on the floor in his direction and go "Haw!" very loud. I more or less dragged Maggie out the back door, her place was on the next floor up, but I couldn't carry her up the stairs, so I wrestled her down on the back porch, and we fell down with her landing on top of me; I landed on the edge of a planter box and hurt my back, then got her down and finally decided it would be more effort than I was willing or able to expend and more outrage than I was willing to commit and gave it up.

The owner lived downstairs, and we made a lot of noise, what with me stomping and all, and a couple of days later Glenn Todd saw Mr. Woodmansee and said, "I hope our party didn't disturb you the other night." And old Frank said, "Did you boys have a party?" He was the coolest landlord in the world; used to bring us fresh abalone oysters, etc. from someone he knew who had a fishing boat.

LOOK AWAY, DIXIE

There are certain incidents that keep cropping up in my mind at certain times, which I guess fit into the pattern. One is what Glenn Todd told me happened in the Texas town he grew up in; Vernon,

Texas I believe. In the summer on hot nights people would sleep on their porches. This was before air conditioning and the poorer people who didn't have porches or who had too many people to sleep on them would sleep out in their yards. Glenn assured me that his family didn't do this, that it was considered "low." Well, there was a teen-aged brother and sister in the low part of town and they made it with each other. Now I guess this was fairly common in that part of Texas but you see on hot nights they did it right out in the front yard and in the hot hammy-headed morning there they would be sacked out together for all to see. So, the more decent-minded townsfolk would complain to Ma and when she relayed the complaint to Emmy Lou or whatever her name could have been she said right back, saucy as could be, "If they don't like it, they can look away."

You goddamn right, Emmy Lou.

PEYOTE

Peyote is a mystical, magical experience, and so beyond words, but out of a feeling of mission and pity for man, I try to find words to help you know the light is there. Peyote lays open the soul of man, so that the truth of God may shine undiluted on the inmost core which cannot help but believe, once it is touched. It unlocks all prisons, real and figmentary. It presents the key to all languages, spoken and inherent. It reveals the absolute splendor and importance of all created things. It strips from us the blindness which we call knowledge, for the living growing being is created and destroyed anew each instant, by each instant. The fully open being is in great agony and joy, for he takes into his flesh terrible and beautiful things, which are often the same. He sees all too deep into the faces of his fellows, sees all the falsity, shallowness, lies, sins, and guilt. And forgives, and accepts, through tears. And he sees all his faults, and knows the inescapable bitter-sweetness of life on earth, among men who die, and loves that sour, and the dearness of all buried in dung. But he will never again mistake the dung for truth or forget the virtue at the heart of things.

CASSANDRA THE MUMMY OR
A BEAT APOTHEOSIS

Mike said something that reminded me of Cassandra, "the mummy from the tomb," as Charlie Plymell called her. She used to say, "Everybody keeps a dime handy for a secret call." Well gee whiz, Cassandra, you didn't have to come right out and say it.

The way I met Cassandra was I went to bed one night when I was living at 457 Oak Street, a recurring address that kept popping up for years. Beth was the first person who found it, when we lived at 668 Oak Street. She rented a room there to write in, trying to become a writer. Because she was married to a painter, 668 was out. A junkie named Morgan lived in the rear of 457 in a maid's room, a low-ceilinged cockroach tank. When I was looking for a place in the paper I saw this cheap one—two rooms for $45—called the number, and they said it was 457 Oak Street. I thought, "What a coincidence!" So I went to look at it, and it turned out to be Morgan's place, but all empty. He had just moved out, but I didn't know it.

I rented the room, which was right across the hall from an old lady pensioner, "Irene" something-or-other. She would knock on my door with a dollar or two in her withered old hand and shit on her tattered old slip, (she couldn't control her bodily functions anymore), and ask me to go and get her some Gallo Wine. She offered me the change if I'd make the run, but at first I did it for free, as a favor, to keep her at arm's length, but she wouldn't stay that far away. She tried to kiss me sometimes, so I started keeping the change, a buck or so, what the hell. It got to be too much to bear, especially the smell of her place. She'd get me to come in there, claiming she couldn't open the bottle or sometimes the can of cat food she'd had me get for her cat. She would offer me a drink of wine, which I'd decline, wanting to get out of there as quickly as possible. Irene quivered with anger at the mention of a rest home.

Then I met Dee, who lived up front in what used to be the living room and the room adjoining it via sliding doors, San Francisco style. It was said the place had been built in 1880 as the Fleishacker mansion. Dee's rooms had fourteen-foot ceilings with Baroque gas-jet chandeliers hanging down. This house had electric wires running through the gas lines, like many old houses there which were built in the gaslight era, only these lines still had traces of gas in them, all wired-up and ready to go off like a live mine. We moved in together for awhile, before I met Cassandra, but we hardly ever saw each other. I would get home about 1:30 in the morning and worked Saturdays too, which pissed her off. So we broke up and I moved back into the room I still had upstairs.

One night I had just gone to bed when there was a knock at the door. I opened it in my underwear and there was this chick standing there. She just giggled and walked in. She sat down on my bed and giggled again. I sat down and put my arm around her and she giggled again. We ended up fucking three or four times a day, which I hadn't thought myself capable of. She was little, about five feet tall, long black hair, around thirty. Every time I'd ask her, she'd give a different age. She must have been pretty once, but she was ravaged by then with tracks on her arms. She took smack and meth, as they were called in 1964, and had scars all over her—from childbirth, appendicitis, fights, accidents, etc. She said that one time she had fallen from a fifth-story window. Her whole life was like this. She had "mi vida loca" tattooed on her arm. Her race was also indeterminate. She said she was part Arab and her name was Sirrha. She claimed she used to make it with her father and had a baby, but then he wouldn't make it with her anymore because she got too old for him.

It turned out that she knew the pill-head faggots across Oak Street (she was a lesbian and a whore also, you see), and one of them had dared her to go across the street and make it with one of the beatniks over there. She was game for anything. The way she picked my room was because the landlady had written "Alan" on the mailbox, and she thought that was a groovy name. Steve Leiper was sleeping on my extra bed at the time, and Janie Chipmunk and other people were also around, but no beatnik could take her sound. They cleared out so quick it wasn't funny. On the night that I met her she was carrying a comic book, a doll, a Rosicrucian manual, a water gun, and a can of Bloody Mary. She didn't drink, but it was fitting. She WAS Bloody Mary. Bloody Mary, full of grace. Silken little sex kitten, the only chick I ever knew who talked all the time when you were making it with her. She never stopped, except in the throes. She claimed that I was the first man she ever came with. Maybe she said that to all the men. I think that a lot of her statements were of doubtful veracity, as if their improbability made them questionable, but this entire book is composed of just such yarns, so who am I to point the finger. All these things are just what I wouldn't have believed myself, if I hadn't seen them.

She had one of the most fantastic raps I ever heard. All about her escapades on Mars getting raped by Green Tony, putting bandages on someone's dick in a hotel room, being crowned in a parade down Market Street. She was a comic virgin-whore eternally set upon by demons. Everything took 2,000 years in her tales, all punctuated by "Ain't that cold, man?" and threats to slash her enemies. "I'll cut 'em up, man," she declared in a husky spade* voice.

One time Cassandra came by with a red-headed dyke and they made it on the extra bed. The next day we blew up and she came back with the red-head and a spade and moved her stuff out. What she left I threw out of the window after them.

Years later I found out that Rick Schwartz had been married to her in Chicago, and by his account, she was very groovy then. He said she was a high yeller, which is what she had accused Dee of being. Dee was sort of dark-complected. I never figured it out. Maybe Cassandra knew what she was talking about.

Charlie Plymell wrote down some of her talk and published it in *Now Now*, or one of his little mags. This was when I ran into her again. I was living around the corner on Buchanan and saw her over on Oak Street with the pill head queers. She threw her arms around me and jumped up and down crying, "Alan! Alan!" when the last time I had seen her I was throwing her stuff out the window after her. Charlie and Ann Buchanan were living with me on Buchanan Street. After Cassandra moved in, they moved out immediately, as soon as Charlie had copped some of her rap.

Then Mike Lewis came by one day and woke her up, shutting the bathroom door. She woke up and wet the bed and came in to tell me, "I haven't done that in six months!" Then she started bitching that

Mike hadn't cleaned out the tub after he took a bath. He said he had, and she said, "Did not!"; and he said, "Did too!" kid-style.

Well, no one could take her. She was crashing after being strung-out for weeks on speed, sleeping a day at a time. I realized I had to close things between her and all my friends. The next day, when she woke up green around the gills I told her she'd have to go. "You hate me!" she yelled and I said, "No, I don't." She said, "You think I'm evil!" and I said, "No." She yelled, "You want me to get busted!" (she was Wanted), and I said, "No, I don't. It just won't work," and offered to give her a ride, which she refused. She walked off, grim-faced and mad, never to be seen again.

She had once told me that she had made it with Philip Lamantia back in North Beach, and that he was a "stone fag." I said, "Then why were you making it with him?" and she replied, "I was a lesbian, man!" as if that explained everything . . .

Cassandra also told me she had tricked a guy who dug her into scarfing her box while she was menstruating. "Ain't that cold?" she said. She also tricked another guy who wanted to eat her, but wanted her to douche first, so she says, "Suck it funky, motherfucker!"

* In the late 50s and through the 60s the word "spade" was common parlance, used generally among "hipsters" of all colors. According to African-American writer Donna Pregent, it was popularized by Black Musicians in the 50s where "my spade" originally meant something like "my secret super cool musician who makes our band sizzling-hot. Nobody knows about your ace in the hole . . . Yet."

David Bearden and Alan Russo, Lompoc, California, 1977
Photograph by James Bearden

PART THREE

MOUNTAIN CLIMBING ON ACID – TRIP I

To keep you up to date while I straighten out the chronicles, Suzy just played a sonata by Clementi on the piano and it was the tune to "We've Got a Groovy Kind of Love." So many pop songs are pulled from classical tunes and you don't know which are which unless you've heard every piece of classical music ever written, so you might be getting euchred by this plagiarized jazz, think it's a great song, and be making a fool of yourself before the great glaring eye of history, or whatever records everything that happens. People, myself included, talk forever about things that are too much to talk about, so I'll limit myself to what happened. The truth, the whole truth, and nothing but the truth. But that could be anything—so watch it!

That eye reminds me of the first time I climbed a mountain on acid in the Sierra. After a long walk across flooded fields—but wait! It was on this walk that we found the scarab. We had come to a stream and gone wading to ease our feet, and when we came back to our shoes there was a beetle on Dave Bearden's boot. Now it just happened that Judith was wearing a ring with a scarab on it, supposedly genuine Egyptian. Well someone said, "That beetle is just like the ring." And we all looked and it was. Same color, same markings, everything. It didn't make any attempt to get away; let us examine it well. It was the same.

Do scarab beetles live in the Sierra? Well, we went on across the fields until we got to where the water welled up out of the ground at the foot of the mountains. We wanted to get to the fountainhead so that the water wouldn't have cow shit in it, there being cattle in the fields. When we got to the fountainhead what was there but a herd of cattle. They'd been spending their whole lives finding the best water and we thought we could just walk in, because we were so neat, and get ahead of them in one afternoon. There was more cow shit there than anywhere else, but we were getting pretty thirsty by then. Finally I saw that the water was being filtered through the cow pies and went into a Chamber of Commerce spiel about how the fine drinking water in the region was mainly due to the high component of cow shit, and we all drank it and didn't get sick; and we had cuts on our feet and waded in it and they didn't get infected. So much for the germ theory.

Then we started up into the hills, and I and the dog, Mr. Bilbo Baggins, a very well-meaning but simple-minded dachshund, became separated from Dave, Judith, and Leslie. I went up the road while they scattered over the hillside, disdaining the beaten track. So when I came to a fork in the road, I took it since it cut back in the direction they were, or so I thought. This was a very peculiar road, deserving of mention as much as anything else, a Forest Service masterpiece of woodsy wiles. It angled off the main road at such a sharp angle that only a jeep could turn that sharp. But, since they have other rigs too, a turnout was provided to make two passes at it. Then there was a short steep sandy stretch and then a berm and a tree across the road. All along the road there were berms, just steep enough that nothing but a jeep could clear them. There were places where they had an angled berm next to a cliff or boulder so that anything bigger than a jeep would hit the rock. It was crafty, I tell you, and I wondered what they were hiding and pressed on. Finally, the road ended in a small clearing with a pair of bulldozer treads and some burnt logs. Might have been a logging deck once but it was pretty small and besides why all the hassle to protect a deserted logging deck?

About this time I looked up and saw that there was a brilliant green peak directly above me. I had noticed it shortly before but hadn't thought of heading for it until I saw that the road ended at the foot of it. I thought maybe it was an outcropping of jade. So I started toward it, mindful of how what appears to be the top of the mountain is sometimes only the first in a series of ridges. As I approached it the wind came up, while there had been no wind all day, and something got going like an echo between the sky, which was very blue, and the sun, which was very bright, and me, who was very spaced. It sounded like thunder, the clap of doom in an infinite but closed room, booming back and forth, a mighty heart pulsing on some inconceivable wavelength. As I got near the peak I began to get scared. I didn't know what was going to happen. My heart was beating fast and I just kept telling myself, the only reason I'm climbing this mountain is to find out if this is the top. Otherwise, the whole thing will look like a plot to lure me into the wilderness.

Well, the outcropping wasn't the top, but it was something else. It was either a rock that looked a lot like a Mayan temple or a Mayan temple that looked a lot like a rock. It was a rectangular rock formation broken up into rectangular pieces, but so regular that they looked like stones that had been laid in place. The green color was from the lichen on it, a fantastic Day-Glo chartreuse. It was spring, and the lichen was in its glory, with a few swirls of orange and purple. It was in patterns, some sort of hieroglyph, or written character in a language I had never seen before but which was still strangely familiar. But I was in no mood for deciphering hieroglyphs. I wanted to climb mountains, and my worst fear had been confirmed, this wasn't the top. I saw another rock on ahead and started for it. A fool's errand, I kept thinking to myself, get lost in these woods and . . . But when I got to the next rock I could see a road in the woods where roads are hard to come by, and this one took a bend right where I hit it. If I hadn't followed a beeline from the rocks I wouldn't have found it.

So I followed the road, which seemed to be heaven-sent, but wondered where could it come out. Was it the same road I had turned off of, or what? It was a good, smooth road; you could drive it in a car, but there were no tire marks on it. It went into virgin wilderness, deep into the woods, where I felt like an intruder in a deserted shrine. I went deeper and deeper, becoming more and more worried that I was reaching a point of no return, where if I went any farther I wouldn't be able to get back before dark, and it would be hard to find the first road after dark. But I was compelled by some lure of the wild to go on, to follow that road to the end.

At one point I could see a ranch in a valley, a spur off Sierra Valley, and I could see Frenchman Lake. I ran when I was going downhill. I got thirsty and since I was used to Coast Range mountains, thought I could find water in any draw. But it wasn't like that in these mountains. The draws were all dry, and there was only water in the valleys. I finally got to where I could see a road and a creek and hear then the hum of water and cars down below. So I cut downhill, sliding and skidding, and hit what seemed to be a bulldozer trail that took me straight to a dam which crossed the stream and led to a Forest Service campground. I washed in the stream and crossed the dam or bridge, just a log actually, and Bilbo swam. He had tried to cross where I did but fell off and tried to climb back onto the log. I called him and he swam to shore, nothing to it. Poor little bastard had all the heart he could hold, but not much brains.

When we got to the road I couldn't tell which way was which so I thumbed cars in both directions. That didn't work of course. Who would give a ride to someone who didn't know which way he was going? So we walked down the road a piece to where there was a guy fishing. I went up to him and noticed when I got near him that he was wearing an automatic that somehow had appeared when I approached him. I asked him where Highway 70 was and he said, "Down that way." Then he seemed puzzled. "Which way did you come in?" he asked, because the only way in was from Highway 70. I told him I'd come in over the mountains with my friends' dog and got lost I guess you'd say. His eyes narrowed, and they were narrow and green to begin with. He had a fishing rod in his hand bent back taut as a whip. I saw myself reflected as a kook in his eyes and went on in the direction he indicated.

No one would stop to pick up a wet dachshund and an acid freak. All the rigs were campers, full in front and private in back, or cars too clean for a dog, or for me either. Finally, I saw a pickup with a dog in back and knew that was what I would have to get. Sure enough, the pickup stopped and gave us a ride, the driver just wanting me to keep the dog off the sleeping bags in back, which he immediately dove for, panicking the people inside them—a guy from Reno and his 12 and 13-year-old sons. I grabbed Bilbo and stashed him down in the corner of the truck and smiled it's all right through the back window of the pickup to the passengers who were now agog. We were whisked in high style down to Highway 70 from where we walked back. Going west I ran into a couple of teenage kids in Chilcoot who asked if I was from Frisco. As I was heading west, mind you, I said, "Well, yeah, the long way round. I just walked in through the mountains," and they nodded and went on.

When I got back to Vinton, Dave, Judith, and Leslie were just straggling back from across the field and wouldn't believe where I'd been, or what I'd seen. I got a Geological Survey map of the area and I couldn't find those mountains on that map. But you'll believe me after the next few stories. You won't have any choice.

MOUNTAIN CLIMBING ON ACID – TRIP II

The second time I climbed a mountain on acid was also with Dave and Leslie, but Judith didn't come along. First we stopped off down the road and took pictures of each other in front of an abandoned one-room country schoolhouse with the name "Summit School" over the door. I don't know why they called it that because it was in the valley. Then we took the road toward Calpine and turned off onto a Forest Service road that was unmarked except for one of those little gabled wooden signs that look like birdhouses but this one didn't say anything. We stopped and went into the woods and found paradise right off the bat. It was pine woods, flat, with a very informal campsite—just a fire pit and a place to sit—not a Forest Service job. Beyond that was a meadow of emerald green grass amidst the pines, bordered by a stream teeming with trout and huge fish too big to be trout, maybe bass or something. The garden of Eden at our feet.

Leslie jumped into the creek with her clothes on and wanted to turn into a sylph or a salamander but we wanted to climb a mountain and there weren't any around. So after driving around the woods, with me riding on the roof of the car navigating, we went up a road but first the ignition needed some fiddling. There was something wrong with the solenoid and you sometimes had to hot wire it with a screwdriver. Dave was doing this, plunging the screwdriver right into the white hot heart of the ignition, with sparks flying, and got a huge shock. Then we found that the sparks had set fire to the pine needles under the car which we had to put out. You gotta be pretty high to start a forest fire with a screwdriver. But we got the car going and headed back up the road from Beckwourth, then turned off on a dirt road and stopped at a turnout so we could turn around. When we got out we saw we were at the foot of a mountain Dave said was Squaw Tit, one of the highest around the valley. It was conical with a tip at the top, which you could see from the bottom but couldn't tell what it was. It must have been named from the bottom. We started up and again got separated.

I climbed steadily, just beginning to really come on, the tune of "Dance the Night Away" by The Cream playing in my head, that continual unresolved not-quite crescendo, using a walking stick and feeling very old in a vaguely Biblical archetype, sensing I had a rendezvous with destiny at the top. There was a long fairly smooth stretch where you couldn't see the top. I stopped a couple of times tasting my blood in my throat and listened to my lungs going at a phenomenal rate, till they idled down, then started up again. I realized the best way if you could do it was to go steadily without resting because you just have to rev up again after resting and you can do things when you're wired up full blast you couldn't do ordinarily. Next, there was a rough stretch strewn with boulders you had to clamber over. Then I found myself at the foot of the peak. It burst upon you suddenly, you couldn't see it till you were right there. Unfortunately, we had left the camera in the car. The "nipple" was a rock formation strange beyond description. Dave called it a huge stone flower. It was an outcropping of boulders 6 to 8 or so feet long, sticking up at about a 45-degree angle as if the mountain had bloomed or exploded at the tip. They were splayed out like the petals of a flower, in several tiers one above the other, staggered like leaves or petals in a pattern familiar from the plant world and the animal world, like seashells for instance.

I started to climb and one rock gave under my foot. That was when I got scared for I realized that they were not necessarily capable of bearing my weight and since they stuck out over me I could pull one down and have a ton of rocks fall on me. So I deliberated a bit and decided if I was meant to make it I would, and if not so be it. The rocks held. As I climbed over them I saw that they were covered with peculiar lichens, some like blood, some like white paint or some

viscous substance that had been poured over them and congealed in layers. Then I got to the top. It was one of the highest points around but jagged and barren and dusty. I began to wonder why I'd come. I took off my shirt and lay down. Then I found out why I had come.*
Unfortunately, I have to leave this part blank. If you want to find out what's at the top of mountains you'll have to climb some.

*See Dylan's song, "Love is just a four letter word," stanza 4 and
  wouldn't hurt to listen to 3 either. Ed.*

MOUNTAIN CLIMBING ON ACID – TRIP III

The third and last time I climbed a mountain on acid was Crystal Peak. No kidding, that's really what it's called; it's on maps, or on signs anyway. You go north from Chilcoot, on Hwy 70 , to Frenchman Dam, go right, over the dam, and follow the signs to Crystal Peak. Simple as that. Well, almost. The signs get woodsy, like painted on trees with red paint. An arrow means the summit is this way, one dot means one mile, etc., sort of halfway between highway signs and smoke signals. We followed the signs to Crystal Peak, came to one road that was blocked, private (think that's the good road), went around to where we couldn't drive much more in a '58 Chevy, though the road would have been passable for a truck or 4-wheel etc., and when we got out of the car there was Crystal Peak above us. Its a fairly conical peak. You can't see its composition from the foot, but you do immediately notice that there's a pine tree almost at the top of it, far past where the other trees have quit, and it's cross-shaped—just a trunk and two branches, spread-eagled into the mountaintop wind, slightly swept back, about as fortuitous looking as an electric flag: annunciatory. So, Art and I head for the top, leaving Paula staying behind to read an astrology book. The pine tree didn't look any more plausible when we got there than it did before, because it was growing out of solid rock. I guess you could say it looked like a plant.

Then we found there was an old mine shaft, a shack, and a road that came around the other way. I guess it was the one we would have caught if it hadn't been blocked off at the other end. The peak is an outcropping, more or less conical, of quartz, mottled or spotted with some black stuff in places, almost like asphalt with gravel, but in other places pure white. When you break a piece of white quartz you find the crystal filaments or icicles imbedded in the rock, clear as glass, but with the intensity of diamond, and ice-like too. We started busting pieces of it against the rocks and chips of crystal were flying through the air. We picked up the fragments, looking for the biggest pieces of pure crystal we could find, and gathered them into little piles, having turned into mad miner rock hounds on the spot. Crystal Peak (I had just taken a half-nap at the last minute) wasn't really high until I got there, when we started feverishly tearing the rocks apart, seeking the heart of puro again, like finding a place high above the world where all the dross was distilled into a pure and shining pearl of great price, the philosophers stone.

We wrapped the best ones we found in a shirt and started down. We found a snow bank in the shade that hadn't melted, scraped off the top, and ate the clean snow underneath, which was very much like the crystal; maybe because it had thawed and refrozen it was very granular. I got to thinking how crystal was used in phono cartridges and in old radios and how the whole peak was made of it. There was no telling how deep down it went. Maybe the mountain was a column of quartz with just a mantle of dirt and trees, etc., the usual guise and garb of mountains. But since crystal is a radio-conductive substance, maybe it really was a transmitter or conductor or something for some cosmic inter-galactic waves. I began to wonder, is that what mountains really are? Not just piles of rock but a crossover point between this world and another? Because that ties in with what happened on the other mountain tops. They seemed to be the thresholds of another world, the domain of the gods, if I may be permitted to say so, the end of this world and the beginning of the next, which one can enter, in the flesh, and do the things one does with gods. You know, that mystical bit . . .

As for what gods, I guess they're the same gods as you get everywhere else: the Father, the Son, the Holy Ghost, and the Virgin Mary, just to square the circle. Christianity never came out even until they let Mary in to fix the odds.

FIRE CAMP

When I was working in the Forest Service (I always say "in" instead of "working for" because you wore sort of a uniform, or were supposed to, and lived in what they called barracks but could've been called a bunkhouse) in June, they had fire camp, in an undeveloped area, i.e. you had to camp out. That was part of the idea. This was when the men from all over Shasta-Trinity National Forest met to get training in fighting fires. I think it was supposed to last three days. It was held at the foot of Mt. Shasta, which is a weird mountain, always "shrouded in clouds" and said to have been revered by the Indians, and for good reason, as soon as you see it you know it's something else.

In June it's supposed to be warm but we had hit the last cold spell of the year, freakish weather. It was drizzling and just above freezing. It would have been better if it had been a little colder because at least the snow wouldn't have soaked in. We weren't prepared for the cold, only had unlined work gloves, no warm socks or boots, no raincoats or warm coats or sleeping bags, and we had to sleep out in these paper liners that we tried to stuff blankets inside of. During the day we just stomped our feet all the time trying to keep them from going numb and kept our hands in our pockets. Everyone had orange hard hats on—it was like a bad acid trip—and everyone looked exceptionally ugly, at least to me. You couldn't have found a more wretched crew.

There were classes which were comically rudimentary, about on the 2nd-grade level, explaining that fires required FUEL and OXYGEN and HEAT, and if you removed one of these, the fire would go out. Then they were going to turn us loose on real live fires, even had all the tools ready. But since it had been raining for two days everything was soaking wet and wouldn't burn. The instructors put gas and diesel fuel on piles of branches but the fire wouldn't catch. All they could get it to do was smolder. We ended up standing around these feebly smoldering heaps half-heartedly hacking away at the ground around them to keep them from "spreading." We were supposed to sleep there again that night and I guess fight a big roaring barnburner the next day, but they gave up and shipped us back to our camps.

On the way back, we plebes were in the back of a truck while the higher-ups rode in the cabs. There was a tarp over the back but a rope came loose and the tarp and rope were flapping rhythmically and violently against the hard hat of one guy, and he just sat there for a long time taking it. There weren't many places to move to, until I screamed, "I can't stand it. Stop that!" and he moved or did something. Maybe he didn't want to appear "candy-assed" and welcomed the urging.

So Fire Camp 1965, which had been talked about for weeks before, was a big fizzle. Despite the added misery, we were glad because we got one less day of the planned misery.

ANIMAL STORIES

Puppy: I'm taking care of four dogs, one cat, one horse, some chickens whose number I have not undertaken to determine, four turtles, one albino walking catfish, and other fishes too small to mention. One of the dogs, a puppy named, "Puppy," was run-over by the lady of the house. His pelvis, I guess, got crushed, and while he can get around, he half-drags his rear end and walks half-assed. He seems to feel that this was visited on him by the Jehovah of his world—his owner—from whom all blessings and blights flow, as punishment for something that he is at a loss to ascertain. And he never will ascertain it, since it doesn't exist. In fact, I suppose it was his friendliness that brought him too close to the car, so now he feels guilty about his love, and it shows. He is self-effacing to the extreme, apologizing for his existence at every turn, hanging his head sideways, and wagging his tail in the low position. Puppy is so abject that when I give him a vitamin in an attempt to restore him to health, if Hogan, an aggressive pup, comes up to him and sniffs he will drop it from his mouth and let Hogan have it. While ordinarily a dog will growl if another dog threatens his food, Puppy feels he has no right to his and will yield it, hoping to earn some canine karma points. He would do anything to regain grace, and there is nothing he can do. One thinks of the Old Testament; the spirit is abroad, its workings everywhere. I hope that if I get to heaven, Puppy will be there, for he has paid his dues and his cause is just. But there is a New Testament too, and it requires more: Power in the land of righteousness.

Young Alan Russo

Superdog: A pickup just went by with a dog standing on the roof; it looked like a black lab with a silver ruff which was flying in the wind. I knew that some dogs like riding in cars and in the backs of trucks but this one was really tripping out on it, like he was the one dog who could do that, with all four feet on the roof. They were going down East Valley Road, which seems like it could be pretty tricky. He had silvery fur down the back of his neck and around his neck and around his ears. Silvery trim I guess you'd call it. He was giving his trim a twirl while wailing down the road with his fur flying in the breeze, almost like the ends had turned incandescent in the wind. It takes some class for a dog to ride in style like that.

The living room windows on the south side just shook. There was no boom or thunder.

Just before that I tried to call Jeanine and the phone just clicked, but sort of a total click, like an orgasm or seizure, and went dead. No dial tone, nothing. I dialed it again and got a busy signal every time I dialed it for an hour or so until it clicked and went dead again. I called the operator who put the call through. It clicked again but this time Jeanine said hello, like it went dead and went through at the same time with the operator's assistance.

I was just telling Suzy that I had a dentist appointment at 3 and she said she didn't know what to do about that, since George had left his shirt at Mickey's last night, when just then the phone rang and it was the dentist's assistant asking if I could make it Friday instead which settled that. If we could just get synched in better we could work things out a lot better and easier. I've been going at things the wrong way, like trying to get a car so I could go see a doctor, finally I called the Physicians Referral Service or whatever it's called and they told me there was a doctor right down in the Village, within walking distance. I didn't find him in the phone book because his name begins with K and I didn't get that far. I got an appointment that day, there was no one in the waiting room, he said his nurse would be right back, when I left 40 minutes or so later, he was still saying she should be back any minute, I don't know if he really has a nurse or not. He spent about half an hour with me, very thorough, looked English or Scotch but has a German name, finally wrote for everything I wanted, didn't ask for money, guess he'll bill me, suspect he's the kind of doctor that gives rich old women their dope.

Dogs Again: On the way down to the doctor's I was walking on the road and just passing a mailbox on a post made out of a crankshaft, when a dog came up to me. It was part Weimaraner and part some other breed and looked to be half-grown; he started smelling my heels. I wasn't sure what his intentions were and thought of picking up a stone or a stick but realized he just wanted to make a "boy and his dog scene" while walking down the road. You throw him a stick, and he fetches it, you know? He was trying to figure out if I were someone who would make that scene. He started prancing and capering around me but going out into the road, sometimes across both lanes, which is very uncool on that road, which is quite curvy and overdriven. Every time he ran out into the street, people would have to slow down or stop. He was constantly on the verge of getting run over, but didn't know it as a young pup and not hip to the traffic rules. I was carrying a near-disaster area along with me like a cloud. I was getting kind of worried because if he had got run over, it would have been right in front of me. I think that would have shaken me up, and also it would have been sort of because of me because this was some kind of friendship dance he was doing. Finally, he took off across a field. Thank God I got out of that one.

But the dog on the roof of the pickup—he was a silver-trimmed super dog transcending the limitations of canine possibility. I had never thought of magnificence or grandeur as qualities that a dog could achieve, but that one at least approached something on that order. Everybody's getting into the act.

Dogs Still: I might as well jot down my other dog stories while they're on my mind. Anything, just so long as it's on my mind. I was visiting some people, I don't remember who or where, and went to sit down in a chair in their living room. They had a dachshund, or some kind of small slithery dog, which, when it saw somebody heading for a chair, at just the right moment, would break into a run and dive into the chair right under your ass so that you sat down on a writhing dog. He had it timed to a hair. Maybe they had trained that dog that way, but I doubt it. He probably was just a freak dog who dug being sat on. Lots of cats, when lying down, will allow you to pile things on them without complaint, to the point of discomfort, and won't pull out until it hurts. Bondage.

The other story is quite a bit raunchier, and I wouldn't include it except for the sake of completeness. I knew this chick from Wichita, Cherril or Cheryl—she's quite a long story in herself—but anyway she had a dachshund named Nietzsche who was a self-debasement freak. He would eat her used underpants if he got a chance, and also Kotex. Sometimes there would be Kotex and panties strewn along the driveway. She had encouraged this trait in him by sitting with her legs spread and letting him nuzzle her crotch, with shorts on, I guess. She was the biggest prick-tease artist of all time. After Nietzsche she had a couple, or probably more, of Siamese cats, all named Sappho. She walked them on leashes, or tried to, in her incredible drag of hip-length

117

boots, sealskin coat, weird hat, etc, freaking people out on the streets of San Francisco. They were easier to freak out then, but have become somewhat blasé since. After the cats, she had a series of standard black poodles, all named Russia, who she walked wearing a Russian-style fur hat. She had a closet full of far out clothes, collected with the help of her husband's mother, who was a buyer for department stores and could get things free.

Her husband was Richard White, the great mad Wichita poet artist piano player dope fiend, one of the Wichita gang I met at W.U. that included Bob Branaman and Beth Branaman, Charlie Plymell, Phil Rohrig, and Roxie Powell. There were lots of other people of course but those form some sort of bloc in my mind and all came out to California after I scouted it. Richard sat in their apartment on Divisadero for 4 or 5 years taking care of their kid Colin, while Cheryl worked at Fireman's Fund, taking Obitrol and Percodan which he got from a highly cooperative pharmacist right downstairs, nice guy, who gave him credit and sold it very cheap, the clerk used to say, "We do twice as much business when D. [?] is working as any time else, can't figure it out," writing music which may have been great, hard to tell because no one could read it, he'd make up his own symbols, jazz musicians would come up to play with him, he played the piano, and say, "What key you in man?" and "What's that mean?" when they came to one of his home-brewed notations.

Which reminds me, what with all the talk about running over dogs, and cats, about the time I almost ran over a kid. I was living with a couple named Bud and Joan on De Haro when this guy comes by with a stolen Jaguar. It had been stolen there in San Francisco, so it really wasn't very cool. I had never driven a Jag, so we took off in it, but I burnt the clutch out getting started. De Haro is very steep, and in San Francisco, the only way you can open up a car and see what it will do is on a steep hill. So I went uphill, but I didn't know that a Jag has an all or nothing clutch. I was sitting there racing the motor against the clutch until a big cloud of smoke came out from under the hood. The guy says, "Gee, that's funny. It never did that before." I finally got it going, and we went to a defunct housing project on Potrero Hill, where there are winding roads and no traffic. I started steering around curves pretty fast when suddenly I rounded a curve, and there was a kid on a bike on the wrong side of the road! I guess he didn't think that there'd be any traffic there either. I hit the brakes and swerved, and he swerved, and I just missed him. Then I got to thinking what if I had hit him, in a stolen car, with tracks up my arms, and a short-sleeved shirt? It would have changed my life.

I stayed in second all the way back.

Mountain: The people next door have a dog named Mountain. It's big, you dig. And it's all'a time mountin'. One time someone brought a bunch of puppies out and Mountain tried to roll four of them in a ball and fuck it. I guess he figured one would be too small so if he got enough of them together it would add up to something big enough to fuck. Doggy logic, with an over-reliance on volume. He follows the chick, his mistress, around when she is wearing a mini with his snout just below the hem, sniffing and wishing. She sort of mounts him sitting on him and patting him, to show there aren't any hard feelings I suppose. Well anyway, it's good to know we're not all alone out in left field.

Fiat The Cat: There is a fat yellow tabby cat named Fiat because he came from a Fiat dealer. He likes to roll and be rolled. If he wants food or out or rolled he just lies down on the floor in front of you and rolls and writhes around. And you rub and roll and ruffle him. Outside he lies down in fresh piles of dirt the gophers have left and rolls around in it and it doesn't get him dirty. It's very clean dirt. There are birds to catch, gophers to eat, and lizards to mess around with. He just trolls around in tabby cat heaven all day.

Judee Sill's Animals: Judee Sill has two dogs and a cat, all worthy of mention. Jasmine is a Basset Hound that has been spayed. I don't know how low she hung before she got fixed but she's too low now. When she comes upstairs, and it's a two-story house, her belly doesn't clear so she has to swarm up the stairs like a seal, belly-flopping, and huge claws scraping away, you can hear her coming, the most grotesque thing I've ever seen. I hear there's a movement to forbid the breeding of Basset Hounds—sure sounds like a good idea. The other dog is a Shepherd who has forgotten she's a Shepherd and cringes in terror at your approach. Sill bred her soul out of her. Her cat looks more like a witch's cat than any other I've seen. Her tail starts out skinny and then gets bushy, and her eye is sly. She has kittens and has the dogs pussywhipped into not eating them. Her method is sort of a cross between witchcraft and conditioning. She rubs up against the dog's face, gives it a good whiff of the smell of milk and kittens and all, and rubs it into its snout. I presume so it will associate that smell with her, to take the exotica out of it, and the dog won't try to eat her kittens. She just does it to the Shepherd. She knows that the Hound is retired. "Out of the list," I think the expression is. When dogs stop being dogs they turn into something awful damn sad, and people keep them for this—licking each other's wounds in a feast of loss.

THINGS PEOPLE SAY

Every night and every day now . . . never knowing what they mean. For one thing, this cop stopped me in Marin for doing 115 or so after I'd been driving all across the country like that, was just wondering how long it could last and that was it; he said, "You've got other people in the car to think about, I don't want any fatal accidents because I'd have to do a lot of paperwork." I said, "I wouldn't want to put you to any bother . . ."

Then driving through Big Sur with a carload of hitchhikers fast around curves, some of them just hung tight; then the girls got scared, some of the boys freaked out too, one got out early I think, and some of them came on with the children con. You know, war is harmful to children and other living things. The last refuge of chickenshits. If you can't think of anything else come on with the children con. So they said, as I'm whizzing around the curves, "There might be some children playing down at the bottom of the cliff and if we went off we might hit them . . ." Now that's what I call thinking ahead . . .

I was back up in Vinton where I lived one summer three years ago and got a case of beer for a kid and shortly afterwards Dave Bearden and I wanted some so I went back to the store but thought I should think of some excuse, why I was getting so much. So I said to Jeff, that's the lady who runs the store, "That beer just doesn't seem to last like it used to," and she says, "Everything's changed." And I said, "Even up here?" and she said, "Yes, it's just like your beer." Which hadn't really changed at all, but me and Dave made that an expression for when some things have changed bewilderingly, "It's just like your beer." He and I have a sort of private language made up of quotes from *Naked Lunch* etc., a sort of shorthand, so we don't have to spell things out to each other.

JOCKEY SHORTS IN THE DARNDEST PLACES

I was thinking about this incident involving jockey shorts and remembered that it was the second time something of the sort had happened to me. This last one was when I had picked up a girl hitchhiker in San Franscico when I was running my Telepathic Taxi Service (just think of me and I'll be there) and asked her where she was going and she says, "Where are you going?" and I say, "Army and Castro," and she says, "That'll be just fine." When I got her to Bud and Joan's, Gary Serber (who deserves a chapter to himself) goes into his act, turns her on to Tussionex, beats on his drum, chants, shows her his woodcut, but I shoo him off and set her into bed and as I'm getting inside her jeans I find she's wearing jockey shorts. She said they were the only clean pants she could find at her place. Hippy you know. But this reminds me that something really strange happened at the same time. She was high on junk and so was very passive and was lying with her arms back on the pillow and the light was dim when suddenly she turned into Susan Branaman. I blinked and she still looked like her. I looked away for a moment but it wouldn't go away. It was like Susan was there. I wasn't high on anything, and she didn't actually look that much like Susan. It really blew my mind, as they say. The funny thing is that the first time I made it with Susan she was on junk and also laid in the same position. Some wires got crossed somehow.

The other jockey shorts situation happened years before when I was living with Joanne in Stinson and we were going to some function where she needed to wear stockings, though I can't imagine what formal occasion we could have been going to. Anyway she wanted to wear hose but didn't have a girdle or garter belt or any clean pants. I guess the same thing as the other time really, only she attached the stockings to a pair of my shorts. I put her on about it and she threatened dire reprisals of some sort if I told anyone. I guess its all right now.

MANTRA-ROCK DANCE AT THE AVALON

I was there—witness to history in the making—yes I was there when Gary Snyder attained enlightenment from Tim Leary at the Mantra-Rock Dance event at the Avalon. And I don't even know them, or rather they don't know me, and it's never been recorded. But first some words of explanation are in order. The Avalon Ballroom was one of the two main hippy acid rock dance halls in San Francisco, beginning in 1966. It had always been a dance hall and always called the Avalon Ballroom, but a straight Guy Lombardo kind of place, until that sort of thing became passé and rock came in. Chet Helms, who ran it with an outfit called the Family Dog, apparently thought the name was cute and kept it.

Sometime in 1967, in the height of the Haight (it is said that old timers pronounced it "Height," and maybe it would have all worked out differently if it had been still pronounced that way), this Swami from New York, i.e., from India via NY, where he was called "the downtown Swami," I believe, to distinguish him from the uptown Swami, moved his show to San Francisco, setting up shop on Frederick just past Stanyan. They called it Krishna Consciousness and chanted Hare Krishna and burned incense and all that. It was very spiritual. Then Allen Ginsberg was in town for awhile and got the idea of bringing rock and Krishna together and conceived the idea of a Mantra-Rock Dance event.

Now if you really missed out (God only knows who might read this), "mantra" means, what? It's sort of a—well, I looked it up in the dictionary so I wouldn't get caught with my thumb in my ear, and it says—". . . one of the sacred texts or passages, chiefly metrical, of the nature of hymns . . ." (see, they had a little trouble too) "prayers, or (later) magical formulas." The only one I ever heard was the Hare

Krishna, but maybe they had some back room mantras for special occasions. Anyway Ginsberg and the downtown Swami, "Swami Bhaktivedanta," as he called himself (perhaps some cognoscenti would snicker at his temerity, but I don't know!) and some rock groups made a date to appear at the Avalon to consummate this holy union. Posters were printed-up, and if I recall right, it was called the Mantra-Rock Dance.

I believe I got a free ticket, "comps" they called them. I didn't go to these things often, but this one was supposed to be special, and everyone wanted to see what would happen. Anything seemed possible then and damn near was. I was standing in the strobe light which is very weird because it breaks up what you see into sections with the intervals when the light is off missing, so that everything moves with a sort of staccato fluidity. One trick people had was waving long strings of beads around, twining them around themselves, so that it sort of turned live movements into a diagram—hard to describe.

So then into the strobe steps Ginsberg along with the San Franscico poet Lew Welch, Gary Snyder, who had studied Zen in Japan, and Timothy Leary. All at once Snyder and Leary start making mudra type gestures at each other. There's another word that could use definition, and the dictionary doesn't have it. They are traditional Indian finger positions and gestures that convey a meaning beyond words—like the V-sign, I guess. What does it mean when you're driving down the San Diego Freeway and a bus full of grade school kids goes by and they lean out the windows giving you the V-sign?

So Snyder and Leary are exchanging these signs, I suppose both were high on acid, and Leary gets to swinging his beads, like making a circle with them with one hand and making gestures with the other through the ring, opening and closing it like a shutter, now you see it-now you don't, which is the essence of the strobe, since you see only what happens during the flashes. He is making some far-out signs, improvising as he went along, until finally Snyder sees the light and clasps his hands together and bows, the traditional Zen indication of enlightenment.

The show itself was a letdown, especially after this impromptu skit. I think the Swami, a simple retired Bengali postal worker, was mind-blown by the Avalon which was packed with thousands of people, many of them high; by the black light show with colors which fluoresced under them, chartreuse and ultraviolet; by the several movie projectors going at once; and the thunderous, supernatural sound of the amplified musical instruments. It must have been a bit much for him when they did the Hare Krishna for an hour at a steadily increasing speed. Ginzy was the only person you could hear. The downtown

Swami never made a peep so far as I could tell. I suppose he just thought it was a bunch of freaks freaking out, or maybe it seemed like a kind of hell to him. They say when Zen masters take acid they have hellish experiences—so he just sat it out, as a matter of courtesy.

There sure wasn't any Second Annual Mantra-Rock Dance, I can tell you that for right now.

AND AS FOR GARY SERBER

He, as you probably expect, was a funny guy. Several funny guys with disparate aspects of his personality. He was into some Zen thing which I can never remember the name of, *Nichiren Soshu* or something like that, and he chanted in his loft over the service entrance, but his chants would go like, "No hole in my arm, no hole in my arm," and things like that.

You see he also was hung up on dope, mostly Tussionex and Desoxyn. He was a real artist at getting prescriptions for Tuss—a hopped-up form of codeine which is almost as strong as morphine but which you could get with a regular script. He had been getting these for years and had it down to a fine point. He called doctors nights or weekends when they can't come to the office and got them to call into a drug store. He has been doing it so long he knew or found out somehow when a doctor with a partner was going on vacation then called the partner and said he was a patient of the one who is out of town and he would call in a prescription. And he got large numbers, 50, sometimes 100. The procedure was complicated by the fact that not all drugstores carried Tussionex. It was also expensive and Gary didn't have any income except a few bucks from mom—to keep him out of trouble I suppose—so he had to share them with whoever else put up the bread. He had to somehow get the doctor, the drugstore, and the money altogether, a real juggling feat. Which he did at least once a day.

He had burned most of the drugstores and doctors in San Francisco and sometimes had to go down the peninsula or over to the East Bay. But you give him a couple of dimes for phone calls and somehow it came up Tussionex. A real artist.

He also had a thing about German planes, especially World War I models. He knew technical details about all of them and claimed there was one where the plane, in effect, revolved around the crankshaft. I wish I could remember how that worked. He would make models of them and when he was high on speed would fly them around the house. Joan's mother, after visiting them said, "He seems like a nice young man, but isn't he a bit childish, flying those model airplanes around?" He also knew World War II German planes, but his interest seemed to end there. He didn't know what kind of jets the new German Air Force flew since they're American. Although he never went to college he could rattle off scientific-sounding data on chemistry etc., and since he knew more about it than I do I couldn't tell how much of it was for real, but I knew he went over the line at times. He complained several times a day that it had been 18 months since he's had a piece of ass. If he would put half the amount of work, effort, and expertise into it that he put into getting Tuss he'd been up to his ears in it.

A real operator who just never found his calling, or maybe he did. He was certainly the best in his field.

KENT CHAPMAN

He was one of the characters of the Height of the Haight that I remember with some fondness, eccentricities and all. Maybe it was his sincerity that endeared him to me. He was a Christian mystic, the only other one I knew, with everyone else being on some oriental trip or other. He carried a copy of *The Imitation of Christ* in his back pocket at all times. For rapid reference I suppose. If he found you sitting down he would ask you if you wanted a massage. Naturally, you would say yes and he would stand behind you, take your hands, and guide you through a series of movements sort of like a modern dance—vaguely relaxing and completely unclassifiable—like a dance with him leading then ending in some kind of mutual symmetry. Never saw anything like it. But these strange spells would come on him. You could be talking to him one minute and he'd be perfectly rational and then he'd turn around and start having a dialog with someone you couldn't see.

It would generally start out something like: "Yes . . . well . . . er . . . ah . . . I don't know . . . no! No!" rising in intensity all along until he was screaming in terror at the end. I assumed he was talking to the devil though I never saw fit to ask him. He slept in my room one night and he went through this all night. One time I asked him, "Kent are you all right?" and he said yes and went right back at it. The thing is, he was a speed freak and I guess something went wrong. But he seemed so perfectly composed and clear-eyed, so lucid with a crisp classic manner, and then he'd turn around and enter into a parley with points unknown. Last time I saw him no one was living at the place which had been my flat, except for him and a few other speed freaks. The front door was broken and someone had written by it, "bad vibes inside bad vibes go away." So I don't know . . . I met a lot of people then that I never saw again. I suppose some went one way and some another. Fill in a leafy wind motif and you've got it.

RICK SCHWARTZ

I was just lying in the bathtub and got to thinking about Rick Schwartz. Don't know if he's still alive, it's kind of hard to tell sometimes. I've been accused of being a bathroom freak, but he's more of one, only it's tied in with junk and probably everything else about him. It's hard to say if he's a junky or an o.d. artist or just a freak or what. He scores big, like 1/4 ounces, takes ungodly doses, sometimes passes out, but if he can navigate, walk isn't the right word because he sidles around in a series of pirouettes, spiraling around with his sweater pulled over his head and spread out like bat wings, and sometimes gets in the bathtub, anyone's, and lies there for hours mooing like a cow, or making noises like a kid pretending he's driving a car. Sometimes he won't make it to the tub and ends up under the table or the sink. If you ask him what he's doing, he'll rasp out, "I'm a cow, man!" if he's mooing, or "I'm driving a Jaguar, man!" if he's making car noises. One time I went into the john at the De Haro pad and he was kneeling on the floor in front of the toilet. The seat was down and there were a lot of little piles of powder on a piece of paper on the toilet lid. He was trying to cut some stuff with milk sugar. There were also piles of powder on the floor and some of it was getting spilled into the cracks in the linoleum around the can. He was so stoned he didn't know which was stuff and which was milk sugar. He was "driving a Jaguar" while he was doing this. In real life, he hardly ever drove stoned without having an accident.

One time he came by with a big bag and asked if he could use a works. I quickly produced a new point. Joan, Bud, Morgan, Bob, Sue, and I waited while he did up. He passed out and slid slowly off the chair and as he went down and out he made a fucking motion with his hips down to his knees on the floor, then a few more bumps before he keeled over. I mopped his brow with a wet cloth but he didn't come around. Everyone else said he was all right since he hadn't turned purple and began digging into the bag. I carried him to a bed and kept mopping his brow. All this time everyone else in the kitchen was taking off, about four outfits going at once. Finally, we gave him a shot of coke and he came around. As soon as he opened his eyes he said, "It's all a matter of balance." Morgan was the only person who helped me with him. I didn't take anything out of the bag until I was sure he was going to make it. Later that night Bob took him by Ray's to try to arrange a deal where Rick would score from Clarence for Ray. Ray refused to have anything to do with Rick, said it wouldn't be cool to have someone staggering around his place; no one could figure out why Bob would introduce Rick to Ray in that condition, or why he would want to anyway, since if they dealt directly Bob couldn't act as a middleman. None of Bob's deals ever worked out, he was a real genius at arranging things so that they got all fucked up; over at their place things were in a constant state of crisis, an interconnected series of disasters. A mosaic of trouble at every level all the time. Susan used to say it was all she could do "to keep her hair on;" quite a show, a real masterpiece of its kind.

Another time over at De Haro Rick and Joanie, his old lady, came by and did up. He hit her and afterwards a drop of blood welled up from the mark and he went down on her arm and slurped up the blood with sucking sounds like a vampire. Later he said, "The funk was so thick even the werewolves got sick." Later I heard that Joanie died in Chicago from unknown causes and he was going there.

Probably won't hear about him again—he's the one who was married to Cassandra.

MARY CAROLINE

M.C. or Mary Caroline or Bobbie, from the old San Francisco Bobbie and Gil team, told me how she got raped one time. It was right after she broke her leg and it was still in a cast, and she was hitchhiking to Big Sur. She was somewhere around Santa Cruz when a guy in a Mustang picks her up. She finds out he's a pool shark hustler type. He turns off the main road claiming he knows a shortcut and ends up driving through orchards. He then informs her that she's just been kidnapped. She says, "What are you going to do with me?" And he answers, "I don't know yet." That was what really scared her. Finally, he stops in an orchard, takes her clothes off, ties her up, and balls her very gently and tenderly with a pistol to her head, saying he was going to blow her brains out when he came. She did her best to bad trip him, telling him she had an inverted uterus, etc., and apparently it worked; he didn't shoot her and said afterward that he didn't dig it very much. Said a friend of his turned him on to it but it was the first time he'd tried it. I guess if he'd had a really good orgasm, he would have shot her. When he read this Glenn Todd said he had read the same rape story somewhere else. Don't know if she was repeating it or if the guy had read it and decided to try it.

When she was staying at the Branamans one time I was there and she was scooting her baby across the floor with her foot between Boogaloo's legs and the baby on her stomach. M.C.'s leg was broken and the kid had cerebral palsy, so M.C. couldn't carry the kid, which seemed to rationalize it, but the baby was crying from being more or less mopped across the floor, so I said "Wait, I'll carry her." I put her in bed, then as I was leaving, I heard M.C. saying to the baby, "You won't ever try that again, will you!" Then I realized she was punishing the kid for getting out of bed, which she could only do by crawling with her hands, as her legs didn't work. This freaked me out, as I had been thinking of moving in there. Decided I couldn't make it.

SOMETHING THAT HAUNTS ME

Some things that people said come back to me from time to time, and I never can figure out what they meant, even after years. One such was when Janet and I visited Joel Brewer, her previous flame, in Berkeley in 1961. He was rooming with Bob Robbins. We, i.e. Bob and I, had been classmates in high school but I hadn't seen him since. I don't remember just what went on there, but I guess I said a few things because later Jan told me that Bob (I used to call him Robin a' Bobbin) said after I left, "What this country needs is a good five-cent Alan Russo." Now, what in the Hell? . . .

THE BITTER BUDDHA-BOY AND
HOW HE GOT THERE

Once there was a guy named Larry, forget his last name, and he lived at my flat in the Haight-Ashbury. He was making it with Tiffany, Suzie Tiffany. She was a beautiful blonde who had an identical twin sister also named Tiffany, only she lived in LA so their territories didn't overlap. I met her sister once and she was better made up but underneath it was the same old Tiffany. Suzie started out calling herself Suzie Creamcheese, but this got too common and there was another chick in the place named Suzie so she adopted Tiffany even though this was what her twin sister in LA called herself. It fitted her too, she was sort of gold-plated, elegant you'd call her.

Well to the point. She and Larry moved in, I forget under what circumstances, but they didn't pay any rent. They were young, about 19, both tall and slim and pretty. She was blonde and very fair and he was dark and curly-haired. They didn't bother anybody and nobody minded having them around. He was quiet and had a copy of the *Book of Ashanti* or whatever, a neo-bible dictated from outer space, that he believed in but didn't push it. After a while, they broke up. She worked for *Western Girl*, occasionally, and started working for the *Oracle* so she had a little bread and rented her own room. He started sleeping in the living room which became a crash pad about that time which became a drag because any time of the day or night there would be people sleeping on the couch and all over the floors and you couldn't use the room for anything. We never could figure out where all these people came from but they did.

Larry had been there for months without ever contributing anything. One time while I was gone Bill Paul kicked him out but he came back somehow so I asked him to get another place if he could, and then Cindy finally kicked him out. Next time I saw him he told me he'd been sleeping in the park. He looked weathered and said it accusingly, like it was our fault he was sleeping in the park. Then after that, he took up station on Masonic, just off Haight by the Weed Shop where they sold cigarette papers. He'd be sitting on the sidewalk against the wall with a salmon-colored blanket wrapped around him all day. We had to walk past him to get to the *Oracle* which was right across the street, and he was always there. At first, I tried to nod or say hi but got no response, and later just averted my gaze in chagrin, because his presence was like a reproach. He got more and more weathered and sun-beaten and looked sort of like a cigar-store Indian, always there as a reminder of our sins, like you're afraid you'll run into on acid.

I was always glad it wasn't I who kicked him out.

HER SONHAUSER

Her Sonhauser was the strangest guy I've ever met; so strange, in fact, that it's questionable whether the word "guy" is applicable, or any other word for that matter. I first met him at the *San Francisco Oracle* offices—the later one at 1573 Haight Street. He just was there one day. I never knew how or where he came from. He looked about 20 with dark hair and bright brown eyes. Jewish looking sort of, not grossly, a pretty chewish poy. Vel, he claims to be from another planet or dimension or something. It was all a matter of lines-crossed and transcended-boundaries with him.

You couldn't pin him down on anything. He would squirm out from under any question and turn it into a joke on you. He mentioned something one time about flying saucers and the Sandia Air Force Base where they do some far-out experiments, but when I started to write the name of the base down he said, "No, forget that." When I tried to get his name straight he spelled it "Her Sonhauser." I asked him if he didn't mean the German *Herr,* and he said, "No, it's 'Her', that's my first name,"

"And isn't Sonnhauser German for 'one from the house of the sun'?" I inquired and he said, "No, just one 'n', it's a name in my language."

He claimed he was from a place, or from something, that exists in a different dimension, you see, so it's hard to say if it's a place, or what, called *Sthronkos*, that's about how he pronounced it. When I tried to get him to spell it he would keep changing it. I would repeat the letters he had said then he would say, "No," and spell it differently, with a sly smile His idea of a joke. He did have a funny little smile that would creep up at the corners of his mouth, sometimes at completely inappropriate (so far as I could tell) times, as if he was just learning how to communicate with people and knew you were supposed to smile sometimes but didn't quite know when.

The other trick he knew was acting threateningly, as if he had been instructed or programmed to deal with people by either smiling or threatening them, which he did when he wasn't in a position to do so. Whenever he didn't get what he wanted he would shout, "You're under arrest!" or "You're all under arrest!" as if he were accustomed to having infinite power at his disposal. His best line was when explaining the situation of his people, who I just now recall were called "Ziriulanids." I believe that's how he spelled it, a European 'r' and a broad 'a'. Anyway, he would exclaim, raising a finger and leaning his head back, "The entire 20th Century is under arrest!"—meaning something to the effect that the earth people had gotten out of line, what with atomic energy and all, to the point that these Ziriulanids had become worried and sent agents in flying saucers to examine the situation, and that the earth was in a sort of quarantine . . . I guess. He talked in a peculiar monotone, sort of like a computer-operated robot or like the recordings you get on the phone, followed by a little smile, to assure you that he was making human contact and if explaining something, he'd say, "Ja?" to see if you understood.

He spoke English with a slight German accent which only got

out of hand when he said "Ja." I asked him about his German accent and he said, "That's only the body I'm using." Judging by his age and apparent Jewish descent, he would have been born around the end of World War II in Germany or thereabouts, and not many Jewish babies survived at that time. I suspect that he had slipped into a loose vehicle left over from the war. With so many people dying, the birth records were pretty sketchy and who would know?

He had done a drawing, or diagram, with a compass and other such instruments which he said were part of a formula for something which I forget. The drawing was at the *Oracle*, but had supposedly been borrowed by Daniel Eggink and not returned. Her Sonhauser was very anxious to get it back. I was very anxious to see it. I went over to Egg's place to retrieve it but no one was there so I spent about an hour crawling around on fire escapes and along ledges, trying to get into windows, etc. I tried everything but couldn't get in. When I got back and told Her Sonhauser, he came up with his "You're under arrest!" line. It was like pushing a button. Egg later denied having taken any such drawing. Dangerfield said, however, the last time he saw it, Egg had it. It was never located. We probably would have put it in the *Oracle* if we could have found it.

I asked Her Sonhauser if the flying saucer people were friendly or hostile, and he tried to dodge the question. I finally asked him if, from the point-of-view of earthlings, their intentions were desirable or undesirable, and he said the latter. I forget his exact wording. He seemed to know quite a bit about the latest developments in physics and non-surgical, inter-cranial stimulation, etc. He would take a brass lampshade and strike it like a gong then move it over your head so that the reverberations produced a spacey effect.

ONE OF MY MAD SCIENTIST FRIENDS

Beth was just by, who used to be Beth Branaman, with her husband Reuben Greenspan, who says everyone is trying to jackass themselves into the heart of the atom. It seems he is a mad genius physicist and claims he has the secret of the atom deal which is with harmonics. You modulate yourself, easy as can be, instead of blasting your way in with brute force, the American and Russian way. You get the resonant frequency of the atom you want, and apply the requisite force on the same wavelength as the atom will resonate to, and get an inordinate build-up of energy—and with a little finesse, there you go: controlled atomic fusion . . . or not exactly fusion . . . but something. He says the government is trying to get it from him, but he wants the Germans and the Russians to beat each other to death. He's Jewish and adjusts his physics to world politics. In 1934 he was in Time magazine about how he had predicted 17 earthquakes correctly, and had done it with Astronomy. When the moon is close and planets are aligned over an earthquake fault is when you can expect it. He was predicting one in California in 1964, and then a telegram arrived saying that it didn't happen. Then the next day the great Alaska earthquake did happen. Just a little bit off.

He's had these lawsuits going for years against the government and companies he has been employed by over rights to inventions he has come up with while working for them. You have to sign a contract that all the rights to what you come up with revert to them. Now he just works on a consultant basis. He's a litigious type, but apparently, he wins some of his cases. He says the Supreme Court has made a landmark decision that the AEC regulations aren't law . . . so now he has the key to the Universe all to himself and is keeping it—like the spoiled brat genius in the TV cartoons. If it won't come out the way he wants it, he won't let it come out at all.

I'M A DIABETIC

Janie Lewis or whatever her name is now (dead husbands . . . prisons . . .) just told me about how Karma caught her, or vice versa, really, and though it was around 1961 and I was around at the time (upper Fillmore, Batman Gallery, first smack period), I never put it together till she pointed it out. Oh, I knew she got diabetes after she started shooting smack and maybe the sugar in it was patently karmic. But she told me how she had been going to drug stores to get needles and telling them she was a diabetic, and after a couple of months, she was a diabetic. Like she said it so many times it came true. The nightmare came true. An "innocent" lie boomeranging into an undreamt truth. A vicious truth suppurating from the corner of the mouth like opium oozing silently/blackly in some field in Mexico. South of the border I sent my life away . . . Now the areas of her thighs and arms where she shoots the insulin have collapsed, big depressions in the flesh . . . gone, sad flesh, forced to give way before the inevitable and intolerable . . . she had a beautiful body . . . Now we sit in the park in Ojai with a hot wind blowing over us . . . ruffling her hair like the pages of a calendar, and she smiles, stoned, into the distance, wanly musing over the years and all (she has never cried). Now she has a little girl with a crippled leg (sins of the mothers?) and wonders how she is going to take care of the kid and die at the same time . . . time gets tight when it is opening and closing in the same time and place . . . it's getting closer all the time to where everything happens at once . . . what someone said time was invented to prevent . . . sounded like a joke at the time, but now I've started to see this same pattern, recurrent, just more perfect and obvious in Janie's case . . . I'll try to come up with some more examples.

Everything is forming patterns whose outlines I'm seeing, everywhere . . .

FAILING THE ACID TEST

For some reason lying in bed this morning with a hard-on wishing Jean didn't go to work so early I thought of the time in the Haight-Ashbury when I threw someone out in the street naked. What happened was I had taken STP and by the time I got back to the flat on Masonic I was pretty much down, or anyway past the peak, and Jon Locke was across the street evidently having a very earnest discussion with Steve Ross. Jon was a friend of Steve Leiper, and had just moved into the living room of the flat a couple of days before. We decided to rent the room because people had been crashing on the sofa and floor and we didn't have the use of the room anyway, so by renting it we would actually reduce the population and lower our rent too. And Jon was a quiet, single guy. But what he did was he slipped some acid to this guy Steve Ross unbeknownst to him. Jon was fresh from

Tennessee and didn't quite know what he was into, and it turned out that Steve, a mousey little guy who had been doing some typing at the *Oracle*, had a history of flip outs and history proceeded to repeat itself.

Jon brought him in. I had something to do and left, and when I came back Steve was freaking out, climbing the walls, screaming something about Jesus. Now the people in the flat above ours were hostile fags who would call the landlord when we got too noisy, so I tried to get him to quiet down but that just made him holler louder. I started checking the rooms to see what kind of shape we would be in if the cops arrived, and in the first room I checked there was Bill cleaning what looked like a pound of grass and I thought oh my god here we go down the chute. So I told him what was happening and asked him to stash the grass. I checked around to see if anyone else was holding and went back to the delivery room. By this time the patient had torn the place apart, cutting himself in the process and was bleeding a little, and had taken all his clothes off. I tried once more too cool him but it just heated him up more. He kept on with the "What's to hide?" bit, "Put it all up front!" But this was in the front room on the ground floor on Masonic right off Haight and anyone on the sidewalk could hear what was going on. So I decided resolute action was imperative. I told everyone else they might as well leave since there was a possibility of a bust, and the residents were glad to do so. This guy and chick who had been babysitting Steve trying to cool him also left. I then made one last plea to him with the same results. So I went to kick him out. Now by this time as I said he had taken all his clothes off and I couldn't find them because he had torn some of the lights out and the others just wouldn't work under such conditions and I couldn't find them in the dark, so I opened the front door, grabbed Steve, he was just a little guy, hauled him to the door and kicked him out. He jumped down the stairs and landed on the sidewalk naked as a jaybird. I closed the door and went looking for a pair of jeans. Steve was now beating on the door screaming "Let me in—in the name of Love!" *Reductio ad absurdum* of the flower doctrine if I ever heard one. I pushed him down the stairs again and gave him the pants, which he refused to put on, saying "What's to hide?" Bill and I then vacated the premises and went down to the corner of Haight & Masonic where the other people who lived at the place were standing. We all watched the denoument from there.

Steve stood on the sidewalk ranting, still on some Jesus jag as far as I could tell. Some spades walked by and were laughing and jiving him; Susan Branaman happened along about then and said, "Put your pants on, Baby," but Steve just stood there holding the pants and bleating his madness to the night sky. Apparently, a trolley bus had derailed and there was now electric smoke drifting down the street which was lit with mercury vapor lights creating a garish scene—a neon nightmare—until finally a cop car came and they dragged him off screaming.

I went back, got the apartment lights going and found his clothes which fortunately had his father's name in the billfold. I called his father, a New York doctor, collect, in Steve's name. His mother answered, happy expectation in her voice—"Steve?" I said, "This isn't Steve," and felt her heart sink 3,000 miles away; heard his father get on the extension, told them what happened, what hospital he would be at, etc. His father flew out the next day and got him out of the hospital. Steve came by and got his clothes. I was embarrassed at what I'd done, but he didn't have any clear recollection of it. He asked if he'd gotten pretty outrageous, then went back east with his old man. Jon moved out in disgrace, or chagrin at what he'd done, leaving the two kids who he'd been babysitting there, which gets into another chapter of the Haight-Ashbury saga.

The incident was in the next day's paper. They were playing the Haight-Ashbury angle at the time, with a page or two each day devoted to what the hippies were up to. It said that when the cops got Steve into the pants they were three or four sizes too big. What they made of that I don't know. I guess it reinforced the impression of total freakiness, which was pretty close to the money.

Alan Russo, Lompoc, California, 1977
Photograph by James Bearden

PART FOUR

THE MAN WHO KNEW GOD

In Wichita the other day I was talking to Justin Hein and recalled the time I went to Mass with him in San Francisco. He is a devout Catholic, and maybe it was Easter, but for some reason I went with him, just for the ceremony and music I guess, but when we got there it was just a sermon. We were standing up at the back of the church when someone else turned to leave. He was a thin, dark middle-aged man, of fiery mien, and he stopped to talk to us, I guess, because we were standing up and so presented an easier target. He had a wooden carrying case of some sort. He said, referring to the priest, "That man is absolutely wrong. I know, because God happens to be a personal friend of mine."

EVEN SHADES

Me and Joan used to live in an apartment on Bryant Street which I just remembered. But first, maybe I should tell how we got the place just to show that not everything goes wrong. All the time anyway. We were trying to get another place which they wouldn't rent to us but they told us about another place. We went there and no one was there so we left a note or Joan did. I thought it was ridiculous. It turned out the landlady didn't live in the building but the tenant took the note to her and she called us up and it was only $80 for four rooms, which seemed like it was too good to be true, and of course it was. She always knew what we did, I don't know how, maybe the neighbors called her up or she watched the reflections across the street, but the few times we had a guest she would be over, knocking on the door with her key, a pointed threat, and saying, "Now I don't have anything against hippies but I have a reputation to maintain in this neighborhood," and would say her husband made her be strict and he didn't speak English so you couldn't say anything to him. One time she told Joan we would have to get matching drapes and keep the shades even. They had to be all up, or all down, or all at half-mast. You couldn't have one up and one down. She didn't want this turning into no hippy pad. Finally, the Brannaman's moved in on us and we moved out from under her and left her with them. Serves her right. By this time she had raised the rent to $200 a month so we had to move anyway. We left the refrigerator behind, which we had bought, and she complained that it had a dent in it. You just can't please some people.

THE WRONG TUBE

I was just now applying some cortisone ointment—been trying every salve, spray, fungicide, antibiotic, etc. I can find in Mike and Joanie's well-stocked hypochondriac medicine cabinet—for the rash at the base of my spine. The doctor tells me it's a neurodermatitis or something, over a ganglion; I think it's from the waistband of my shorts. Anyway, I put the tube on the john but noticed it was right next to the toothpaste and thought that Thea, their daughter, might use it by mistake which reminded me of the time I brushed my teeth with vaginal jelly in Stinson Beach.

I woke up before dawn and wanted to brush my teeth, but I couldn't turn the light on because JoAnn was still asleep, so I stumbled to the sink which was in the bedroom and grabbed what I thought was the toothpaste. Now we just happened to have a big family-size tube of Crest that was almost exactly the same size as a tube of vaginal jelly, which just happened to be right next to it and sure as shit, I grabbed the wrong one. It didn't feel exactly the same, it was lighter and crinklier, but I had just woken up and wasn't thinking too clearly. I put some on the brush and started in. I had already swished it around before the taste, or feel, hit me. It was one of the worst things I've ever tasted; can't say for sure it was the worst because those melted vitamin pills that mom always put on your plate were enough to make you barf so it's got some other pretty strong competition. But anyway, there I was with a mouthful of vaginal jelly and suddenly realizing what I'd done. I frantically turned on the water and washed my mouth out, then washed the toothbrush and brushed my mouth out, then used toothpaste to try to get rid of the taste. It's got some kind of acid in it that kills the sperm. All this commotion woke JoAnn up and when she found out what had happened, she laughed her head off.

"Funny girl" I used to call her. Real sweet but with a bitch streak. "Bad beautiful bitch" I used to call her too.

THE GREAT FLOW

The one about brushing my teeth with vaginal jelly relates to the time JoAnn bled all over the bed. It was the same place, and the landlord wanted to sell it, apparently because he was so appalled at the tenants he had and wanted to hang up the whole thing. So, he had prospective buyers coming by. Now JoAnn sometimes had irregular periods, would always tell me her period was late to put me uptight, and when it did come sometimes it came with a vengeance. Well she was using Tampax and those things will let you down sometimes, can't handle a flash flood, and when we woke up one morning she was lying in a pool of blood. All over the sheets, soaked into the mattress, her ass and stomach and legs were covered with blood; apparently she had been turning over in it and you'd think it would have woke her up, or maybe she did it to spite me. Anyway, we pulled the sheets off but a lot had soaked into the mattress. Then after we were downstairs some people came by to look at the house. After they went upstairs I thought, "Oh my god the bed!" That ungodly big bloodstain was still on the bed. I've always wondered what they thought, or said, if anything.

That was the same place where the landlord, who had grey hair on his back, bought a new refrigerator because the old one had broken down, it seemed, and after we got the new one in it didn't work either and we found it was just the outlet that didn't work. I don't know what he did with the new refrigerator.

HASH-HASH?

Me and Bud and Gary were going on a drugstore run. I was just going along for the ride you understand, and going through the Tenderloin I saw a guy in Bermuda shorts standing on the sidewalk talking to the sky, which was pretty blue I must admit, and a couple of blocks later a woman walking across the street fell down as we went by, and then we parked by a Walgreens. Gary went in to try to score and Bud and I sat in the car. After a bit a foreign sailor (seems the Turkish fleet is in port, you'd see sailors from all over the world in San Francisco and they all wear basically the same outfit) comes up to us, the window was open, and says, "English?" I said, "Are we English? No, we're American." He again says, "English?" and I say, "You mean do we speak English? Yes, we speak English," and nodded affirmatively which I guess was all he needed, and he said "Hahsh-hahsh?" and made a smoking gesture. I said "No, go to the Haight-Ashbury," which he didn't understand, and then he went into Walgreens. I wonder if he tried to score from the Pharmacy. I guess "English" was the only English word he knew so that's how he started out. Imagine trying to score in a country where the closest thing to the word you want that you know is "hahsh-hahsh" for grass.

BLUE, BLUE SKY OF HOME

I passed through Tennessee one time to visit Steve Leiper, who was living with his parents on Signal Mountain, near Chattanooga. He was growing some pot and we were bopping around in the hills, hobnobbing with some hillbillies he had made friends with, right fine people too, only thing was you had to listen to nigger jokes by the hour. I believe now they tell hippy jokes but this was back in 1962 or 1963. I understood one of 'em preached on Sundays, but he told nigger jokes too. It's just their nature. And they always repeat the punch line, slap their thigh, and say, "Yessir!" Me and Steve would try to force a smile, feeling too guilty out of liberal sentiments to laugh. The hillbillies were trying to drill a coal mine but they missed the vein. One of them had lived in Detroit and could have made good money up north, could put a car together from parts—an engine from this one . . . etc. '53 Fords were his specialty for some reason, and yet he couldn't understand how an internal combustion engine worked. The hillbillies said they'd rather live down here on relief, because there aren't any niggers in the hills.

Well anyway, we were hiking around the hills and stopped and smoked some pot and I laid back and looked at the sky, which was very blue, and said, "Gee, the sky doesn't get that blue in Kansas." And Steve looked up and said, "Well, you know, Alan, it doesn't get that blue here either."

ALL UPS AND NO DOWNS

When I was about 18, some friends and I were driving across Western Kansas or Eastern Colorado, which isn't much different. We got to a rolling stretch of road and experienced a sort of a roller-coaster effect with the dips gentle enough that you could take them fast, but the hills fairly steep and just the right curve for what happened next. Which was that I would be going up a hill, and the next thing I knew, I was going down the other side and then up the next one, with the part in between—going over the top of the hill—missing. Sort of a strobe effect, flashing from one hill to another with a lapse in the continuity. After a few times, I really got scared and thought I was losing my grip, so I pulled over and had someone else drive. It wasn't until later that I realized what had happened, that the centripetal force going up the hill drained the blood from my brain, and I would pass out and regain consciousness on the downgrade when the blood returned. I was turning on and off like a light, not as fast as a strobe but a lot closer to it than was right.

I WISH I'D GONE TO A SCHOOL LIKE THAT...

Mike McClure reminded me in Laguna about the time in San Francisco years ago that I ran into Janie, Mike's daughter, at a party and got to talking to her. She was in the third grade and I asked her what she studied, and she said, "We learn language, math, science, etc." I said, "Have you learned 'the Truth' yet?" and she replied, "No, we learn that in the fourth grade."

AN ACID TRIP

And speakin' about nothin' much in particular, I recall the time I took acid, starting out on De Haro—but first, let me explain that Morgan and Joan had been taking acid for seven days, sort of testing the proposition that you couldn't get high for over three days, and they came by and Morgan accused me of putting him down to Lisa, and then I dropped a tab. Now Bud and Sharon had slept there the night before but here I've got to backtrack a bit; because the night before I had tried to make out with Sharon, a beautiful 18-year-old chick who however was already hung up on junk, and she got pissed off, saying "The chemistry's just not there," and finally they went to bed on the couch or whatever that was in the living room and I ripped off my shirt and threw it at them saying, "Wipe yourselves off with this after you're done!" Implying they were taking advantage of my facilities by sleeping there and I was getting it back by throwing this scene. And it was a very favorite shirt of mine, the dark blue job from J.C. Penney's in Wichita I'd purchased years ago, and some chick, I forget who, had cut off the sleeves after an elbow wore out, and it was such nice soft cloth and such a nice pattern, a cheap imitation of some expensive style which I've never run across, that I always kept it, and finally threw it into their astonished faces.

Well as I was saying, the next day I had to take acid to meet the challenge posed by Morgan and Joan, had started to come on, and Sharon came in the suede skirt that Susan had somehow conned out of a store—she saw it in the window and had to have it and talked them into letting her charge it though they didn't know her from anybody; being leather it never got dirty except for the increments of crud on it and Susan had turned it over to Sharon. I stuck my head up under it and nuzzled her ass, and she was holding a shell, undershirt kind of thing over her bosom saying something about how she didn't want to inflame me, and I pulled it down and pinched her on both nipples at once, my aim was remarkable, and she went into the kitchen and bent over to pick something up, I guess, and I came in behind her and goosed her and much to my surprise my finger went clear up her snatch, which was very wet, I suppose from the night before, and she turned around, but never during any of this did she utter one word of objection or reproach. I went into the living room and held up my finger in front of Morgan and said, "You wanna smell my girl?" and he said, "No, I don't wanna smell your girl!" Then Morgan and Joan and me left, after a very complex scene about cars, where nobody could get it together with anybody about who was going where. We finally walked to the little park on Potrero Hill, getting more spaced by the minute, and I wanted to go get Susan high and all of us have a love-death together, and we found a red-haired chick sitting in the park and told her our situation and she says, "The I Ching say, Man must have limits," and I said, "If you can find any let me know"; then someone pulled up in a car and we went to Morgan's where there were these 11 people and a dog sleeping on the floor, it was in the Haight Ashbury you know, and I was getting to where I didn't know what to do; I had my Post Office badge on and a white shirt and a necktie which I kept telling people was to hang myself with in case we got busted, and a windbreaker and all as straight as I could make it, and Morgan kept saying, do some pushups, or go run around the block; and then we went out to start the blue Chevy that we had borrowed from Bob and Susan, who got it from Steve Leiper, who wanted to take a tire off it to put on Jay Thelin's Woody. The Chevy had good tires, too good for it, no doubt bought with a phony credit card, you know you could look at it and see where the tires came from, and we had to put water in the radiator which leaked, and someone brought a wine jug out, and Morgan perched a foot on the bumper, the motor wasn't even running, and said, "Sounds to me like you need a valve job," in a Kansas twang which to me was one of the best lines I've ever heard.

Well, Joan had a terrible time pulling the Chevy away from the curb because it was parked on a hill, but she wouldn't let me drive because of my previously expressed suicidal impulses; we were going over to Bob and Susan's to turn her on and finally made it but things got weirder yet because Rick, Joanie, Bud, and Sharon were there and watched I guess in shifts while I fought cosmic battles with Bob and Susan's kids, who at one point had me down and all but out, were jumpin' on me, and me saying, "No it isn't possible!" Utterly defeated by two little children, it's the ultimate degradation; I finally took my windbreaker and chased them off and banished them into another dimension; sometimes I'd look at Sharon and she'd look like a beautiful 18-year-old chick and the next minute she'd look like a fucked-up freak, who could go either way. (I never heard of her after she hitched off to Big Sur but you know which way they always go.) And then Bugsy, the Branaman's boy, looped the cord to the Venetian blinds around his chin and when he let himself off the chair the blinds went up. When he got back on the chair they went down. So I went over and grabbed his heels and let him down, and the blinds came up, and then I pulled him up, like a pump handle, and the blinds came down; we finally ended up going to Big Sur that evening, Bob wanted me to go for my money, and I wanted to turn Susan on, which didn't quite happen. When we got to Pacific Grove we stopped at a gas station and a Mexican cat who was walking by recognized Bob and laid a bottle of Percodan-Demis on him. We slept in Bill Bathurst's shack and all I got to do was suck Susan's tit, which had milk in it, but Bob knew something was going on—a half-assed trip.

GOOD DRUNKS

I ran into two good drunks at once, and that doesn't happen often either—the grace of God when it does—in the Hub Bar in San Francisco. This was at the foot of Haight Street on Market, across from the Hub Drugstore, sort of a connection place, mainly because it is open late at night and for some reason there aren't any all-night drug stores in San Francisco. I was in the bar killing time, I guess, waiting for the store to open though I don't remember why, and there were these two guys there. One was dark, lean, with the air of an undertaker, and in his early forties. He was the straight man, more or less—they did sort of a duet—and the other guy was in his early fifties, grey-haired and pink-faced, the joker. Both trying to bounce their joke off the other persona. The gaunt one kept raving "Roses! Roses, BLOOMING in the middle of the Sierra desert!" That's what he said, "Sierra." And the other would say, "Yeah, but you ever try to grow spaghetti?" Then the Straight Man would say, "A Rose Garden," or he would have said *Garten* with such alacrity if it had been Germany, "A Rose Garden BLOOMING! (great effusiveness suffused his face as he said this; he seemed overjoyed, whether with some memory or just being able to put down such a line) in the middle of the Sierra Desert." And the smirking pink-faced guy says, "We tried to grow tapioca, but the *Mah Jongs* ate it all." To which the undertaker replied, of course, "A Rose Garden . . ."

And there was the guy, I ran into him several times, probably different versions of the same archetype, as Charlie Plymell would say: "they worked out of the same union." You know, the red-faced wino, beaming conviviality, who gets on the bus or subway, maybe with a transfer he just found, or he might pay 15 cents for a captive audience, and roams up and down the car with some routine like, "There he was, top of the ninth, and what does Mays do, he drops the goddamn ball!" Over and over again, to everyone, like a punch line, "Top of the ninth and he drops the goddamn ball!" A joke between him and the scoreboard, with people yelling, "Sit down before you fall down." His face just gleaming like a puppy-dog's tail, like he had a revelation of some cosmic comedy, "DROPPED the ball, you see, top of the ninth!" and he wanted to share this with everyone he could and had bought a streetcar of ears.

The scenes drunks pull on buses and streetcars in San Francisco remind me of things I've seen on subways in NY, though I don't guess those were drunks. One time I saw a couple, an old man and woman, both blind, walking down the aisle arm in arm singing hymns and carrying a tin cup. Another time I saw an old man with a little American flag stuck in his hat, and all kinds of funny buttons and things, you know the kind that fly the flag of madness, walking down the aisle playing the trombone. I forget the song. These artists would start at one end of the train and go through it like a combine through a field of wheat.

I hear there is a cop on each train now so maybe you don't get that kind of show anymore.

WHAT'S WRONG WITH A SOFT TOOTHBRUSH?

I was just brushing my teeth with my new toothbrush. I lost two in Big Sur and should buy them by the case, what with getting drunk and running around I can't hold onto them for long. I remember I got a firm one and then remembered the time I bought one in San Francisco. I was having gum trouble and the dentist recommend getting a soft toothbrush. I went to a drug store and said I wanted a toothbrush. There was a spade mailman standing around. The druggist asked what kind I wanted and I said, "The softest you've got." At which the mailman said, "Um HUMH!" like he was onto me, knew where I was at.

I've always wondered why he said that. What did he think?

THE MAN WHO DIDN'T LIKE GOD

In 1964 I went to a Lemar demonstration in Pershing Square in San Francisco. Lemar was an organization dedicated to Legalizing Marijuana, hence the name. It was run by a lawyer named J. Richard White, and Chet Helms, later of Family Dog fame, worked for it. I went to the demonstration for the hell of it. A bunch of people were walking around with signs, and since it had been publicized, there was a group of anti-pickets, even a few uniformed Nazis, who always turned out for these things. And to top it all off there was an old man picketing the anti-pickets, who were Christians. It seemed that he was a very old Italian atheist from long ago and he didn't seem to be very concerned about pot but was very exercised about the others who were carrying signs about God etc. I talked to him, tried to tell him that the other pickets weren't against God either (I guess he assumed they were because the Christians were against them) and that God was a gas. But he wouldn't have any of it. He said, with a look of unfathomable despair, "No, no, I don' lika God."

BUS-BUSTING BY THE BEACH

Me and Janie were going back to her place but then she wanted to go someplace else. So I said, "You wanna go to the beach?" and she said OK. We drove down there and went into the parking lot. There was nothing else there except a Greyhound bus. It was a late model Mack I think and had its lights on. The bus driver was behind it working on it. It struck me as kind of a strange place for a bus to be. When we got out of my car I went over to see what was going on. What was happening was the driver was standing behind the bus kicking it in the rear. On the bumper. Again and again. Like he had got mad at the bus and had taken it out behind the bushes and was kicking the shit out of it.

KIDS SAY THE DARNEDEST THINGS DEPT.

Tonight Thomas was talking about the baby he claims his friend Oscar's mother is going to have and slipped and said Oscar was going to have a baby. I said, "Can Oscar have a baby?" and Anna said, "No, silly, boys can't have babies, ESPECIALLY if they're little children." As if the two impossibilities added up to a double one.

Last night Sue said a hippy came into her classroom and the kids got into a discussion about what hippies were. One said, "They smoke a lot," maybe associating the anti-smoking campaign on TV with hearing that hippies smoke pot. And Anna spoke up and said, "No, they drink a lot of booze." Then one real little kid said, "No, they smoke marijuana." Sue says it went on from there and she wishes she had a tape recorder. So do I.

Then Anna brought up the Donner Pass incident. I asked her what happened, and she told the story only they just got stuck in the snow and ran out of food and died. They never ate each other. I guess she heard someone tell a bowdlerized version to the kids.

The same night I think Anna started saying everything was a Psychology joke. She would tell a story that didn't make any sense and say it was a Psychology joke and said we were Psychology jokers.

THE PRETTIEST GIRL IN THE TENDERLOIN

One night I had a sore throat and went down to the Eddy-Taylor drugstore in the Tenderloin. This is the red-light district and as I was driving along a whore crossing the street said, "Want a date?" I figured what the hell and said "Ten dollars." She said, "Park." Then she got involved in some scene on the sidewalk and I went on. After I got the syrup I noticed how many whores there were and thought I would cruise around and see If I could find one that really turned me on. After walking all over and not seeing anything very exciting I finally saw one; tall, light for a spade, and beautiful. I was going up to her when she said something and I realized. She was a BOY.

NAPA

Reading *One Flew Over the Cuckoos Nest* I remembered the time I visited Napa. I went up with Bill Howell and his wife to see a friend of his who had got drunk and freaked out, a guy named Barney. They let us into the visiting room but I think it was before that we saw an old guy wandering around the halls in his bathrobe, chanting in a monotone, "Where are Shaugnessey's shoes? Where are Shaugnessey's shoes?" with no one paying any attention. Bill said he must have just had shock treatment. Then in the visiting room an old man came up to me and said, "Do you know me?" I shook my head, and some attendants came up and said, "Come on, Mr. Stone," and tried to lead him away, but he persisted and they said "Come on Mr. Stone," again with more of an edge to it and finally dragged him off as he was yelling "Don't you remember me?"

ODD ENDS

Suzy just reminded me that when we went to see the light show or whatever it was at the art museum I stepped into the pool at the entrance. There wasn't a curb or anything around it, and I was looking around, drunk, and walked right into it. There is a statue in the pool which I seemed to blame so I kicked the base of it. Then I went to the john and wrapped my wet sock in toilet paper and this in some other kind of paper, which I carried into the auditorium, a suspicious-looking bundle.

Which reminds me of a strange bundle I found in San Francisco. I was walking back from the park with Lisa and was going past the bus stop shelter on Stanyan when I saw a package, about six or eight inches across, wrapped in waterproof paper and very thoroughly taped up. I nudged it with my foot and it was soft, like meat. Some spade chicks were walking by and laughed. I examined it, curious but uncertain, and asked Lisa, "Shall we open it?" and she said no so I went on. I'm sure someone else opened it. It was hard to resist, but I suspect it was some kind of weird put on, and I didn't want to be the one who got put on. Maybe it was a fetus, or a heart, or just shit, or something you couldn't even identify. Another close call.

MAGOO AT KNIFEPOINT

Topanga, 1961 about, I was at Richard and Cheryl's place and I turned Richard on to peyote, thought it was a noble venture at the time. He was just coming on and sitting around in god knows what state when Cheryl starts demanding that he take her to a Mister Magoo movie in Hollywood that I guess they had agreed on previously, but she, who never had and never has, couldn't understand the existential complexities of driving from Topanga to Hollywood and seeing a Mr. Magoo movie on peyote. She wouldn't take his equivocating evasions for an answer, and went in the kitchen and came out with a big old kitchen knife and I, figuring he might be too limp to handle it, being astronomically limp to begin with, barely able to get off the couch to eat his white grapes sometimes, plus with the peyote having known what good effects, pinned her arm behind her back and took the knife away. For which she cussed me out. Well, of course she did want to see that Mr. Magoo movie. And they went, too. Richard said he stayed out in the lobby. No effete snobber, mind you. I dig Mr. Magoo as much as I should. It's just the total picture, you might say, and I must do a section of his dietary habits. When I first met Richard, he was about 18 and Cheryl 16, luscious as all gittout, her I mean, and he was on white

151

grapes and chocolate milk, and red in the face from taking speed and having a mild heart attack, and later in San Francisco for years he lived on Campbell's bean soup and iced tea, while later still in Wichita again it was canned peaches and sour cream. He didn't seem the model of health, but according to Richard, all his stories must be taken with an oodle of salt; when he got on the methadone program, he did a complete physical, and everything checked out A-OK. And there's more, much more . . .

RICHARD & CHERYL WHITE

For a long time, Colin used one of those little potties and the shit would sit in it all day. Richard wouldn't dump it so it sat there till Cheryl got back. I asked him why they didn't get one of those adapter seats for the john but they just didn't have one, that's all. It was their way.

Soon after they came out to San Francisco we were smoking pot as they called it then, and she, who wouldn't turn on till years later, apparently got a contact high and came out in a diaphanous nightie with a saucepan on her head and did a song and dance routine where she said she was Johnny Appleseed. For a long time, not many people would say a good word about her and considered her an albatross around Richards's neck. She was very possessive, and it wasn't till later in Wichita again when she was pregnant and he was about to leave town and she called me up and asked me if I knew where he was so she could talk to him before he left, not weepy but straight, almost noble under the circumstances, that I saw things in a different light. But I had to lie to protect him and didn't tell her where he was and felt shitty about it afterwards.

He was staying at a pill head whore's house, name of Flo Ann Miller. Phil Rohrig used to make it with her, would say "I came by to see my old girl flow." Wrongest characters in town would congregate there. Bob Winders, the second toughest guy in town, who would beat you up for the time of day, used to be married to Flo; it was said he was on a list the Wichita Police Dept. had where if you killed him they guaranteed you would get off. Rex Hotchkiss, ex-football player butch pill head, was the toughest guy in town. 210, big black eyes, a hair-trigger temper, and the only guy could beat up Winders. Ronnie Wikel, an old buddy of Bob B. and his sidekick Ernie Chapman; you couldn't get any pot except from pill heads then because the heads were basically pill heads and the spade scene was impenetrable, or almost, but Ronnie could score from them but there you go again. It had its points though, for at that time you could still get the old kind of Cosanyl with dihydrocodeinone over the counter, 76 cents a bottle at discount stores, some places even sold it by the pint, $2.30 or so. You could also get mescaline from Light and Co. in England while you couldn't get either of these in California, $6.58 a gram postpaid. But that was later. Around that earlier time, I was turning Wichita on to peyote. It burgeoned into a big scene a couple of years later. When I went back and was at a party I heard a frat type saying about peyote, "I had a chance to get in on that but didn't." Now I hear there's a big scene at the U. Richard turned Rex, the butch pill head, on to Cosanyl, and he laid back and nodded out and moaned, "You took my strength away." Well, I guess it was all he had.

Richard had sort of a queer streak, though he hardly ever made it with guys—he did with Phil and that was why Cheryl never liked him. Richard would do things like leave a note on Dave Bearden's door in San Francisco that would end "Don't eat me till I get back," and send me letters that said "I want to phuck you," but would never say or do anything about it, like it never happened. You could just leave it hanging in the never-never if you wished. I don't know what else you could have done.

CHERYL AGAIN

I just remembered that in the part about Cheryl I forgot to mention that she could make her pussy talk. Or at least it could make some kind of noise, hard to describe, sort of like a fart only wet and sloppy, sort of a raspberry sound. Sometimes at parties or whenever the occasion seemed ripe to her, she would rip a few off. She had to stand with her legs spread some and lean forward. I guess she would do almost anything to get attention. Sometimes at parties, we would get her to do it for kicks 'cause it was so freaky. One time Bob Lavigne was there and we got her to go over by him and do it. He about turned green, fag artist feller. It brings to mind the man in *Naked Lunch* who taught his asshole to talk, only hers just knew one word. Maybe she could modulate it some but it was basically all one word: "cuuuuunt." She also claimed that she could draw up water with it and squirt it across the bathtub though I never got to see that one.

When I saw her last summer she was getting fat on Dr. Pepper, the friendly pepper-upper, because Richard was strung out on Cosanyl and they hadn't made it in two years. It was funny, she was the biggest prick-tease in the world. Like she'd be sitting on a stool with her legs spread and would whip up her skirt and give you a glimpse of her snatch under her pants, but came on very puritanical, wouldn't make it with anyone but Richard and when he couldn't make it she did without, and prided herself on her abstinence. When she told me they hadn't made it in two years she said, "That proves you can get along without it," or words to that effect, sort of like she was conducting an experiment in abstinence, a touch of triumph in her voice, and she was equipped for such an experiment, if that box could get by without banging I guess any could.

In all fairness, I suppose I should mention that once Cheryl let me eat her feet. I worked on them for an hour or two, sucking the toes, rubbing the soles over my face, etc. When I was done, she said, "Well, I must say you did a thorough job." I'd only do it with a pretty girl— doesn't make too much difference what their feet are like, they're little more than a symbol, and there's so little aesthetics involved in feet that it's hard to imagine a pretty girl who didn't have nice feet . . . like her, like her feet.

ART GROF'S TIME CYCLE

Last time I saw Art Grof was in the entrance to the Straight Theater on Haight Street. I was walking to the park with Lisa and her kids, and found a joint on Ashbury, rolled tight and thin like when they sold them in Kansas City for fifty cents apiece in 1948. Art was rapping with some chick, had a methed-out looking English cat with him, told me he had relationships with hundreds of people in San

Francisco so that he could meet new people and have a ready-made relationship to step into or something like that. I told him I'd been by his place several times since the phone was disconnected but he was never there, and that a Latin chick had answered the door in a short leather jacket and panties the last time. She asked who it was first. I said, Alan. Maybe she knew someone else by that name; anyway she opened the door, didn't hide behind it, eyes so dark they could have been all pupil, couldn't tell if she was that high or that exotic, there was a pleading look in her eyes. I guess she wanted to get raped. I never think of those things in time.

He said, oh, that's so and so, and recited her lineage, about 10 different races. I asked him when he was most likely to be at home, and he said toward the end of the week. I thought that was a good line. A bigger time-cycle than normal. We found another joint in the park, a bomber. This one got us high; we smoked it walking along the main drive through Golden Gate Park when an unmarked car drove by, would've sent a twinge of panic through me but I didn't feel a thing, shows you the change in atmospheric pressure that has gone down.

THE GREAT LEMONETTE SCORE

It all started back in Edgetown, betcha don't know where that is, southwest of Oliver and Mount Vernon, Wichita; it was at the edge of town when they built it, but the town went over the edge and became Ridgewood. Well I delivered *Eagles, Wichita Eagles*, there, got the papers at Edgetown, delivered them, and at the Edgetown Grill and the adjoining grocery we would get soda pop and little pies and all that kinda stuff; one time I bought a package of sweet rolls and couldn't eat it all and the chick says, "You're eyes were bigger than your stomach," and she was right, but anyway that was where I got turned on to Lemonette in a machine I believe, where you put in a coin and slid the bottle out through cold water and along slots till it came out at the end like a computeroid puzzle and pops out when you hit the straight-up position; well they had Lemonette in that thing, and that was where I met it.

It came in tiny six-ounce bottles and was the best and indeed only lemon pop made. The same company also made Grapette and Orangette which were the best in their respective fields. They were awful small but your connoisseurs would go for it. After moving to California, I never saw it again until one day in 1967 in a Mexican restaurant on 24th I believe I saw a bottle of Grapette. I asked the people there where they got it but they couldn't cope with that; I looked in the phone book but found nothing, finally looked at the bottle and wrote to their world headquarters at Camden, Arkansas and they wrote back and said their San Francisco distributor was City Bottling. I called them and they said, "Yes we have Grapette but we make our own lemon-lime stuff so we don't use their formula for Lemonette." Then I found there was a full-fledged plant in Redwood City, so called them and the chick says, "Yes, we have it in 8, 10, and 16 oz. bottles and the little ones cost $1.60, medium $1.65, and large $1.90. Best deal obviously, so I bustle on down in the Divco milk truck we hauled *Oracles* in, found the place on the industrial mudflats, a Quonset hut, very small, and the chick and the boss were both gone, for a quickie I suppose, so I talked to the guys in the plant, young guys. The plant wasn't running, and they said they didn't have any big ones of Lemonette bottled, and it would be too much trouble to fire up the machine for one case, but when they found I had come clear down from San Francisco ("Like, really?") they laid two cases on me free, they felt so bad, of small ones, and said "If you come back don't bring the bottles, don't tell the boss"; didn't even charge me deposit on the bottles of course since they didn't want to see them again, and it was partly part of the Haight Ashbury let-it-flow trip everyone wanted to get in on, they were doing their little bit, and I roared back to town with two cases of Lemonette. Oh I forgot to completely explain why you couldn't get it in San Francisco. City Bottling had the franchise for San Francisco, so no one could make Lemonette there but them, but they didn't, and the Redwood City place did but they couldn't infringe on the San Francisco franchisee's territory, so I had the only Lemonette in town ever; I put one case in the *Oracle's* fridge and one in mine at Masonic and tried to turn San Francisco on to Lemonette. I was thinking of setting up a smuggling operation, just charge enough to pay for the gas, but never got around to it. And of course, it didn't taste quite as good as it did 15 years ago; it never does—does it.

NEW YORK/TRIP EAST

Don't know if this is newsworthy but I was just thinkin' about the time in 1967 me and Joan Alexander drove East and back from San Francisco, thought I'd write it down, what the heck I can always throw it away, like the song Glenn Todd sang "I'm not afraid to darn/ I'll go out and buy some yarn/ That's what socks are made for." Which reminds me of a song David Bearden wrote to the tune of John Henry: "Henny Penny ran up to Cock Throbbin'/ Said, Heavens, the sky is falling in/ Cock Throbbin' just broke the arrow in his heart/ Said, that ain't nothin' but my hammer suckin' wind, chickenshit/ That ain't nothin' but my hammer suckin' wind."

He sang that to his boss, a logger, and he said, "Shit, Dave, that don't make no sense." But onward.

We got a drive-away lined up in LA, a blue Mustang convertible, flew to LA, and drove east. Got stopped four times going east and not once going west. First time was in Arizona where a Highway Patrolman gave me a ticket for going 75 or 80 which is what I was doing, but I didn't have to pay it at the time and never did. He knew the car was a drive-away but didn't hassle us. He saw the credit card we were getting gas with was another name, and he pulled into a gas station right behind us. I didn't see him till I got out of the car and there was another cop saying, "Can I see your driver's license." He asked whose credit card it was and I said, "Her father's." Very cool cop, and Arizona's supposed to be a fascist state.

The shit hit the fan in New Mexico. I drove all day and Joan drove all night on speed, we got to Tucumcari at dawn and stopped at a restaurant. There was a Highway Patrolman in the restaurant who evidently had followed us. He was the rankest cop I've ever met which is saying a lot but he sure had cop instincts, maybe they're inseparable; anyway he saw the California license plate and stopped us, looked at the papers, and it turns out you have to get a permit to drive a drive-away across New Mexico and we didn't have one. So we follow him to the Judge's office in a motel and the cop says it's going to cost us $100, just to fuck with our heads. The judge calls the drive-away agency collect and tells them he's got the car and it'll cost them $87.50 to get it loose; and we call them and they say they're going to try to get out of it; and we call their headquarters in NY or someplace to try to get the west coast office to send the money because we were stuck there until they coughed it up. We could have left but not with the car. There was a stash of hash, acid, and Dexedrine under the ashtray between the bucket seats. The cop had searched the car for dope and opened the ashtray and fiddled with it but didn't take it out, while we were 'bout shittin' our pants. He came within about an inch of it. We were there all day at the Judge's office from dawn till 4:30 when the money arrived by wire. The judge apologized for the delay. It was obvious from their glee that he and the cop were going to split the fine. The money order was made out to me so I guess there was no record. So we had to drive TWO nights from LA to Tulsa instead of one, jeez, was I pissed off. As soon as we got into Texas the grass turned green instead of brown, the people at the cafes were friendlier, and I've never felt the same about New Mexico since; and all those communes are there but if that's typical of the authorities they're in the wrong state.

We got to my parent's refuge in Tulsa, rested up, and took off again. Went to Wichita, saw Richard and Sherril (never can remember how she spells her name), spent night at Janie Robertson's, last time I ever saw her, Charlie Plymell's first great love, don't have a picture of her, unfortunately, she was really beautiful when she was young. Then it was on to New York.

We drove straight through from Wichita. It was late May and going through Illinois we heard over the radio it was 95 in Chicago. We did get stopped in Ohio. The reason was I got a nosebleed and had blood on my shirt. When I stopped at a highway patrol station to ask directions the dispatcher saw the blood and pretty soon further down the road we were pulled over. I explained the blood to the cop and why Joan was driving a car with California plates and a Massachusetts driver's license; he didn't even ask whose car it was. He asked me what I did and when I said I was the circulation manager of a newspaper he said "Oh!" and let us go. The trip was to be a combination of business and pleasure as I was lining up dealers for the *San Francisco Oracle*, etc. If he had known what kind of paper it was, I don't know if he would have been so impressed.

We drove all night and by dawn, we were on the Pennsylvania Turnpike. We got out at a Howard Johnson's and it was 40 degrees and blowing up a storm. I thought, hm, didn't know the nights got so nippy here, surely it'll warm up later, but when we got to NY it was 42 and windy. We had just caught the last cold snap of the year. We had to break out coats and sweaters and all I had was a crumpled, bloodstained trench coat I'd brought with me across the continent. We came into NY over the George Washington Bridge because Joan knew some people that lived uptown, and somehow we got off the wrong exit. The New York freeway system is medieval-looking, leading to cobblestone streets, and we ended up in a tennis court. Her friends weren't home, and we felt alien and tired from driving all night, it was like dropping into a different world, all vertical and grey and ugly and cold and windy; people stared at us. We went to Columbia University to look up some other friends of hers. We parked and walked to Broadway and at the corner of 115th, right in the middle of the intersection, was a middle-aged colored woman in her go-to-meetin' dress, lying flat on her back with her legs sticking straight up in the air, holding her white hat on her head with one hand and smoking a cigarette with the other. A student went up to her and offered to help her up but she was right where she wanted to be. God knows why, I suppose. People going by smiled and took it in stride. Later, on a side street we saw an old woman scuttling along the sidewalk with a newspaper held alongside her face talking to the buildings. I recognized her from when I lived on West 97th; either that or she was "working out of the same union," as Charlie P. used to say. Time-space warp. We ran into Joan's friends at Columbia right off the bat, went to the cafeteria, and couldn't figure out which way to go in the line. I saw a ham sandwich and asked a guy behind the counter how much it was and he said "Look at the sign," but it wasn't on the sign. New York for ya. I realized the day before had been my birthday so I got a piece of cake.

Then we made the mistake of going downtown to the Lower East Side on Second Avenue when we should have taken the FDR Highway. By the time we got there I was having an ulcer attack, because you can't see the lane markings and people dart back and forth while dodging double-parked buses and trucks like it's some kind of dodgem real-life game. Sheer madness reigns. I parked the first place I could near where we were going. A car is an albatross in New York. We thought the Lower East Side would be about like the Haight but we hardly saw any hippy-looking types. I was standing at the corner by Beth & Reuben's place and here was this great ancient fire hydrant and I started to talk to this old guy about it, being fresh from San Francisco where you could rap on anyone, but when the guy finally realized I was wasting his time talking about a fire hydrant he walked away in utter disgust. There was a hole in the street at this intersection so deep that cars hit bottom going through it, and it was a weekend so it was going to be there a while. A hippy-looking chick did walk by and I asked her if this didn't seem strange and she said no, and I realized New York was a mass psychosis, a state of hell that all the participants agreed tacitly to accept as the only reality and not to question it. You couldn't talk to them about it, it was like asking what color water is.

After New York it was up to Boston where I met Joan's parents and their maid who would sit in the kitchen when she wasn't busy and talk to herself in Lithuanian for the rest of her life. Her parents put us up in twin beds; mine didn't have twins so we had slept in a double while in Tulsa. Morgan and Sandy ran into the same thing. At her parents they slept in separate beds, at his they started out in separate ones and then merged together.

Going down a turnpike in Oklahoma on the way back I was lying down in the back seat while Joan was all night driving on speed when there was a big sideways lurch. I sat up and asked what happened. Joan didn't say anything so I said, "What HAPPENED?" and I guess she had got herself back together by then and told me she had been doing 100 or 110 and lost control and sideswiped a guard rail, just grazing it. A little bit harder and we would have rolled and rolled . . . As it was she just knocked a little bit of chrome trim off and the people we delivered the car to didn't even notice it. Wonder how many lives this cat has used up, never counted 'em.

FLASH & SUPERCOFFEE ROYALE

Ray just came by to borrow a buck for Terpin hydrate and derailed the previous narrative which I couldn't quite wrap into anyway and we went outside to sit on the bench in front that's on the main drag of Cherry Valley and it's Saturday morning and everyone, I mean EVERYONE, comes to the Post Office to pick up their mail, and the PO is right next door so you see everybody including young girls; and Gil the New York Okie from next door crawls out looking kind of purple and Allen Ginsberg comes by and sits down, followed by Peter Orlovsky of course since Ginzy can't drive, and then a young woman rides up on a bicycle and says, sort of to the assemblage of old geezers on the bench, "Do you know who I am?" And I didn't even think hard, assuming it was someone else who it was supposed to be, but turns out it is Maureen Owen, whom I hadn't seen in eight years, and she had published some sections of this very book in her NY mag *Telephone*, and I had just started to write on the book today for the first time in the better part of a year, and last night Ray gave me an amp of adrenalin as, he put it, "sort of a joke," really completely a joke, and I brought it out; we were drinkin' beer and by now Ray was on his second bottle of Terpin, which I had scored, copped rather, and in the friendly (really) neighborhood drug store there was an old lady filling some prescriptions in front of me saying something to the druggist about quarters for the laundromat and he says, "Oh, you mean for the washing machines, I thought you meant those one-armed bandits." And she says, "Oh fuck them." A little old lady! And then she says, not by way of apology or explanation but just in general, "I've been taking too many pills the last two weeks." After she left, I said to the mildly after-smiling druggist, "What kind of pills does she TAKE?" and he says, "I guess she's a little hypertensive and they have to give them something to keep them down. She used to be a nurse." And I say, "I guess she knows what she's doing then," and he says, "They get to know a little and then they think they know what they're doing," and I quoted Pope, "A little knowledge is a dangerous thing," but as for the amp of adrenalin, I pointed out, it was the last thing I needed and explained however since I shot up a mixture of speed and coke I was in imminent danger of blowing up from a sudden excess of blood pressure; it happened for the first time when I was high and has kept recurring ever since, a feeling in my brain and ears and face like I'm going to explode. Since then I've found several other people who have it too and one time I was having one of these, I call them terror attacks, and I grabbed a book off the shelf, just for something, anything, to distract myself from myself, and it was at my father's place so the book was a psychology book because he's a psychologist, and I open it at random and the first sentence I read goes something to the effect, "There can be no question that anxiety states can elevate the blood pressure sufficiently to cause a fatal occlusion," like I was wondering: CAN you psyche yourself into dying this way, and I pick up a book and it says, "YES, you CAN, Alan." If anyone ever had reason to be paranoid . . .

Also, today I invented a new drink. I never drink in the morning but this being a Saturday and all I basically combined Coffee Royale with my way of making coffee, which is to heat up a cup of milk till it simmers, gotta watch it close now, lest it boil over itself, and mix with instant coffee and sugar. MMM good, and also can be a vehicle for supercoffee, i.e. with gelatin or powdered milk, for a high protein shot. But this time instead of adding gelatin or powdered milk I added whiskey; it tasted good, smooth, call it Supercoffee Royale.

NICKNAMES

I've never picked up nicknames in my life till these last few months, and now I've got two of them. In Cherry Valley where I "live" the kids call me "Crazy Jack" because I chased a bunch of them with a hammer. At work they call me "Kamikaze." It turns out that they've called me that from the start but I just recently found out when someone said it over the intercom. "They're sending Doug, Rich, and Kamikaze up to 17" and I asked about it and found it dated from when I had just started there, working in the hole, the excavation for a parking garage. I was using a chipping hammer, sort of a mini-jackhammer that looks like a machine gun, with a grip and trigger, and I was sitting around with nothing to do for the time being and noticed a guy standing on the sidewalk onlooking. The machine gun metaphor occurred to me and I picked up the hammer and aimed it at all the men in the hole and turned it on—it goes rat-a-tat-tat—and sat back down. Then I noticed the guy I was working with was looking at me and I picked it up and shot it at him. It was he who gave me the name. Exactly why I don't know. But it fits better than they can ever know, they've never seen me drive, and when I found out about it I asked and a guy told me the whole story, and I told him I liked it, and now they call me that to my face occasionally, though as sort of a put down. I let them know I knew by taking the intercom and saying this is K. "We're sending trash down on the elevator," which for some reason they call the buck-hoist, and I say to the operator below, "Ground control can you read me? Come in ground control." And he says, "What the fuck?—over," which is a private joke on that job due to the intercom system, and I say, "This is Kamikaze, take it away." And he laughs and says, Okay Al." For some reason, people I work with always call me Al while my friends call me Alan, but now what friends I have called me Al and the rest call me 'Crazy Jack' or 'Kamikaze'. I have more ex-friends . . .

WAAAA!

Gregory Corso broke my flyswatter, the rotten son of a bitch. I mean, not just because of that; he's a rotten sonofabitch all around. Ray Bremser says he introduces him as "a good poet and a bad person." Which is being fair, I think. He's short, 42, doesn't have as many teeth as he might and has a big schnoz which does manage to turn up at the end, and girls, some anyway, think he's cute. Someone at Ray's said, "Well, anyway, Greg, you are cute as a bug's ear." And someone interjected (Zap), "you mean cute as a fat tick." Which also I think fair. As an inmate of a mental institution once said, "Does any bachelor of arts under the canopy of heaven have the guts to let the chips fall where they may?" I'm trying to be fair about Corso even tho he fucked with my head last weekend, ripping off a chick I was trying to get a thing going with.

SUNFIGHTER

I drive 50 miles to work in Albany, and I live west of Albany, so going in the sun is in my eyes all the way and coming back I'm looking into the setting sun, and it's the same trip all over again in reverse. I pull the sun visor down and put on shades and try to keep my eyes on the stretch of road between the visor and the road, but going uphill this narrows it down to nothing, and all I can see is 15 feet of the road in front of me. Don't mean to be bellyaching, but you see I face Old Hannah two hours a day, and there are no proper authorities to complain to, you wanna do what I do that's the price you gotta pay. You wanna talk to me about seeing the light? Man, I am done seeing it already. God fuck you over almighty; Corso tried to tell me that I hadn't seen the light, but I saw altogether too much of it already.

DEEP TWELVE

This morning lying in bed, I had a fantasy. There's nothing unusual about that, but this one was a little different; that is, it went a little farther. In it, I was fucking a woman, but it was an idealized version of myself, with a huge cock and she says, "I have what every man wants, and you can only reach it with your penis." So I fuck her deep and touch bottom. But that isn't it, and something deep within her calls to something in me, and I get a bigger hardon and stretch her, and that still isn't enough and it gets still longer and tears her, and that's what we were looking for—she is impaled, torn and bloody on the savage scepter of my cock, consummated halfway between crucifixion and hari-kari. She literally wants to be fucked to death, to have it go clear through her, the ultimate extension and only possible fleshly apotheosis of sex . . . this isn't S&M—it goes deeper than that.

I remember David B. showing me the leather patch on his Can't Bust 'em jeans that showed a pair of mules each pulling on one leg of a pair of pants and he said, "That's what women want—to be cleaved apart at the crotch."

Well, that's where childbirth comes in—the baby's head, the new life tears the mother apart, bursts into the world, so what's wrong . . . ? (Echo chamber effect—what's wrong, wrong, wrong...?)

ALAN RUSSO'S DREAMS

The Goal-Line Fall: Last night I had a football dream in full color, and usually I don't dream in color. The ball carrier, wearing a helmet that looked vaguely reminiscent of a hard hat, fought his way through the tacklers, fell just over the goal line, had a heart attack, and died. He kept saying, "Oh my God! What the hell? Oh no! What the hell is this?" That's what happens when the gettin' gets good.

Hotel Dream: You guessed it; it was a strange dream. As usual, it's hard to convey just how strange! It seems that I had rented a room in some sort of rooming house, and when I went in I found a little girl sleeping in my bed. I decided to consult with the management, thinking that there had been some mistake, but there was a woman there signaling to me not to do so. But I went to the manager's office anyway, which was like an old-time elevator in the basement and told her about it. She showed me a floor plan of the place, displaying which rooms were vacant . . . but first, someone showed me the numbers of the vacant rooms written on the back of her hand. 1115 was one of them, I think. But these rooms were all too expensive . . . and the floor plan was funny because it was like a calendar with a room for each day. I went back to the room and the woman was still there, dark-haired, but without eyes, like in Orphan Annie. I can't explain her explanation very well, but it seems that some time dimensions had got crossed, and she had rented the room in one of them and I had rented it in another. I had just wandered into another time, and she didn't want the manager to know. Her husband was there too. I said, "Well, there are enough beds." It wasn't laid out like a hotel room, but like a room in a crowded house. I think that some sex interest was creeping in at this point. Anyway, I wouldn't stay at that hotel unless I was writing a book.

A Dream—Significant, No Doubt: This morning I woke up about 1 o'clock and after that drifted in and out. First I dreamed I was trying to turn the lights on, but they wouldn't go on—a recurring nightmare incident. Then I turned around to try another switch and ran into what I guess was a spirit. It's hard to describe the feeling. It wasn't like a solid body, more like a mass of compressed air. At the time I don't think I thought that I was dreaming. I found myself back in bed and decided that I'd turn the lights on for real. But the room wasn't the room I was really in. It was like a big old San Francisco-style of room, and the same thing happened—trying to get to the light switch, I ran into that thing, which scared the shit out of me! Then I really woke up, in the real room.

Later I dreamed that I was writing, but the paper was somehow feeding into the doors of a shed or barn. After a page was finished, I'd have to open the doors to get it, and there were piles of *Oracles* and some other papers in there and people who were trying to arrange the stacks of paper while I was typing with the doors closed, so that when I opened the doors, I had to fish the page out from behind the papers. It seemed to be their idea of a joke. I decided that things were getting out of hand and went to work on a book of collages. They were sort of like cellophane and didn't seem to be pasted together. One of the people in the shed said, "So and so went to the drugstore and asked for a something." It was intended to be funny, but the humor was rather obscure. There were several cryptic things like this, and then some eggs. Three-dimensional things could fit in the book of collages. I was wrapping hollow Easter eggs around the collages, only some of the collages were too big. The eggs formed something like cradles around the collages. In the end, there were three collages, but I only had two eggs left. On the last page was an egg. It was like a hard-boiled egg with the shell removed. I decided that this was the most important object and to use one shell for it and to split the other for the other two.

The Clearest Oil You Ever Did See: I had a dream the other night. I have a lot of dreams that I don't write down, which bothers me greatly, but I'm like that and have other things to worry about. I caught this one in time.

I dreamed I found some clear oil, cooking oil. It was understood to be olive oil, the way things are implicitly understood in dreams—I didn't even see the bottle. It was completely clear! Not yellowish at all, but absolutely clear! This inspired great wonderment in me and I called Mike and Joannie to come look at it. It was in a metal measuring cup, so you couldn't look through it, but you could see the bottom of the cup, and it was as clear as . . . well, as baby oil. That's clear, but there was something miraculous about this; it was clear and edible. Some gap had been bridged between the physical and the spiritual—oil in the Bible representing grace pouring down from heaven. It wasn't tainted like regular oil. It was the solution! The solution to how to live a physical life without being fouled, for oil is the grossest of foods, and yet this was as clear as water, as clear as glass. The Corruption of Being was dissolved in Grace. If this can be clarified, what cannot? I held the chalice in my hands . . .

. . . and now it is a hot afternoon and I am drinking wine and wondering what to do. I'm going to write about a bus trip. My dreams will have to handle the oil department.

Oowee, Tragedy: This is just a dream, yeah, just a dream . . . I was riding in a car with Janet, my lost true love from Wichita, and in the back we had a box with a helpless little animal in it. I can't remember what kind it was, but it was very small and helpless. I was holding my hand over the top of the box to protect it. We went by a telephone pole with an eagle or hawk perched on it, and it saw the little beggar and swooped down on it like a shot. I raised my hand to grab something to hit the bird with, but in that instant it snatched the little animals and flew away, right before our eyes. Naturally we were mind-blown by this.

That night we slept together, but Janet wouldn't make it with me unless I could explain it away, make it right, redeem the horror of life for her. And I couldn't. And I guess that's where it's at.

Auditorium Dream Sept.25th: I dreamed that I was in an auditorium. That is, it was a place where people were gathered to listen, but it wasn't set up like an auditorium. People were sitting around on the floor, etc. The program notes were like a newspaper, but also sort of like a menu at a restaurant, with meals in boxes. There were featured articles, like about an education program the Black

167

Panthers were starting, and a singer would sing a song about it. Joan Baez did a song I thought was about the most beautiful song I'd ever heard. Joni Mitchell was there, or a chick who looked like her. Joni sang a song, also from the menu-newspaper, and then they showed a movie on the wall, like at the Fillmore Auditorium. It was of Howard Hughes, taken in the '40s or so, where he is stumbling along singing a bawdy song or a sea shanty. I began to giggle, and then other people, who had been taking it seriously, started to laugh. It reminded me of when Bob and Sue Branaman and I used to go to science-fiction and monster movies in the Mission District for chuckles.

Dream Lover, Where Are You-Oo-Oo: This morning I woke up, or dreamed that I did, with someone in my arms, that is, someone lying more-or-less under me and to my right, which is the side I sleep on. Like I was lying on my right side with someone under my right arm and shoulder. This was kind of odd, because so far as I could remember, I had gone to bed alone in a single bed. So I felt the party, as in pinching yourself in a dream, and sure enough, there was someone there. Every time I felt, there it was, so I thought to ask who it was, and did, all in my sleep. It answered in a boy's voice, and that was when I realized that I was dreaming. If it had been a girl's voice I would have gone along with it and tried to figure out who it was, but since it was a boy's voice, I knew it couldn't be and was just a dream. Then I awoke, and it was my right arm pinned under me that I had mistaken for a person—some physical stimulus that sprouted into a dream where I dreamed that I was awake.

Dream of Janie Chipmunk: Last night I saw Jane Lewis. She had just got back from Germany, but she didn't hug me or kiss me, which surprised me. She said, "Alan, I'm a ghost." She was thinner but didn't look bad. Then she asked me if I knew anyone who had a douche bag, and I said, "No, no one I know uses them." Then I remembered that Beth had one and told her. She was going to the phone to call her when it started ringing. I woke up, and the phone was ringing. It rang just twice, and when Mike answered it, no one was on the line. Mike and Jane Lewis are brother and sister.

From the Vision of Zosimos: And while I said this I fell asleep, and I saw a sacrificial priest standing before me, high up on an altar, which was in the shape of a shallow bowl. Fifteen steps were leading up to the altar. And the priest stood there, and I heard a voice from above say to me: "Behold, I have completed the ascent up the steps of light. And he who renews me is the priest, for he has cast away the density of the body, and by compelling necessity, I am sanctified and now stand in perfection as a spirit (pneuma)." And I perceived the voice of him who stood upon the altar, and I inquired of him who he was. And he answered me in a fine voice, saying: "I am Ion, priest of the innermost hidden sanctuary, and I submit myself to an unendurable torment. For there came one in haste at early morning, who overpowered me and pierced me through with the sword and cut me in pieces, yet in such a way that the order of my limbs was preserved. And he drew off the scalp of my head with the sword, which he wielded with strength, and he put the bones and the pieces of flesh together and with his hand burned them in the fire until I perceived that I was transformed and had become spirit. And that is my unendurable torment." And even as he spoke this, and I held him by force to converse with me, his eyes became as blood. And he spewed out all his flesh. And I saw how he changed into a manikin (i.e. a homunculus) who had lost a part of himself. And he tore his flesh with his teeth and sank into himself.

That's me all over the place, yuk yuk.

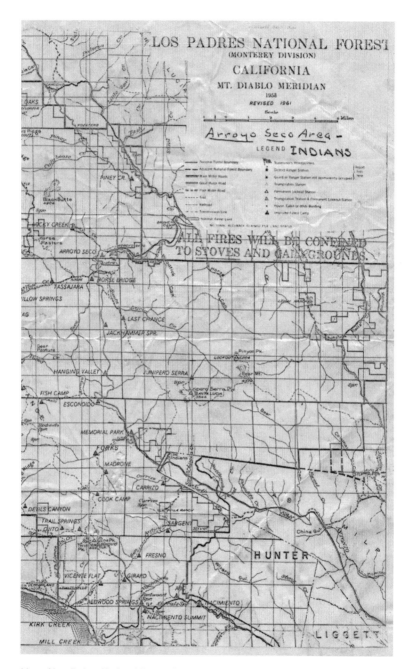

Map of Los Padres National Forest, California

PART FIVE

THE BIG YELLOW TAXI AND HOW IT GREW

It goes something like this: What do you get when you cross a plastic Jesus with an Electric Tibet? A Big Yellow Taxi, that's what. There are only a few people in the world who would understand that, even of the ones who were there when we made the movie, so maybe I'd better explain . . .

I guess you could say it started when I ran into Morgan in San Francisco. He was with his new chick, Sandy, who was a big Kansas Heifer with big boobs, who loved Morgan's ass to distraction and had a little 5-year-old girl, Angie, who goes up to every guy she meets and says, "Hi, I'm Angie." Only she likes black cats the best. Ed Strange was with them, a 16-year-old runaway wanted for GTA (Grand Theft Auto) who runs around with older people to avoid getting busted. I had just moved out of Janet and Butcher's place because things kind of blew up there. I had got drunk and disorderly and they and Cheryl all went to bed together. I capped the jug of vodka and split, kicking the door in parting.

So I found Bud & Joan's place, which was sort of a fluke, since I didn't have their address, just knew what part of town they lived in and what kind of car they had, and found it by the car. Joan's sister Sue was there with her husband Sherry and their three little girls. Joan looked a lot more like her sister than I remembered. Sherry had made a quarter of a million or so off designing toys, games, automated nurseries, etc.—mad genius, ex-speed freak who drinks a fifth of vodka and smokes half a lid a day. He makes red line joints by taking all the tobacco except the last 2/3 inch or so out of a cigarette, fills it with grass, marks the joint where the grass ends and the Pall Mall

171

begins and smokes it down to the red line. So you don't end up with any roaches. He does things the way he likes.

Their oldest girl, Lauren, barks orders like a drill sergeant at the next younger one, Sharon, who absolutely obeys her. If you tell Sharon to go in the living room, she'll say, "Lauren told me I can't go in there now." And if she says anything Lauren doesn't like, Lauren will snap, "You think that's funny, Sharon!" The littlest one is a love bug who says, "Close your eyes and give me your hand," and kisses your hand. One time she was sitting on my lap and we kissed and she looked into my eyes for a long time with a look I couldn't interpret—like curiosity tinged with fear? You won't find a 4-year-old looking into your eyes that long very often, they move around a lot. But onward.

The scene was that sister Sue and family were about to go to India for nine months, with what mission I never completely ascertained, but I guess it had to do with hash and gurus and avoiding Possible Prosecution for some Movement activity Sherry had been involved in. But Bud, Joan's hubby, wanted to get some land and wanted to turn Sherry on to Big Sur and California and get Sherry to put up the down payment. There are several reasons why this didn't happen. For instance, Sherry would totally freak out from time to time and his money was tied up in stocks that were down, but we went to Big Sur anyway. And so did Morgan and Sandy who wanted to go back to Nacimiento to camp.

So we got a two-car caravan together with Bud's VW bus, which is equipped with a camper body called Dor-mobile (an English outfit), where the top opens up into a canopy kind of thing so it sleeps 5, and my '59 Olds 4-door hardtop with 113,000 miles on it which is disintegrating rapidly. Like every day something comes off. But it's all heart and has never let me down. We understand each other pretty well.

Between the cars, we had thirteen people and lots of gear. One of the people was a guy that lived upstairs of Morgan who we just took down to Santa Cruz but is memorable for an expression he contributed to the trip. We were talking about cars and I said Olds was the best American car made and he said, "That's above the point." This became one of the recurrent expressions on the trip which was characterized (in part) by certain other expressions which I might as well run down now. We would say, "That's above the point," when someone said something that was in another dimension from the topic as conceived by the other person, or that missed the point by a matter of order rather than degree. Another common one was "to get on one's case"; which isn't new, but was used a great deal on this trip, as in, "Keep your hands off me, or my old man'll get on your case;" or "Get off my case," which later blended into one I hadn't heard before, "Get outta my face," or "Keep outta my face." A very basic one which I heard for the first time there, though others tell me they had heard it long before, was "Shine on" and "Shine it on." Shine on meaning something between fuck you and get off my case. To shine something on meant to hell with it, to pass on it, as in "Just shine on that, let's split, man." Like if someone is putting you on about something you can say, "Shine on, man," in a good-natured way. Shine something on could also mean to deceive or dump, as in "I'm not tryin to shine you on, baby, we just don't have room in the car." It is a very versatile expression capable of almost limitless permutations.

Another one was "Clean up your act," or "You'd better clean up your act," which could be used to put someone on when his freakiness had broken cover through some act or word.

A minor one was when someone was so fucked up they couldn't function you'd say, "You're a passenger," which came from a drunkenness machine you breathe into and if you're too drunk to drive it lights up, "You're a passenger." Another one that came up occasionally was, "Get back!"

It's hard to explain the nuances of difference between this and "Shine on" and "Get outta my face." It's more of a joke, like you were talking to a dog, when someone's animal nature or weird side somehow corresponding thereto had manifested and you were calling him on it and shooing him off. It could be said with a waving-off backhand gesture. "Get BACK, man." Funny how both this and "Shine on" occur in Beatles songs tho with different meanings.

And so we set forth—me, Morgan, Sandy, Angie, Ed, and the guy from upstairs with a half-gallon of about half-vodka and half-orange juice, the remainder of Sherry's screwdriver fixins, in my Olds; while Bud, Joan, Sherry, Sue, and their kids went in the VW bus with the grass. We went down the coast, stopping to smoke with the other car-full while getting juiced on the vodka. After a confusing scene in Santa Cruz which I can't sort out enough to tell about we continued on down to Partington Ridge and went up to where the Branamans live. We figured it would be a good way to turn Sherry on to Big Sur, with the view of the ocean, mountains, organic garden, and the sort of commune with separate houses for each family. Bob wasn't there but I gave Susan a bottle of iron pills. The fog was in so you couldn't see the ocean, and the garden was going to pot since Roland left, with weeds choking the strawberries and overshadowing the cabbages. Paranoia was more rampant than ever since the health department had been up there; they (the Branamans) had moved out of their house, which wasn't legal for habitation, just before, but they wouldn't let anyone sleep there so we camped by the gate, another sign of the increasing uptightness. The Dor-mobile with the roof opened up into a tent-canopy looked like a Fellini fantasy; while me and Morgue and Sandy slept together in sleeping bags which for some reason we put on rocky ground on a slope so that we were on the verge of sliding downhill all night. I couldn't sleep, played some games with Sandy and Morgue, but nothing serious.

It took us a while to get going the next day—when we got to Nacimiento Bud had a flat tire and my car was overheating. But taking care of those matters was minor compared to getting the whole menagerie together that morning. Morgue and Sandy are hangup artists second only to the Branamans themselves. It takes about half a day for M&S to get in gear while Bob B. can take a whole day such that you begin thinking about waiting till the next day, but it'd be the same thing all over again, so you just drive all night, then he will pull a disappearing act and you have to hunt him up and find him whittling a gargoyle or something. I know someone who says it took him three days to get Bob going. There was some discussion about buying land in Salmon Creek, where it turns out Linus Pauling owns land and Sherry knows Pauling, so everything seemed to be clicking but nothing came of it as I'll explain later. We finally got going and made it to Nacimiento that afternoon. I believe it had got to the point where things were taking so long that there was talk of staying another night at Partington but I had said I was going on whether they did or not. The original idea of two vehicles was a backup in case one car had trouble. This was becoming more of a possibility since Bud now had no spare and my car was acting up, but I would have gone on anyway so they rolled out with us.

Now to get to Nacimiento from the coast, which isn't a very good idea, you go a few miles south of Lucia and there is a sign pointing inland which I believe says Nacimiento Reservoir. It's not a large sign and the first eight miles is unpaved, apparently to discourage people from going that way. Then you come to a crossroads and it's paved from thereon. I'll try to get a good map of the area, the Forest Service map I have doesn't really make it. I tried making maps myself but they lacked a certain something. After about four miles past the junction, there is a campground on your right. This is what we called "the other camp" since we stayed in the next one, about 150 feet down the road and separated by a small ridge. The two together are Nacimiento River Campground.

Unfortunately, I don't have any pictures. Bud took some movies and a spade soldier took some polaroids that didn't come out too good and he took them with him anyway. Both camps are right alongside the stream, which isn't much of a river. The other camp was upstream from ours which I guess is why a lot of us got the runs. Our camp had five fireplaces, three trashcans, and a faucet from a spring that would have kept us from getting the runs but it got hot early in the day and we never got up early enough to fill our jugs from it. There were two sets of johns, one a covered two-hole privy and one that was just two cans out in the open which were nearer but no one ever used them except me when I got the runs and I started using them out of necessity despite the howls of derision this engendered. There were two entrances, one at either end of the campground, and neither one was very good. I never tried the one at our end of the camp. I came in the far one frontward and backed out of it, otherwise, I would bottom out and couldn't take any passengers in or out. Everyone had to pile in or out at the entrance. The trees along the creek were live oak, the biggest I've ever seen, 100 feet or so high, and some other trees which I guess were elms, also very tall. The hills were scrub and pine. The weather was warm to hot during the day and comfortable at night.

Ranking high among the place's charms were the nearby facilities. Just four miles down the road was a swimming hole, called Hippy Hole by the rustics, where you could actually swim and dive off rocks and go naked, etc. This was in the Fort Hunter Liggett Military Reservation, which I will have to explain since it played a crucial part in the whole movie. From the coast to a couple of miles past the camp it's National Forest. From there on in it's Hunter Liggett. So the first part of the road is a Forest Service road and the rest of it a military road; the whole thing is government property and the road isn't a state highway or even a county road. Consequently, the Highway Patrol doesn't patrol it. Due to its remoteness, the Monterrey County Sheriffs don't come by with one notable exception as I will presently relate. The MP's patrol the military base but don't bother civilians as long as they don't speed, with some exceptions which I will also detail. Hippy Hole was on the base but the MP's only ran off GIs, since it was off-limits. This resulted in an authority vacuum—our campground was in National Forest, and the Forest Service doesn't have police power. They would have to call in the cops. The MP's would come by our campground sometimes but just to fool around. So there was almost total freedom which we proceeded to take maximum advantage of.

Another facility which made it all possible was the food available from Hunter Liggett. Their dump was fairly nearby and people would go there and scrounge through the trash and pick out whatever was usable. This was mostly cans, though you might find almost anything. I found a head of cabbage, two loaves of bread, and a towel. But mainly it was cans of things the soldiers didn't want, which for some reason were Ham & Beans, white bread, cake and other desserts such as pudding. It was hot in Hunter Liggett and apparently the heavier things were found to be cloying. The same thing is said to happen in Viet Nam—the countryside strewn with millions of cans of Boston Brown Bread, fruitcake, etc. Also at Hunter Liggett you would find little packages of all kinds of things, and field kits which contained a meal and some cigarettes and a little roll of toilet paper. Before we got there the scavenging was going on unimpeded and there was a big ammo box full of cans. However, the shit started to hit the fan right when we arrived like it always seems to do, like we were the straw etc. Someone had ripped off the box of C-rations and so the army guys were bulldozing over the dump as fast as they dumped things in it and the MP's were running people off. But we developed other sources of supply—a National Guardsman I met at Hippy Hole. You see the Guard and Reserves were having summer maneuvers so there were thousands of soldiers, who weren't really soldiers but just guys avoiding the draft, around; anyway I had him bring by a case of food. A black power cat who came by the swimming hole laid a bunch of food—big canned hams, bread, etc. on the MDM agent and us; and the biggest score was when Wiley Cat put on his army uniform and went in with some army dudes at night on speed and raided the mess hall and came back with flats of eggs, I don't know how many, 20 lbs. of bacon, and a great big cake about three-feet-long. And then there was the time Debbie Strangeways was going to trick a spade mess sergeant for some food but I'm getting ahead of myself. Suffice it to say that the US Army was instrumental in feeding the cast.

Now as for the cast—well first maybe I'd better put things in a bit of chronological order. When we got there we had a big troupe of our own and there was also a VW bus with Rick and Karen, friends of Joan or Sherry or someone from Buffalo there, tho how this worked out I don't know, so we sort of had our scene at that end of the camp going for a while. In the morning Karen, a beautiful dark little chick, would do her makeup in front of the side mirror of the bus, and since she had to stretch to see in it and was wearing sawed-offs, this made a pretty picture. The next day Bud & Joan and their gang left, without doing anything about checking on land, the excuse being Bud didn't want to drive back that way without a spare, which I can see but still, there was a feeling of a copout, or maybe he was afraid of running out of dope. So they split as did Rick and Karen so that end of the campground emptied out and we were left with the others. Who were the real cast.

I guess you could say the honcho of the place was Fred, who we called Tarzan. He seemed to consciously play this part since he went around in a leather kilt sort of thing and did Tarzan-like stunts such as climbing trees, diving from a cliff into the swimming hole, etc. There was no question of what role he played—he was king of the jungle, about 27, tall, tanned, and lean. He had an old lady who everyone called the Old Lady. I don't know how old she was but she was leathery and dry and delighted in telling you about her diseases and would show you her sores. She soaked up oil like a sponge, as I found out at the swimming hole in an incident that comes later. She had a daughter who we called Debbie 2 because there was another Debbie, and Debbie 2 was a lovely part-Mexican 16-year-old with big conical Mexican-style tits with protuberant nipples, who had a young-love affair with Ed. Now the other Debbie, who we called Debbie Strangeways, was a blonde JD type who had an ID which said she was 18 and she claimed she was wanted for probation violation. Practically everyone around there was a fugitive, runaway, deserter, or some sort of freak who had dropped completely out to where they couldn't even make it in hippy scenes or Big Sur. It wasn't really a hippy scene here, but something beyond it; due to lack of authority people who were 86'd from everywhere else had gathered there, like a pirates-haven in the south Pacific. Debbie S. was a classic young blonde tough-talking reform school slut, a big prick-tease, who had a kid but was, if not as good as she used to be, which is unverifiable, still pretty good, with fairly erect tits and still-pink nipples, nice legs, and a weak jaw somehow indicative of her sluttish mind and nature. She had formerly made it with Kim, a cute and gentle-spoken young cat newly out of the army, and was now with Duane, another star of the show.

Duane was harder to cast than Tarzan. I guess he would be sort of a Robin, the Junior partner of the hero. He was about 19 or 20, tall and thin but muscular, hippy-looking with long (fairly long) hair and little round shades, but there the similarity ended. He had been through some sort of scrapes with the law (everyone had a story so it was impossible to distinguish fact from fiction—Tarzan supposedly had done time) and claimed to have done more than he seemed to have had time for, like driving in road races, etc. But he was strong, fast, aggressive, knew something about guns, karate, sharpening knives, dope, and anything else that might come up. He was quick and uptight, like a natural speed head. I can't recall him smiling much—

one time he said "Pyorrhea" and spat some red stuff out, but we were drinking rosé and I said, "Come on, that's just wine," so he spat some on a rag and sure enough it was blood. It was oozing out so fast he could spit some out every few seconds. I gave him one of Sandy's 500mg. Vitamin Cs. I guess he hadn't been eating a well-balanced diet and was on the verge of being in catastrophically bad health while being in super good shape at the same time.

There was also a kid of 12 or 14 named Tommy there for a while who stayed with adults as a cover, like Ed with us. He and Debbie 2 had a brother-sister thing going. And there was a fat-faced dark-haired guy from the next camp who also ran around with Debbie S. when she wasn't with Duane, so she was pretty well covered. She would never take her clothes off at the swimming hole but bathed every day downstream at a place that could be dimly discerned from our camp, I went down and watched her one day. She called me a dirty old man, I suspect everybody in the camp did behind my back, but this was part of her tease act. Oh and they had a German Shepherd named Brute, supposedly short for Brutus but the abbreviation had overshadowed whatever former intentions may have existed. For tho just half-grown he was extremely aggressive and would nip at any stranger and bark up a storm even when you came back from the john. This was part of what made us uptight about Tarzan and Duane—they seemed a bit too violence-prone and gun-happy, but it turned out that some of this was directed at Charley, a cat whose camp was right across from theirs.

For some reason, Duane had taken a dislike to him, tho he seemed like an innocuous feller and Duane not only didn't call the dog off Charley but, it was said, he sicced the dog on him. And we felt some of this animosity and were uptight but finally got it straightened out. It was through a balance of power that this came about. Ed acquired an old Remington .22 rifle from a guy at the Army airfield named Buford P. Clapsaddle. I forget how he met him but for some reason, he supplied us with guns. This .22 was an autoloader but the clip was gone so it was a single shot, there was no trigger guard, etc. Now Tarzan and Duane had a .22 rifle and a .410 shotgun, while all we started with was a .25. So this gun evened up the odds. We went into King City and got some mini-mag ammo and came back with a

Remington leaflet. We showed the leaflet to them and from then on we got to be friends. Things had seemed to be coming to a head that day. A flock of bluejays had arrived and Duane was popping them with the .410 and when we got back there were some tailfeathers on our table, like a warning or some voodoo. But it turned out what he had been doing was when some straight hippies pulled into the grounds that morning and started to set up their camp, he would blast a bluejay right in front of them and they would pack up their tent and split. You had to be prepared for heavy action. It took a bit for us to adjust but once you got in the swing of things, i.e., totally insane, it was lots of fun. Well anyway, it turned out the feathers were there because someone had said something about making a headband, and all was cool. The cast was together and we were ready to roll.

I should mention that the first day after we got there was the day of the Great Raid. Morgan, Ed, Bud, Sherry and I had been shooting at the unused johns when a straight-looking couple in a sports car took off toward Jolon and I thought, they're gonna call the cops. And sure enough, after a while, a car pulls up and the driver says, "The cops are coming, they're at Hippy Hole." Everyone who had anything to hide scattered. I took the .25 and scrambled madly up the hillside, where I ran into Charley, who apparently was wanted for something, and he showed me where the box of C-rations was. It was tight on the ridge, so someone from the other camp could have taken it. I stashed the .25 and came back down. After a bit two Monterrey County Sherrif's vans and a pickup went by, without even slowing down, and then a car, which slowed down, took a good look, and continued on. Then the people in the sports car came back, I realized they hadn't called the cops, and we began to get the story, which seemed to be that the police had heard of a rural guerilla group up there and something about hanky panky at the swimming hole. So they organized a whole expedition, and had come charging down the road to the hole, which wasn't cool for any of those vehicles except the pickup, and surrounded the place with rifles and moved in with shotguns and grease guns, wearing flak jackets. They even had a matron so they could search for girls. But due to their indiscreet mode of entrance, everyone was dressed by the time the cops got there and they didn't do anything except check IDs and just busted one guy for being drunk and 17. Why they didn't stop at our camp I don't know—it couldn't have looked much wronger—I don't know what it would take to please them. As for the guerilla story, the only thing I could ever figure out was that it had to do with Mandy, a chick who was doing an MDM (Movement for a Democratic Military) thing, going into Jolon and rapping with the soldiers and passing out newspapers published by the MDM. She was staying at Ponderosa, a higher class campground a couple of miles away, but I don't know if the cops checked there or not. It might have been a combination of rumors about that and the crazies up at Hippie Hole. It was remarkable how fast information, however distorted, got to the authorities. Things travel faster in a vacuum.

There were some other fairly steady people who must be enumerated. Drifter, for one. Like everyone else, he had a story or rather several, he told everybody something different. He was evidently a spade but said he was Puerto Rican and couldn't understand Spanish. And he had some other stories, all to explain away the unblinkable fact of his blackness. Which was only an issue, I suppose, because Tarzan and Duane, especially Duane, hated "niggers" and thus didn't take much of a shine to Drifter. He was tall, bushy-haired and vacant-eyed. You could see why they called him Drifter. He latched onto us because we were the most prosperous people in the camp, with a car, food, wine, just about everything. Sandy had set up a kitchen by the table and a medicine chest in a crate nailed to a tree so we were the establishment of the camp, or part of it, with Tarzan and Duane sort of handling the law end of things. First time I've ever been in a situation where people like Morgan and me were the most stable and affluent ones around. Sandy's domesticity helped out getting all this together. Whenever anyone needed something they came to us. Naturally, Drifter started hanging around our table, the focal point of the camp, eating what we ate and drinking our wine, etc. Sandy finally got pissed off and made him wash some pots. She was capable of getting very salty. He took to sleeping in my car, sometimes he'd sleep in the front, I'd sleep in the back, and sometimes Angie would sleep in the front. Both of them barfed while so doing, but Angie also pissed. Drifter tended to sleep all day and if we wanted to use the car we would have to wake him up. But one day we couldn't wake him up and everyone went around saying, "Drifter's dead!" but no such luck; when Morgan dragged him out he woke up. We finally ran him off somehow and he was staying at Mandy's camp at Ponderosa, but before that, I believe he moved to the "other camp" until he and some other freaks got drunk and noisy and this retired cop and his retired cop wife who had a semi-permanent camp set up there fired a shot with their .38 so Drifter and the freaks came and sat in the road by our camp and played the guitar and sang till Tarzan ran them off.

Drifter was known to rip things off. There was a constant problem with theft since there was no regular supply of anything and plenty of people in need. One day after we scored a ham it disappeared—some eggs also were gone but were found downstream, apparently the work of a racoon—and it was said that some acid had been stolen from the other camp. Duane blamed it on Drifter, who had been there the night before, and we formed a vigilante committee and took off. On the way to Ponderosa we met a pickup that had been at the camp the night before and left in the morning, so we stopped and searched it. Then we continued on to Ponderosa where there was a ham, but they had one stolen too, and Duane went into a harangue ostensibly to another cat there but right in front of Drifter, about how there was this certain person who, whenever he was around, something disappeared. We got together and I said, "Personally, I don't think Drifter did it." And Tarzan said, "Neither do I." And that settled it. Cooler heads prevailed, but Duane would have got on Drifter's case on mere suspicion.

HUSTLING AT JOLON

Jolon was the nearest place where you could get gas or beer and wine or anything else for that matter, except C rations. It was just a gas station and combination bar and cafe with a few groceries sold, and it was about 16 miles from the campground. But it was kind of fun. It was at a crossroads in Hunter Liggett, where the road into the woods met the road to King City. The soldiers would gather there for lack of anything else to do. There was a bench outside for some reason and we would come in and my radiator would often be overheating and

I would knock the cap off with a jack handle because the first time I took it off by hand I got a geyser of rusty water in the face; so I would knock it off which looked kind of funny and then we would fill the radiator and put water in gallon jugs which we carried with us. And then we would get beer and mess around. Speaking of knocking the radiator cap off with the jack handle, this once resulted in an incident that typifies our Jolon scene. After knocking the cap off I laid the jack handle or tire iron or lug wrench, as you will, on the fender, put water in the radiator, and shut the hood. What I didn't know was that the end of the tire iron was protruding over the engine compartment so that when I slammed the hood shut the tire iron got caught between the hood and fender. The hood had a 2-position latch and the first one caught, so you couldn't open it, and it was shut tight enough so that we couldn't pull the tire iron out. We finally worked the tire iron around to the front where we could pull it out. Naturally, people watched and though I suppose it was the kind of thing that could have happened to anyone, it always happens to me. Anyway, you never knew what sort of impromptu action might crop up.

The first time I saw Mandy, the MDM agent she was rapping with some soldiers about war or armies or something like that. One day Morgue and I and Debbie Strangeways went in and there we were with this little blonde slut in the midst of thousands of horny soldiers. It seemed she had turned a trick or two before and the occasion was obviously ripe. The first taker was the truck driver who brought the gas in. He gave her a beer and offered her five dollars to blow him. They went in the gas station restroom before I even knew what was happening; she claims he came in the sink so I guess it was only half a blow job which is all a nickel is worth anyway, though he gave her another dollar in parting. Then some spade regulars who worked as cooks came up to us. One older cat and two young ones. We got to rapping and the older one who was the head cook said he would lay a bunch of food on us if they could get a piece of Debby. She was in the john at the time and I didn't think she would go for it and they were walking off when she came out and said she would and I ran after them and we arranged it for later that afternoon. When we got back there were MP's all over the place and the head cook was there but it seemed something had gone wrong and our food had been hauled off and dumped, and all he knew was that it was in one of the trash cans nearby. I looked around and found it, and we pulled the car up and began feverishly pitching food into the car—a huge can of frozen peaches, 20 lbs. of flour, 5 quarts of milk, and a can of desiccated peppers, which went a long way. There may have been more but the big bag the food was in broke and we were in a hurry which was apparently justified because just as we took off a couple of MP jeeps and a Monterrey County Sheriff's car came in the other way, so it looked like we just cleared out in time.

Later Buford P. Clapsaddle, our gun connection, told us the MP's or CID's or someone were on our case and were cruising around in a bronze Super Bee trying to set us up. They were very uptight about any fraternization between the soldiers and the hippies; at the boundary line between Hunter Liggett and the National Forest there was an off-limits sign and the swimming Hippie Hole was off-limits too. I guess they were afraid the soldiers would get dope from us though there wasn't much to worry about there since we hardly ever had any. Which reminds me that one time at Jolon an ambulance outfit came in and I asked one of the medics if he'd sell me some morphine. He seemed to think I was kidding and raised his fist in mock outrage but I said I was serious and he said they didn't have anyway. Morphine used to be abundant around military bases but a guy who had been a medic in Viet Nam said he had only given it about three times. I guess they're afraid of the soldiers taking it.

The army must be getting harder to run all the time.

ROUSTED AT HUNTER LIGGETT

At the base headquarters there was a PX where you could stand around in front and get someone to go in and buy things for you, cigarettes and beer were much cheaper there, and we were also using the phone because the one at Jolon was out of order; and while we were doing this they played a tape of a bugle over a loudspeaker from the main building, a California mission-style thing, just across the street. First, they played a tune and people didn't do much but then there was another one, which I am told is called "Retreat," and everyone stood at attention and I guess we were supposed to be saluting the flag but they were all facing different directions and there wasn't a flag in sight anyway. The comic quality of the situation was heightened by the fact that the gas station attendant was standing at attention with the water hose in his hand running on the ground.

Morgan and I started saluting each other and a telephone pole and goofing off when an MP in a sedan drove up. He said he had got complaints—don't know how word travels so fast there—and would we show a little respect while we're on the base and finish our business and split. Our business at the time was waiting for someone to come out of the PX with some beer but we were pretending to be waiting for someone to get out of the phone booth. So we almost got busted for failure to show respect.

THE OPEL KADETT'S BRIEF CAREER

Kim took off for LA with some scheme to get 13 keys and came back a few days later without any keys but with a blonde chick and an Opel Kadett. We managed to get them to drive us into King City once—I was going in almost every day in my heap, always trying to get through a day without making a run but something always came up, and it was good we did because that was all anyone ever got out of that car. The next day Chuck and Kim and the chick went swimming at Hippy Hole and after a while, Chuck came back bloody and looking like death. I asked him what happened and he said, "I almost got killed." It seemed the chick had been driving and an army truck had been coming the other way and she went off a cliff and Chuck jumped out and the car got totaled though no one was hurt badly. The MP's and Forest Service materialized quickly and radioed for the Highway Patrol, but the chick didn't have her license with her and when the cop found this out he said, "If you don't have a license why'd you call me?" then turned around and split without giving her a ticket or anything. Shows how much THEY cared. Guess it was outside their territory.

Editor's Note: *"Big Yellow Taxi!" Cast assembled. No script. No camera. No film. High concept. Cinéma vérité. All the Way. And Beyond! (R.D.)*

DOGFIGHTING IN BIG SUR

Just went through Big Sur again, which is part of a longer story, but I am reminded, ahem heh heh of a party I went to there.

It was on the Summer Solstice, so of course all the Big Sur characters got together at Coast Gallery and played Beatnik music, bongos, and stuff just like in the old days, but with electric guitars too now. People tried to dance but it wasn't rock music, so you couldn't do rock dancing, and besides, they think they're a cut above hippies. They were selling wine, Rotta Organic wine, for 35 cents a cup, and Pat Cassidy had a jug or two of his own. I finished one and couldn't bring myself to ask for any more, so I asked what kind of deal he'd make me and he said, "Fuck, it's free," and gave me a glass and started to hand out joints. But then he set up like a stand and started selling it for 25 cents a cup. He'd ask someone going by, "Want some wine?" and they'd come over, and then he'd tell them it was 25 cents, and they'd pay. He did this to some of his best friends and made all of them pay. One guy tried to wrestle the jug away from him and everyone else went along. It was some kind of game that I probably didn't completely understand. The Sur is all a big seminar or session or happening or school. But Cassidy didn't need the money; he had a roll of fifties in his billfold.

Well, I got really ripped on the combination of the wine and grass pot-entiating each other and went into my outrageous drunk routine, which includes fighting dogs. I only do this when I'm drunk in Big Sur and can't do it sober. I would pick the biggest dog around, German Shepherd or whatever, grab him by the snout, and throw him around. They won't fight because you've got them intimidated. The dogs would run from me. Turnabout is fair play, every dog has his day, and I tried to tackle one and skidded on the gravel and skinned my arms and other places.

I got so many cuts that day I'm not sure where they all happened. I climbed up a wall and cut my head on a stone, then I lost my balance and fell into some sort of flowerbed and cut myself on the concrete edge, or something, right by the bandstand, so everyone saw and even a little girl kept coming up to me saying, "You're drunk." Finally, I drew a line in the dirt with my toothbrush and walked it and said, "See, I can walk the line," assuming she was familiar with that routine. She said "So what? You're still drunk." I don't suppose anything I could have done would have impressed her, since she held, like a magic amulet, the knowledge that I was drunk.

BIG SUR

A while ago I went up to Big Sur to see what was happening and maybe make it with Susan too. It wasn't the easiest trip I've ever made; on the way up I started to have one of my "attacks" as I call them, stopped and dropped a Valium, noticed a tire was shot and thought I'd change it but found the spare was in pretty much the same shape and drove on into the unknown. The Valium didn't help much and I stopped in Santa Maria which is more a detour than a stop since you have to go miles off the freeway to get to town, didn't know that, finally found a liquor store and got a bottle of red Ripple, chugalugged it in the parking lot, feeling very gauche, but jeez, whatcha gonna do, drove on, cool finally, got to Gorda and went to Mary Caroline's place and much to my surprise who was standing at the door but Ely, the big fat Jewish junky friend of Bob and Sue from LA. I still don't know what he was doing there, but there he was and I said, "This must be the place," and he repeated this and we talked rather stiffly for a half hour or so till I finally found that the day before he had taken 2000 mikes of some fierce shit and didn't remember who I was. Then someone asked us to help push a truck, driven by Crazy Richard, who had given Ely the acid, and Ed Day was there, and a glowing blonde cat who introduced himself as Ted. Ed introduced himself too, we've met each over and over again and never recognize each other, and we pushed this truck, and I had just hurt my back and knew this was folly, but couldn't think of any way to get out of it without appearing chickenshit, and hurt my back struggling uphill spinning our feet through puddles, but finally got it going, then this Mayan looking chick came up to me and said, "I saw you pushing," and we got to rapping, looking each other in the eye, but I thought she was with Crazy Richard. Turned out she used to be married to him, but I didn't know where it was at, then Susan and

Bianca arrived, but before that Mary C. returned, and Crazy Richard dumped two bags of ice in the sink, and I asked what it was for, and MC said, "It's to put on my tits, they've got milk in them and they hurt." It seemed she had just had a miscarriage. So I said, "I'll suck them," and she said, "Will you come every four hours for a year and a half?" Well, that nonplussed me. Then I got into the whole Big Sur thing which is so intense and complicated I can't get it all down. Ed came back hysterical and said Ted had chased him down a mountain shooting a shotgun at him, tumbling over cliffs all the way, wanted to borrow a gun but no one would loan him one, then MC flipped out and told everyone to get out, said, "Thank you if you love me but I can't bear your love right now." Her baby had just died you see, and so we split.

Me and Susan went and laid down in the Travel All driven by George Abend, but she said it wasn't the right time or place, and we had to wait hours for him to get back because he was hung up with the local witch or some such story, and I was going to follow him up to Roland Hall's place on Partington Ridge, but I ran into the cliff backing up and was delayed a few seconds and when I got down to the road he was nowhere in sight. I was completely bewildered but finally took off north, driving fast, and never saw him again; seems like I could have caught an International in an Oldsmobile, then ran into some kids whose VW had run out of gas and took a guy and chick clear to River Inn and Redwood Lodge but it was three in the morning by now and every place was closed, though found where the road to Partington was, but had to take the kids back to their car; I slept in my front seat since there wasn't much point going up at four in the morning not knowing where I was going, next morning I drove up but didn't know where to go, went back to Gorda and got Ed Day to guide me, but on the way up we stopped at Girard's, and Jim Cook was there, Captain Cook was still cookin', and this Apache chick named Yvette went with us, never did figure out how this was arranged, but instead of going north to Partington we went south to Pacific Valley for a jug of wine, and once we were that far Ed suggested we go on down to Gorda, his aim was to make it with Yvette while Mary Caroline was up in Palo Alto burying her baby. Ed said I could ball her too, then while he was at it some friends of Ely's from LA arrived, one was freaked out drunk and caused a ruckus with Anderson, the owner, who thought he was on dope. I have to skip many interesting details because they came too thick and fast, but when they were done I went in and Yvette was lying naked on the bed, though when I came on to her she said, "Would you let me go to the bathroom to wash?" but we took off again; once we were in the car she says to Ed, "Can I put my pants on now?" And pulls them out I don't know where she had them and puts them on. I've never understood that scene.

We finally got up to Roland's place, high up on the ridge, where you can see the ocean far below, often covered with clouds, like being in the sky; all of Big Sur is like that, it's not just a change of place, it's almost going to another level of existence, and Bob and Susan had pitched their tent under an avocado tree by a garden where Bob was doing a transcendental gardening thing, moon, stars, and all, and we got drunk and all I remember is trying to ride some kid's bicycle and falling off three or four times and rolling down the mountain, and they had these big dogs and I was grabbing them by the snout and throat, and next day Bob was apologizing and Susan was saying he had been "naughty," but I can't even remember what he did, I didn't know he was so drunk but it turned out he had drunk a half gallon before we got there. Well next day Ed and Bob and Yvette and I went down the mountain as they call it with her curled up in the mattress in the back seat, and went to the Hot Springs where she disappeared with no more ado that she showed up with, and we finally went to a party at Girard's, or maybe it's like that every night; anyway there was this chick named Gaynor or Gainer who was freaking out and singing "Bali Hai," the part about "your own special island, come to me, come away" and bugging everybody, and I finally picked her up and carried her off and me and Bob went to the Hot Springs and had an orgy with her in the baths, then finally left her there, still singing, and went to Bill Weejohns and shot some smack, and left with Zebe, who Bob told me was some kind of guru who would bury you in manure and sprinkle you with water for four hours a day to purify you, and he smoked a joint and refused to turn Bob on, I guess because he didn't get a taste, and he ended up driving and drove my car half off a cliff at Roland's, perched with one wheel off the ground. Next day a guy came up who said he was Tamara's brother, and a Digger, and Rhoda from San Francisco, the usual stream of visitors the Brannaman's get, but it was uptight because it was someone else's place, and I was uptight too but had to wait all day to get Roland to tow my car out. And I took Susan down to Sarah Kahn's, who it turned out used to make it with Charlie Plymell, where she was supposed to pick a bunch of vegetables and we kissed goodbye, never did make it with her; she blew some pot smoke down my throat though, and when her lips are puckered up they're the most beautiful thing in the world. Well anyway I thought about stopping off in Gorda and checking Dorrie out but passed, they had pushed my car out of the parking lot once before, very tense scene there. This is just skimming the surface of what happened there in a few days. I suppose if I had any nerve I'd go back there and try to make it, the home of the brave and land of the free, Big Circus someone called it, the tournament of superheroes.

I lost two toothbrushes on that trip, but somehow two suede jackets, women's, turned up in my car, one with a pair of glasses in it, that Bob had worn from the Hot Springs, having lost his coat somewhere; and Yvette left a man's Xtra-large polo shirt which she was wearing for a dress, it rode up over her ass and I slapped her on the butt and said, "So that's why you wore the pants," while she was lying in Ed Day's arms—things are pretty loose there. She offered to babysit for Susan, said "I love children" but you might never see her again either.

THE TEMPLE OF POWER

Historical notes of Underground History Department:
Years ago, I walked by the Southern Pacific Hospital around the backside, and their power plant for emergency use was there, sort of below street level, and I looked in and saw the inside of the plant. There were these big boilers and turbines and a raised floor between them on which there was a brass tripod. On top of this little table-like thing, which had long slender legs, was a sort of samovar-shaped thing, like a teapot with a long spout, and it was also gold-colored.

The only rational explanation I can think of is they kept oil or some fluid in it for the machines, but it had a highly sacramental look to it. I guess the boiler man started tripping out on power and its relationship to life, keeping the hospital alive and saw this setup in a store window . . .

COSMIC SPECULATION HIGH ON SPEED

As to the Big Bang theory versus the solid-state theory, the B.B. theory should not be construed as "true" within any meaningful human time-space frame. That is, even if within some ultimate view there were a cyclic process, its workings would be over a period so long that its movements would render it static for our purposes. If human efforts can produce significant changes within solar years, cycles involving billions of such units may be regarded as of academic interest, except insofar as the directionality of the dynamics of the process affects these efforts. On the other hand, the solid-state theory should not be interpreted as meaning an unalterable stasis, since by any estimation the system is in such a state of flux that the only question is the degree of its volatility and its direction, if any (as argued by the B.B. theory) and, I would suggest, its potential for direction.

I would further suggest that philosophical questions of origin and aim be allowed to settle themselves, if they will be so kind, within the process of practice. Theory may not, of course, be totally divorced from practice, and it is in the light of a somewhat different theory that I outline possible courses. However, the ivory tower gloss needs to be rubbed off these issues so that they may be seen for what they are: the potential blueprints for man-planned development of the cosmos. On an idealistic basis, I have qualms about even suggesting such a fundamental revolution in the status quo, but I believe that factors which have escaped our control, such as the suicidal life-pattern on earth, stimulated by other factors, have rendered far-reaching planning, or at this stage, speculation, necessary. With the upcoming technology and personnel, the gap between speculation and technology is little more than standard R&D time spans. I foresee a telescoping time dimension in which apparently vast state-of-the-art gaps will be bridged with a speed not hitherto considered possible.

I propose merely a schema of the more or less immediate historical panorama confronting us and a few of the paths open therefrom.

In this view, the cosmos may be regarded as infinite for immediate practical purposes. Therefore, infinitely more energy AND matter is available to us than any present or envisioned technology gives us the means to deal with, or cosmology depth to conceive of. The sudden jump from nuclear fusion to quasars is an illustration of the depth of field. The former, unconceived of a few years before, gives man undreamed of powers within the system within which this is the ultimate energy exponent i.e., the solar system, while the latter, discovered a few years after, is a corresponding exponent within a much greater (or higher power?) system. Although the quasars are the most distant "bodies" yet discovered, this is no reason to assume that the system within which they form the corresponding force is at the limit of the universe; rather, it should be taken as the second factor in a progressive formula.

Since conventional physics acknowledges its inability to explain the order of energy emitted by quasars, which to an earlier mentality would have been interpreted as a message from a higher being, supernal in all respects, and commensurable to none of the strictures of our level of existence, an unorthodox approach may not be out of order.

I suggest that the prevailing dynamic in the larger system, which includes all that is known and undoubtedly more, may fairly be described in human terms, as chaos. . . i.e., one in which a ruling order has not been established. I do not mean to deny by this that a higher-order may be intended which man is meant to implement, which, being accomplished, would abolish chaos, but just that this is the reigning condition. By reigning, I mean prevailing, since it is just the idea of the conscious and deliberate ordering of the present state of affairs that I mean to attack. In order to make this point, I need to draw a distinction between our immediate surroundings— the solar system—which has been demonstrated to be a clockwork mechanism, though one with many disconcerting quirks, and the known universe, which shows no signs of being orderable by an extension of the methods which have achieved what understanding we have of our limited system, but which seems on the contrary to operate by laws of its own, if any at all, and the operant principle, as manifested to us, is chaos. This does not require such a severe mental wrenching as might at first appear. The solar system is largely within our grasp, both conceptually and physically, as recent acrobatics [sic] have shown. It is a closed system, with only occasional intrusions from outside. Electromagnetic radiations from outside do not appear to affect its mechanical functioning. Although it no doubt stands in a gravitational relationship with the rest of its galaxy (this relationship being undetermined), it operates independently of the rest of this galaxy. It may be significant that the solar system is near the periphery of the galaxy. Conditions near the center might be much more determinative. Perhaps in the boondocks, something unique, or unusual has arisen: an order, comprehensible by the inhabitants thereof, and extensible, by means of certain principles derivable from this order by these inhabitants to further realms. However, these principles cannot be assumed to exist, *a priori*, in these other realms.

Here a clarification is necessary. I first proposed a schism between operant principles in the solar system and the rest of the universe (an objectionable term, implying an unproven uniformity) and am now arguing for an extension of these principles (though not the very same, as I will show). The difference is that the traditional assumption, which I call into question, is that this common principle already exists, while I postulate that it does not exist outside our system except where it can be demonstrated, which at present is nowhere, but that it can be introduced.

This postulate rests on a hyper-Copernican view of the universe which is based on nothing but appearances, which, however, are all we have. It is that in our solar system we have a germinal unit, or one might say a base or launching-pad, which contains within it a revolutionary, or evolutionary if you prefer, principle: consciousness operating through adequate means to achieve ends which accord with the designs of the initiatory power. I will not here debate whether this power comes from elsewhere. Assuming the uniqueness of this cell, it could well be an element thereof, and not received from a "higher" source. Within the scope of this argument, it could be either self-generated or from a trans-cosmic source, without affecting the argument. The point is that it develops within this system alone, and does not exist within the known universe outside it, and has no counterpart outside it. While the marvelous plan and design of the "creator" who is posited by the selfsame design and plan, is abundantly evident on earth and throughout the solar system, it has by no means been demonstrated elsewhere. The galaxies appear to hold together fairly well, but over a sidereal period how well is not known, and the fairly well-ordered galaxy which our well-ordered solar system is a part of may be an exception, the orderliness of the galaxy, if any, perhaps being a paradigm of our system, or vice versa, and certainly not applicable to some more unruly aggregations, such as gaseous nebulae and novae. Taking the known creation as a whole, no comparable order seems to exist. Granting the difficulty in judging this point due to the disparity in scale, still many discordant elements are irreconcilable with a model of the universe based on the nearer examples.

Scientific discoveries may establish basic underlying principles, but at present, they tend in the opposite direction, and indicate a cosmic free-for-all with no purpose except to "do its own thing." Which is approximately what I think it has been doing since it began, if it did. How or whether it began is a bootless question at present, the B.B. theory that all matter emanated from an infinitesimally small point being more mystical than anything

I would [not] dare to advance without more light. What matters is that we are in medias res, with certain forces to deal with, and rather little time in which to do so. The prospects are staggering. We are by no means limited to the solar system. This system may have already been irredeemably damaged by radioactive wastes, and seems to be a territory disputed by several highly destructive factions. What is open to us is the virgin wilderness of the open skies. It has been estimated, for what that is worth, that 90% of all the material in the universe is inchoate in the form of interstellar gasses, largely hydrogen, being the basic constituent. No one seems to be doing anything with this stuff. What's stopping us? Gasses could also be used to create viable atmospheres on the planets in our solar system.

Scientists and technologists could devise limitless uses for this, the only truly raw material readily available to us. I merely wish to suggest the possibilities. If fully utilized, and intelligently employed, this matter would become the basic stuff of reality. It could dwarf the presently constituted creation in volume, and its intelligent integration could make the "starry wonders" look like an ill-managed fireworks show. More importantly, it could be used to create a world "nearer to the heart's desire"—man would then run his own show, subject only to his own limitations, instead of having to accept a menial role on a dying planet. If successful, man would become the major creator, and what had passed for "god" would appear for what it was—an automaton incapable of transcending itself, like the computer that can only answer the questions its users can think of answers for, its apparent design a chaos that worked, well enough, and just barely well enough, to produce something to supersede it, and continue the process, which might be described as giving birth to god. In a "spiritual" sense, the Big Bang theory might be considered to be vindicated by this—this evolutionary process, which could be called life, sprang forth from the heart of matter, took an order, whether through accident of plan, and seized control from its progenitor, whether from outside influence or due to a dynamism generated by itself, and went on to shape its own destiny. It is hard to imagine how existence, however construed, could fulfill itself more wholly.

The dangers are in proportion to the opportunities. If the power of thermonuclear fusion in the hands of man is capable of destroying our world, the higher powers indicated by the quasars, beyond physics, could perhaps destroy the universe. Man has the capacity and the proclivity for either course.

Alan Russo's rooming house in Santa Barbara, California, 1977
Photograph by James Bearden

PART SIX

THE ADVENTURES OF ALAN & DUMPY

Editor's Note: *Walt "Dumpy" Townsend was a Shoshone Indian who attended the University of California at Santa Barbara in the late 1950's on a football scholarship. Dumpy was a hefty man with the typical American Indian wide shoulders and thick torso, with proportionally more modest arms and legs, the legs being bowed. His facial features were solemn and dignified, and not given to expressiveness. He stuck around his friends in Isla Vista after graduation, being a laconic, alcoholic bon vivant with sharp perceptions and a good brain, which Alan Russo, swimming in the same social, Beat, intellectual, wastrel waters understood. Here follow some adventures which Alan remembered. It is unknown if Dumpy wrote anything, or if he remembered anything, either. (D.W.)*

DUMPY RETURNS TO SANTA BARBARA

Dumpy showed up the other day with his bag of possibilities and a plan to drive to Laredo to get some peyote. Your "possibilities bag" is like a small duffel bag, or in this case, a laundry bag containing immediate necessities: change of clothes, shaving kit, etc. Dumpy says it's an old cowboy term, like from Zane Grey. I don't know if you can get your troubles in one, but you can get your possibilities in. He's been knocking around like this since I've known him, rootless Indian, crash-diving through white man's limbo for an evaporating ground more elusive than the game. "Anytime the hunter gets captured by the game, anytime the stranger gets stranger than the land, the stranger gets banned."

We finally got hold of a map and found out that it's about 1800 miles from Santa Barbara to Laredo and he doesn't know how to score there, anyway. But it's legal, because he's an Indian. Then he called across town about mescaline and wound up going down into the village for some beer. *Sic transit.*

Possibilities. A bag. Nothing goes right. A light across the desert of endless night . . . never make it across the desert on these tires . . . shoe soles. Dumpy is starting to grow a mustache which makes him look like a 225 pound General Nguyen Cao Ky. Bob Branaman came over and got me to go to the airport with him to drive Jeanine's car back, so we have two VWs now, up to full strength. Everywhere I go there are plenty of VWs and not much else. Sometimes three or four to a house! Should have one to a person. Bob has a '49 Cadillac that's like driving the *Queen Mary*. He gave me directions to the freeway coming back and I got incredibly lost. The last time he gave me directions, the same thing happened. I went to two gas stations and the first one misdirected me. God, did I get lost!

I've been disoriented since I got here.

The ocean is to the south instead of to the west.

NATURAL PHENOMENA

This afternoon Dumpy and I went up into the mountains to La Cumbre Lookout Station. From there you can see the ocean and the other side the mountains at the same time. On the way up we passed a canyon where Dumpy said that in the summer birds sing all night. Their calls echo up and down the canyon, ebbing and flowing like a liquid tide of song.

I've seen the ring of fire around Wichita, Vortex of the continent. On summer nights when there are storms you can see it quite clearly, sometimes all night; a circle of lightning completely surrounding Wichita, and around that, tornados, which never strike Wichita, the eye of the Vortex. The old Indian legend has it that they don't hit where two rivers meet. In Wichita this dead, dull void of low pressure hits you in the pit of your stomach when you get there, a wave of near-panic at the uncanny stillness at the heart of a maelstrom a thousand miles wide. It's all happening, but this unbearable deadness is the pivot that makes all that possible . . . like a compensatory sacrifice.

The only things that I've ever seen turn Dumpy on, that he would get enthusiastic about, are nature things, especially animals. Like when he described the Indian songs his people sang, where the rhythm imitates the hawk's flight—the old Indian spirit still stirring in the broken flesh. One of his arms slashed-up on a plate glass window, the other fucked-up by Valley Fever, which mainly Indians get, and which he got working at the camp for the white men, cartridge-loading, capsule karma, comes back on you so quick you can see it move before your eyes.

MEMENTOS AT MONTECITO
AN EMPTY MANSION

Dumpy just found another drawer of 19th Century artifacts: strange little strainers with clips, maybe for some kind of teapot long-since broken, a peculiarly-shaped spoon that says "Trinidad, Colorado" and the motto *Nil sine humane*, a knife with a specifically-shaped blade for some particular purpose, and so on. *The National Geographics* in the closet go back to 1916. There is a Geological Survey map from 1905, old pictures of relatives and classmates, more recent objects equally unidentifiable, a butter knife dated 1871, a baby spoon hand-made and engraved "Willis W. Knowles," (This used to be their business). There are quite a number of walking sticks, some carved and painted in an unfamiliar fashion; a silver tray, sort of like a soap dish, full of beads; another butter knife with strange notches, made by R. Wallace in 1835. There are many more closets and drawers. In the living room there's an 1881 A.J. Holman Bible with complete concordance, gold leaf, silver clasps, shellac cover, parallel columns, inscribed "From Mother and Father to Willis W. Knowles and wife, Christmas, 1890." I wonder how old that makes his baby spoon?

WHADDAYA MEAN, JUST MANURE?

Every time I delve into the back closet I find another gem. I have before me the *Department of Agriculture Farmers' Bulletin #21, Barnyard Manure, 1894*. It is prefaced by a letter of transmittal, which starts:

"Sir: I have the honor to transmit herewith for publication as a farmers' bulletin, an article on barnyard manure. Prepared under my direction by W. H. Beal, of this office. I feel sure that the importance of manure produced by domestic animals in the economical management of our farms is not sufficiently appreciated, and hope that the presentation of the case in the spirit of the best practice allied to the most thorough research will serve to increase the attention paid to this essential element in successful farming."
— A. C. True, Director

The bulletin starts out: "A well-kept manure heap may be safely taken as one of the surest indications of thrift and success in farming." Figure 1 is entitled, "The waste of barnyard manure." It shows a barn with piles of manure alongside it. A liquid is seeping from the piles into a stream that runs nearby. On the right a man is approaching a horse, while on the left a cow looks at a man standing in the doorway to the barn. It's a heartbreaking scene, when you consider how valuable that manure is, which you have to read the bulletin to fully comprehend.

I guess you might say you have to read it to fully savor it.

DUMPY & ALAN IN SANTA BARBARA

The other day Dumpy and I went to check out Isla Vista and its incredible Playboy scene, with luscious chicks sunbathing in every other front yard. We drank a lot of beer, and when we got back to "The Spread," there was a gallon of San Martin Burgundy and a pack of Gauloises just inside the door. We drank the wine.

Dumpy's next plan was to go to his parents' place on the reservation in northeastern Nevada with a stop off at the whorehouses in Elko. We would borrow a four-wheel-drive vehicle from one of his friends and bop around the mountains on the Rez. We were just about to leave when Mike and Joannie arrived. They had been planning to come up for the weekend, which gave me a convenient excuse not to go to Nevada. It might be fun, but I didn't want to leave the cat home alone. Our latest plan was to leave today, but Dumpy is still asleep or maybe reading a *National Geographic*. I better check.

The room he's sleeping in is full of those *National Geographic Magazines*, plus a glass-top table inlaid with silver and parquet teak. In the closet, I had found an 1862 gun made by Wesson before he met Smith, but couldn't tell if it was a bullet or ball firing job. It would work, except somebody had broken off the hammer and stripped the screws. It's a .41 carbine with an octagonal barrel. The room is all windows, and we can watch the chicks play tennis from here. We have some kind of Fools' Paradise here, too good to be true, and it is. The owners are dickering to sell the place, and people are constantly going through with blueprints. Things that seem too good to be true generally work out to be just that.

OWYHEE

MOUNTAIN CITY NEV.

Looking North on 51

Well, we really did go to Nevada. We left in chaos. Mike and Joannie left at the same time. I was trying to lock up the house, but we all kept remembering things we had left inside and I kept climbing back in through the windows and then locking them, so it got harder each time. We left in the afternoon, too late to get there that day, so we stopped off at Dave Bearden's in Sierra Valley and found that Dave gets out of jail on May 15th. We went on the next morning and stopped off in Elko, which is the junction with 51, the road into the reservation. Officially it's the Duck River Reservation, but everyone calls it "Owyhee," the name of the town there.

Elko turned out to be the wildest town I'd ever seen. First we went to the Pioneer Club, where we ran into Dumpy's Uncle David. The Pioneer is the ground floor of a hotel with a cafe running around the wall. The bar is a hang-out for Indian drunks, cowboy drunks, and other white drunks who dig getting lushed with Indians. The paying customers sit at the bar drinking Coors out of cans, while the people who can't afford that stand around drinking port, and those who can't afford that, or who just can't stand up, sit against the wall, or under a table, or in the few lounge chairs, as if the place half-remembers it's supposed to be the lobby of a hotel. Several people sit two to a chair, nodded-out blissfully, Indians and whites dozing on each others' laps. There are cuspidors along the brass rail of the bar. As long as you can sit up against the wall it's cool, but if you pass out on the floor they call the cops and have you hauled out. You get in the way, plus you could die there, and this way they know who's alive. Dumpy says one of his uncles died on a drunk and his buddies dragged him around to the bars for the rest of the night, propping him up, which ties in with their funeral customs, which are quite strange and said to still be practiced in the remoter boonies. They keep the bodies a long time, in cold weather anyway, and go through rituals reminiscent of *The Tibetan Book of the Dead*.

Dumpy knew where the red light district was, so we went there. It's between the railroad tracks and the Humboldt River. The Southern Pacific main line runs through town. When we left the Pioneer, it was sunset, pink over the mountains, with the railroad crossing lights flashing red and the bells ringing. The cat houses have locked screen doors. You ring the bell, and the madam, who is also the bartender, or one of the girls answers the door. The girls line up in their undies and you choose one, or if you don't see one you want, you order a drink and a chick latches onto you and asks you to buy her a drink. The drinks are classic road house splits, or little cans of Coors. The girls are about half white and half "black." I didn't see any raving beauties, but balled one at the second brothel. At least her face was in place. They have to be 21 to work, but California is crawling with teeny-boppers that are better; in shape anyway . . . but these jobs are automatic and fool-proof. She asked for fifteen dollars, as had a girl in the first house, and I didn't haggle. Later, Uncle David told us that they would go as low as five. You can pay whatever you want. They grimace at five, smile at ten, and sigh at fifteen. Dumpy balled a high yeller who had nice soft thighs and ass. She was sitting on the stool next to mine. When she got off her ass brushed fleetingly on my thigh, and she said, "Oh pardon me." I thought I might 69 her, but Dumpy had already taken her, and they were gone a long time.

While you sit at the bar, the madam-bartender talks to you; professional conversationalists, some of them. I couldn't face the thought of 69'ing the high yeller after Dumpy had balled her, and she was the only one I saw there who turned me on. While Dumpy was "in a room," a guy came in and said to the madam, who was pregnant, that she was going to have a boy, because the sex of the infant is determined by the partner who is in control at the moment of conception . . . and it wasn't her.

We went back to the Pioneer and picked up Uncle David and took off for Owyhee after a few more drinks and scenes, of course taking a fifth of port with us. Dumpy was out of money by then because he gave twenty dollars to his whore and he started to borrow from me. We stopped at a bar on the road. The lights were on and there was a semi parked in front but the door was locked. A guy opened the door and asked, gruff-like, "Whaddayou need?" He sold us a six-pack. We got to Mountain City and stopped at a bar there. I was getting out of the car with a beer in my hand when a compact bus with a light on top of it pulls up. I was worried for a minute, but the deputy was just checking out the action. As long as you can function, they don't bother about the niceties. We went into the bar, and the deputy came in too. He was wearing boots, jeans, windbreaker, and a cowboy hat. I couldn't see his gun, but it appeared to be an automatic, judging by the bottom of the holster, probably his own .45. Dumpy had his badge ready to flash just in case, but the deputy went on to kibitz the poker game in the back. We got some more beer, picked up another Indian, and headed for Owyhee; a car full of drunk Indians, but that's par for the course.

Mountain City is the last outpost of white authority. After you enter the reservation, the only cops are the tribe's own. They have their own cops, judges, jail—the works. We dropped off the extra Indian and went to Dumpy's parents' place, which was a big house trailer, it being about 2:30 a.m. by this time. Every night lately we weren't getting things wrapped up before 2 or 3 or 4. I went to bed and Dumpy woke me up early the next morning.

First, we visited his grandparents next door. His grandmother is a serious Bible-quoting, peyote-eating woman who only went through the 2nd grade, but writes and reads well. Grandpa's mind is alive enough to be bugged at his body being as dead as it is. We then took off in a Jeep station wagon, but it was too wet to go into the mountains, so we bopped around and went to visit Dumpy's Uncle Willis. He was just about to brand his cattle. Driving a good Ford Stake-Side, owning a nice new house, he was the president of the local cattlemen's association, but we got him drinking and he turned into a shit-faced drunk Indian, just like all the rest. There's a big thing up there about who got who started on a binge, because they can go on for months, while somebody's friend or relation will feed his cattle and try to keep things together. But it's a constant struggle, always on the brink, with the women trying to keep the men in line. It's a tough job, but they have some tough women up there. They don't have lush on the reservation, so they bring it in from Mountain City. We went back to Dumpy's to get his car for the run. His father was silently pissed-off because we were supposed to be going someplace with him, but we went on to Mountain City instead. Uncle David bought a gallon of wine at the grocery, but Dumpy took it away from him and traded it in for beer. We had to push the car to get it started again down the dusty main street, and then we went back to Uncle Willis' to have a drink until Willis' wife came home—a good, tough Indian broad. Then we had to load the trailer with hay and go out to feed the cattle where Willis found a dead calf, the 30th one that year. Willis' wife took Uncle David home to Grandma while Dumpy and Uncle Willis and I followed in the Jeep. Uncle Willis wanted to go back to Mountain City, but we learned that Grandma was fixing us a big supper which served as an excuse not to let Uncle David and Uncle Willis get smashed. We went to the folks' place and had venison steaks, etc., after which I went to bed early. But Dumpy went over to Grandma's house and sang Indian songs. He made a couple of runs into Mountain City after all, and woke me up at four o'clock wanting to talk. That was the end of that night's sleep.

The next morning Dumpy's mother had gone to work in the school cafeteria, and his dad had cooked up sausage and potatoes. We ate breakfast and then split. One of Dumpy's aunts had given us ten pounds of smoked rainbow trout, exquisite smelling, delicately smoked stuff; the best of fish. But we forgot about it and left it behind. We stopped off at Grandma's, where she gave Dumpy hell. Then we went to Uncle Willis' to look for Dumpy's coat. Uncle Willis was recovering from the night before, in the basement, where his wife makes him go when he's drunk. The coat wasn't there. Then we stopped by the school to say goodbye to Dumpy's mother and drove to the gas station, where Dumpy's father showed up with the coat which Dumpy had left in the Jeep. He wrote a check for the gas since Dumpy had run out of checks.

We went to Mountain City where Dumpy ate a hamburger. I drove us on back to Elko, and we looked for a whorehouse that was open, but it was still too early. The one with the groovy high yeller was closed, so we settled for a glass of orange juice and another hamburger, with onions, which made Dumpy fart for several hundred miles sleeping in the back seat, while I took back roads instead of the interstate, because I thought that it was shorter that way. Driving across Nevada in a VW is very frustrating, because you can't go as fast as you could in a real car. It's uphill for hundreds of miles, just slightly enough to slow you down. Then the downhill slope is half a mile long with a curve in it. The wind is always blowing dust. It's rough country up there, either hot or cold, and all made of rough stuff. It's abrasive at its best.

It occurred to me that Owyhee is not in any state, since it's partly in Nevada and partly in Idaho, and not governed by either one. It's also not very clear what time it is there, since the Idaho-Nevada line is also the line between time zones, Pacific on the Nevada side, and Mountain on the Idaho side. Nobody ever knows what time it is. When you ask them what time they're using, they say, "How many kinds are there?" That seems to be typical of the place. State lines. It would still be snowing in the mountains while it was 80 degrees and flooding down on the plain.

ANOTHER TRIP TO SAN FRANCISCO

Well, we've done it again, folks! This time Dumpy and me and Ken B. went to San Francisco in a blue '65 Mustang fastback almost exactly like the one when Dumpy and I went up there in 1966, only with a hot engine. Ken drove fast, and if we hadn't stopped off at some wine tasting rooms, we would have made good time. We went to North Beach, ate in Chinatown, and then went by our friend Art's pad where this chick had answered the door in her bathrobe asking who we were. I said, "Alan," but she didn't know me from Adam, I don't think. I asked if Art was there and she said "No, but is there anything I can help you with?" I said, "Can we come in and talk about it?" and she let all three of us in to wait, trying to sell us grass for $20 a lid, and acid and mescaline for $3 a hit. Then she went out and was gone for far too long. We talked to some kids in the front room about acid and mescaline, which was the point for them. When she returned she came back panting and sort of flushed. I got the impression she had just had a quickie. She half-laughed and said, "Well, what happened was blah blah blah . . . ," but the truth of what had happened seemed so transparent to me that I cracked up partly because we had been smoking grass. Then she pulled out what she claimed was a hit of "organic psilocybin" and oh yes, her black velvet blouse was hanging off one shoulder. That was what she went out for. Dumpy bought the "organic psilocybin" off her for $5, although I tried to point out to him the improbability of it being any such thing, without coming right out and calling it a scam in front of them. But Dumpy will go for anything. He was taking Dayglo poster paint as mescaline for a while.

Then we went over to Lisa's where there was a set of drums in

207

her living room and some people, one of whom who turned out to be living in my old pad at 1136 De Haro and immediately asked me to put in a change of address because he was still getting my mail. He also worked for the Post Office in the zone for Bryant Street and delivered the route which included where I used to live at 1088 Bryant and still got a little of my mail that just got forwarded on to him at 1136 De Haro. He knew more of my old addresses than I did, almost like he'd been tracking me, or trying to avoid my mail, which caught up with him at every turn; he was getting my mail from three different addresses, so when he got some to Bryant he had no choice but to forward it to himself. After he left I asked Lisa and she said he would be a good person to talk to and we went over to 1136, where he and Bob Erickson lived; Bob who has turned into a hippie astrology freak, disciple of Gavin Arthur who, he says, wants to reincarnate through him and his secretary, and his chick and some other chick come in and Peter, the mail connection, who wouldn't do the thing. I slept there while Dumpy and Ken went to a hotel. I tried to make it with the spare chick who wasn't very good looking, and she gave me stories about how her old man was a Hells Angel tho she had only been in California a week and a half, and he was nowhere around, and finally that she had an infection of the cervix, so I gave up. Ken and Dumpy came by the next day and we went back to Art's and started talking to the kids in the front room again. It finally appeared that Art was there, which the chick from the day before had hoped to conceal from me, so that they could get our trade instead of Art; but just before she went out again, Art came in. Oh, I forgot to tell how she changed her clothes the night before. She had on a bathrobe, and when she went out, she first pulled a pair of jeans on under the robe. Then she undid the front of the robe, pulled a sweater kind of thing over her shoulders, a Goodwill job, then slipped her gown off and pulled the sweater thing the rest of the way down. If we'd known her better she would have just disrobed in front of us.

Well, we finally got Art to score for us which pissed the other people off, but it took a lot of trips around before it happened, much better price, complex scene afterwards of taking them around, seemed they didn't have a car, it took hours to get out of there, met

208

Art's new chick, Vicky, very young looking tragic baby-faced whose first words on seeing Art were, "You got any smack?" I said, "What's a nice young girl like you doing taking smack?" She was also going around in a bathrobe housecoat thing which didn't even close in front, so she was constantly pulling in shut between glimpses of her tits. Finally, we were going to take Art, Paula, Vicky and someone to a thing at Speedway Meadows and Art said we were just waiting for Paula to get her coat on. I finally went into their room and Art was sweeping the floor. I asked if they were ready and he said no, "Paula just needs to put her coat on;" then she said, "I'm ready," and we left, but ended up dropping them off somewhere because they decided it was too late to go to the park, and they had stalled us just long enough that we hit the traffic on the freeway and turned off on 17 at San Jose. Ken got bugged in Santa Clara and just started going down the streets with the least traffic; we made pretty good time but ended up back in San Jose and stopped at a park by a river. In the park there was a stage with a choir of Mexican kids in brilliant blue satin robes and white kids were running around in white robes. I thought they were choir boys but Dumpy pointed out they were judo outfits, so I took off my shirt and did 20 one-handed pushups without really going all out, almost like I stopped at 20 for a round number, and that's twice as many as I had ever done before tonight, then I did 20 again, half-drunk, but had to push to make it. But it was like I had burst through some barrier, like a 4-minute miler running a 2-minute mile.

When we got back to Montecito the party was in full swing with everyone crazy drunk and it went on from there. John Crawford was there, turning everything into an intense soul-to-soul encounter but he had quite a brew to stir that night. Howard was outrageously drunk and I started calling him a fat drunken slob to his face and pushing him around. John told me I was a successful failure, then things came to some kind of a head when I went through the kitchen to go to the john and Howard and Elaine Dvorak were sitting at the table with their feet kind of close and one of them made some jocular remark which I forget, to which I replied with a jocular remark to the effect that they were playing footsy, and no one can remember what happened after that but it seemed to me that she was playing off Howard, who she thought she had pretty well pussy-whipped, against me, trying to get Howard to take me out in defense of her, and I called her on it and slapped her very lightly, just to where the soft flesh of her face stirred against my palm, and Howard said, you slapped her and I said what about it, and when he arose to defend her or whatever I went out to the closet and came in with the shotgun which was unloaded, just to show him I was ready to go all the way. Elaine grabbed the gun, which I took back, and then the three of us stood with our arms around each other and talked it over. Mickey came in just then for a drink or something, was leaving, apparently not realizing what had happended or not wanting to know, and maybe Elaine didn't want him to either, but we called him over and told him what had happened and all four of us put our arms around each other and talked it over. I slapped myself hard twice to make any reparations that might be coming.

Everyone was telling people they loved them that night. Howard told me he wished he could figure out how to tell me he loved me and John speculated about how I'd be in bed, lotta backroom stuff upfront. I saw Dick Phipps and a vaguely Latin-looking chick and thought she was Betty, and made some remark about her dress involving the fact that she was pregnant and she didn't answer. I thought she still hated me after all these years so much she won't even talk to me, and later found she wasn't Betty but Chip Chapel's girl. After a bit, Bob Knowles came to the door and said the neighbors were complaining about the noise.

Everyone eventually cleared out except Dumpy, John, Howard, and me and we had a spot of bother evacuating because we didn't want Howard to drive but he wanted to get his car back, so Dumpy took the keys out of his car to try to get him to go with us in John's car but finally rode home with him, then went with John and me up into the mountains, and we heard the birdcalls up the canyons, then went to a cliff up on the ridge, where Dumpy offered to push me over if I wanted him to. I passed; we went through drunk college routines, but high too and just plain cuckoo, and didn't get back till almost 5 AM and Dumpy was supposed to get Ken's car back to him by 5 so he could get to work. And next day I had to go work on Meynet's garden, but got a late start hangover and all; he was supposed to go to France

Sunday and this was Friday and everything was getting more and more impossible. The truck wasn't big enough and Bob Knowles who I was supposed to borrow the shears from was gone but I went over and finished up what I could and told him I'd rent a truck the next day. Funny thing was he didn't seem to know it was Friday and the banks would be closed the next day and he wouldn't be able to go down and straighten out his account, and he was supposed to be straight.

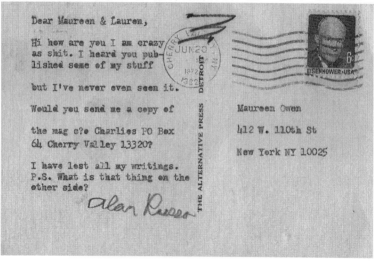

Dear Maureen & Lauren,

Hi how are you I am crazy
as shit. I heard you pub-
lished some of my stuff

but I've never even seen it.

Would you send me a copy of

the mag c/o Charlies PO Box
64 Cherry Valley 13320?

I have lost all my writings.
P.S. What is that thing on the
other side?

Alan Russo

THE ALTERNATIVE PRESS

Maureen Owen

412 W. 110th St

New York NY 10025

Postcard to Maureen Owen from Alan Russo in 1972.
Owen published "The Daylight Special Fiasco" and "Expressions"
in literary magazine *Telephone* #5, Fall 1971.

PART SEVEN

THE DAYLIGHT SPECIAL FIASCO

The Daylight Special still runs daily up and down the coast, though the Lark is flown forever (do they ever come back?) and you still see it, driving between San Francisco and LA, though you probably won't hear its whistle blow (horn now with the diesels) because you're on the freeway, and it just blows at the remote crossings where you're not likely to be, at least not when the Daylight Special goes by. No more the days when the black and red of the engine burst through the blue of the morning sky like god's fist furrowing the future before it. The old gods die, new ones are born. Coffee colored dirt in the grey-blue morning. Tragedy like a hillside raising its sleepy brows to the city spreading in the yellow morning to its feet. I'm tired but I'll make my rest. Isles of the Blest. If this isn't paradise, MAKE it. And if it turns out to be hell, then fake it. Whatever it is, you'll follow the law and take it. I've forgotten why I started to write about the Daylight Special.

THE GUY WITH A DIME ON THE SEAT

I was waiting for a bus on Mission and ran into Richard Brautigan, who was going the same way. We got on a bus and sat down after exchanging some pleasantries about the failure of his first novel. After we sat down, this guy—he was small and dark, 30ish, not apparently drunk but just somehow fucked up—was making demands on a straight-looking guy who was sitting opposite of us. The little nut was standing up and telling the one sitting down that he had a dime on that seat and that it was his seat, that he had somehow reserved it, and the other cat didn't have any right to be sitting there. This went on for a

213

while, the freak all the time harping on his dime, until I finally said to the sittee, "Well, lets see what's on the seat?" So he stood up, and sure as shit, there was a dime on the seat. The freak took it back, seemingly feeling that a wrong, which he considered par for the course, had been done him. It wasn't until later that I realized what I should have done— told him the fare was 15 cents, not ten. You know, ask a silly question.

IN MEMORIAM ROGER SCANNELL

The night before last Dumpy and I were waiting for Eli to come back to Branaman's and were reading a copy of the *LA Times*. Great front page with a banner headline BUCHER BEACHED and a picture of the Queen Mary or is it Elizabeth II arriving in New York for the first time. Inside was a biography of Roger Scannell who had just been found hanging from a Venetian blind cord. He was the biggest stool pigeon in Chicago and the biggest puzzle was how he got by till he was 38; it was almost his birthday, and no one, but no one, had a good word to say about him. Not even the cops. They said even they couldn't trust him because sometimes he would set someone up, that framed him, to get even with them. One anecdote was how he took a chick around with him, and someone, a cop or someone else, asked him how he avoided hotshots, and he replied, "Whadda you think I keep her around for?" She always went first, probably she and everyone else knew the arrangement and this forestalled attempts, since all you would do is kill her. He was also a compulsive thief, one time he and a cop went into a gas station, and when they came out he pulled two cans of car wax out from under his coat. This blew the cop's mind because he had been standing right next to Rog and hadn't seen him filch them and he said, first, "Don't do that anymore when you're with me." And second, "Whadja do that for anyway? You don't even have a car." To which Roger winked, "Maybe I'll steal one to go with it."

He stole, lied, and finked partly to support his junk habit and partly for kicks, or maybe they merged in the middle to where they became indistinguishable, "life-style" they'd call it now. Hardly a week went by he didn't get beat up, constantly playing the odds between the cops, the hoods, and junk . . . win a few, lose a few. Finally lost the big one, but considering how long it took them to bring him down it constituted some kind of victory. Made it through the darkest wilds Chicago was capable of providing, or being goaded into, to where it required police aid to keep him alive, and on to where even that didn't suffice. Unless he really did hang himself, which no one believes, though the official report was suicide. They figure he was too selfish to kill himself, plus maybe subconsciously, they feel poetic justice would be foiled that way. And out there that's the only kind of law there is. The article, which I wish I had, concluded with the words of one veteran observer that every time he brought it up everyone said: "It couldn't have happened to a nicer guy." Didn't say if anyone came to the funeral, if any. So there's a real live, I mean dead, antihero for ya. Here's one hat off for Roger Scannell, superfink.

While we were waiting for Eli to get back some of the people he had left there, apparently to meet Bob, but no doubt working into several scams he had going too at the same time, asked what time it was, since it had been quite a while since Eli had left, saying it would just be a little while, and Bob says, "It's about time he was getting back." Titters of laughter, their collars were a little too white to appreciate that one fully. Back door line. I finally went into the kitchen and ate what was left of the spaghetti which I had been avoiding, though I hadn't eaten all day hardly, figuring that would bring him back if nothing else would; you lose your appetite on junk, so it was like washing your car to make it rain sort of principle and it did, I was still in the kitchen polishing it off, when they came in.

Which reminds me of the time I was taking the Mission bus back from working at the Post Office late at night in San Francisco when a drunk spade got on the bus, sorta long hair before the natural craze, and announces loudly to everyone on the bus, "I'm Jesse Gorilla!" Then turning to the driver, who was also colored, he said, "Whatchou got to say for YOUR-self, you black-assed nigger?"—eliciting a laugh from the negroes on the bus, who were neither embarrassed nor uptight, but just digging the show. Then he turns to the first passenger, a middle-aged white woman, and says something like, "I'll bite your head off if you say one word you bitch!" She flinched at each word like bullets were hitting her, like in the Hungarian uprising of 1956 where they showed pictures of the Hungarian police getting mowed down by the "freedom fighters" and you could see the bullets striking them. Well I was sitting on the other side one seat down and knew my turn was next, and was thinking about knocking him out the doors; it was one of those trolleybuses with double doors in front, but just then the driver starts up, closes the doors, and Jesse says, "Let me out!" Which was fine with the driver, and Jesse debussed after one more declaration that he was JESSE GORILLA! I was just making preparations because I knew there wouldn't be one good word in the barrage aimed at me, and I didn't want to hear it.

THE GENUINE OUD PLAYER

On New Year's Eve, I went to a party where Howard Crawford was on apple cider the whole night. He had a gallon jug with him and drank the whole thing. He got the shits, but never got drunk. I guess it was some kind of demonstration of will power. I didn't feel like drinking that night, but when I got there and saw what was happening, i.e., a party in its early stages, with a few people sitting around rather stiffly, I realized that there was nothing to do but get drunk. Which I did.

Now this party was supposed to be a costume party if you wanted to wear a costume, and there was big burly spade guy in Arab clothing with a robe and burnoose, and I supposed he was a guy from LA coming on with the African hype. But then, around midnight, a hush came over the crowd and the guy starts playing an oud, a large lute kind of thing. And he really could play it! He was Hamsa el Din from Nubia, who recorded for Vanguard. I looked at my watch and found that it was one minute after twelve. I told the people sitting near me to pass it on, but not all of them did. Everyone was being too cool listening to the genuine imported oud player. Joannie, from Isla Vista, was sitting by the floor furnace with its rectangular grill and she had red boots on with square toes that were just about the size of the spaces in the grill, so I tried to cram her toes into them.

Someone had put a lot of dry ice into the bathtub and closed the door until the room was full of CO2 vapor, and then they opened the door, hoping to fill the whole house with CO2. But it just crept out along the floor like an ill wind. Somebody else put dry ice in the punch bowl and I sniffed the fumes trying to get high. The next morning I had a beastly hangover.

NUTHOUSE CATS

I went down to LA with Dave and James Bearden and their families to do a tape with Mike Lewis's recorder, which never happened because first we smoked a bunch of hash and drank everything in sight and then someone came by with a lot of acid and the session disintegrated, plus somehow I don't think it would have worked anyway.

Kids crapped out on sofas and some people crashed in the backyard and finally around 6 in the morning, I happened to look into the next room and there was an empty double bed. I thought obviously no one was going to sleep there that night and I might as well try to get some sleep, when I noticed that there was a cardboard box full of canned Chinese food next to the bed on the night table— chicken chow mein and all that, lots of it. I was grokking on this when Mike's wife, who hates me, suddenly materialized behind me. I guess she had been sleeping outside for some reason, and she said, "Are you looking for anything in particular?" which startled me and confused me because I really wasn't looking for anything. I had just found something by accident, but her tone was very uptight like I had found something I shouldn't have. I said, "I didn't know anyone was here," which may not seem to make any sense but I meant partly I thought the room was unoccupied. And she said, "There isn't supposed to be."

I mumbled an apology and drove off into the blue-eyed morning and I've been wondering ever since, what in the world do they do with Chinese food in bed? What inconceivable freak scene could that be? Do they just like to pop open a can of chow mein after balling? Or is there some other explanation too simple and accidental to think of?

THE WEST HOLLYWOOD ESCAPADE

Don't know what eventually became of Phil Rohrig; he went to Hollywood and tried to get into scriptwriting and didn't make it. When I went down to LA in 1965 he was still at it with a story of how one director or producer had accepted a script of his and then they changed directors and the new one didn't like it. He said he'd been at it for four years but some people tried for ten or fifteen before they made it so that wasn't so bad. Well, the first night I called him he was just in the process of moving. He and his wife or chick who called herself Gigi had a bunch of poodles and managed apartments; that way they got fancy West Hollywood pads free, but the poodle shit got them evicted. So, I helped them move which turned out to be more hassle than I anticipated since someone else was helping him who was also moving and we had to move his shit too and didn't get done till around 3 in the morning. I had just been drinking beer courtesy of the management but Phil had been drinking some brandy. I found out he'd been lushing a lot and getting out of hand, like pilfering things out of parked cars while walking down the street drunk.

After we got the stuff moved into his new place he and Gigi had a spat and so there was no one there but him and me. He then went out and came back with a couple of bar stools. He said there was a place nearby that he'd been casing and it was wide open and he tried to get me to help him burglarize but I tried to talk him out of it. He went out again and came back with a rocking chair. Sure was a lot of moving that night. Again, he tried to get me to help and I tried to stop him, with our almost coming to blows this time. He then went out and came back with an oriental painting and an armload of clothes—a London Fog trench coat, some cashmere sweaters, sport coats—and I realized how serious this was getting, that he was copping thousands of dollars' worth of stuff. He told me they had a stereo and color TV etc. so this time I went with him, mainly to try to keep him from getting into trouble.

On one of these escapades, Phil had pulled a heavy china base clock down which hit him over the eye so he had blood running down his face and he was wearing rubber gloves. Just as we approached the place, which to my mounting dismay was only two doors down, one of his poodles came running up, apparently, we had left the door ajar. He took it back while I stood around on the sidewalk. Just then a Mustang pulled up and a woman got out and went up to the door of the apartment. It was about 4 by now and not many people were abroad so I suspected this was the chick he was robbing. When he came back I didn't say anything. He then went up to the door of the chick's apartment, remember he had a stream of blood down his face and long rubber gloves and looked like something out of a horror movie. She said, "Who ARE you?" and he turned around and said to me, "Let's split." We went back up to his place but he went out again. He returned and said he had listened at her door and heard her calling the cops. He went out once again because he knew the cops were coming. And he returned with the cops because he'd run into them and the woman claimed he was the man she'd seen. I was stretched out on the bed pretending to be asleep. There was so much stuff lying around that we had just moved in that the cops couldn't tell what was stolen, especially since they didn't have a description of the loot. So after he talked his way out of it for the time being, the cops just said, "Don't go out anymore tonight." Then after they left he did go out AGAIN. I would have stopped him but I didn't want to get out of bed till I was sure the cops were gone and by then he was gone too. This time he didn't come back. I found out later he had run into the cops, which was predictable since they were still right out in front, and the woman had identified him again, and so they busted him.

I didn't know that at this time, just laid around in bed for hours, with a funny scene going on with the people downstairs who had a black Great Dane and around dawn kept walking it around the bedroom window. I was getting very paranoid and finally I decided to split, but the trailer we had been using was still attached to my car since Phil's car had broken down during the process of moving, and I didn't have a wrench to take the hitch off with and it was Sunday morning and none of the U-Haul places were open and I didn't know which one he got it from anyway; so I called a friend and asked if they had a suitable tool and they said yes, but on the way over I just pulled over on Sunset Blvd and knocked the hitch off with a jack handle and left the trailer sitting there on Sunset Strip in the grey LA morning. And after all this shit they felt I had let them down.

Next time I saw Phil he had got out of jail with no charges and he said he'd got rid of all the stuff. Then he and I were out in front of the place he was managing trimming the hedge when a car pulled up. He handed me a watch, an Omega, and said, "Stash this, it's the heat!"

A couple of plainclothesmen walked up and they went into the apartment house. They had a search warrant and a description of everything he had stolen, plus some things he hadn't, for insurance purposes I suppose, and he still had those fucking bar stools which he got for Gigi and one sweater. They were looking for me too, knew my name and that I'd been there that night, but fortunately, the woman hadn't got a good look at me and described me as tall and dark. I guess they thought I was the gardener. I stood there with the rake in my hands wondering what to do, then finally went up to the Strip and watched some Hell's Angels types getting busted. When I came back, the cops' car was still there, so I went to Barney's Beanery and had a beer and when I came back a second time the car was gone. I went up to Phil's apartment and no one was there. I heard he got 9 months.

Later I checked the Wichita phone directory and his mother wasn't listed anymore. Then while visiting Richard White in Wichita we went to a supermarket and there was Phil with his mother. She was living in the same house but she wasn't listed in the phone book because she had remarried. Phil said he got only 3 months for the LA burglaries but he now looked shrunken and bitter. He shook hands only when I extended mine. When he walked Richard back to his car Phil shivered in the night air and declared, "I'm afraid." Richard says he visited Phil after that and Phil said he had been in a nuthouse and that he had "failed."

PAT PENDER

Now Pat Pender (think that's how he spelled it, from Greek *Pindar* was his story), was a real character. He'd be a character in anybody's book. George Goyer met him by accident in the South Bay, don't remember just how. The South Bay, in case you didn't know, is the area roughly between Santa Monica and Long Beach, so named from the Santa Monica Bay, with which it has very little relation. Millions of people know where it is and no one else does. Anyway, Pat was in his sixties, living in Hawthorne in a shack on an alley, on a pension from the Canadian Army, and he had some obscure nerve disease where his nerve endings were deteriorating or something. I forget the name of it.

He was shrunken and hunchbacked, with a goatee and looked sort of like a retired Satyr. His skin was flaking like dandruff but deeper, and had a peculiar color in places. He always wore a vest and flannel shirt and suspenders, and shoes without socks (too hard to get on, I suppose.) He used his hands like hooks, because he couldn't bend his joints much. He might have been good looking once; it was hard to tell. He knew many languages and was teaching himself Turkish I believe it was, at the time. Here he was coming apart in layers and he was learning Turkish. I believe he even had a rationale for how it was going to come in handy someday. In the South Bay. He had a sharp mind, frayed at the emotional edges by paranoia, self-delusion, dogmatism; I believe he was a socialist of the kind who thought communism was an abomination and socialism the salvation of the world; he always had copies of the Progressive Labor Party paper around, *People's World* I think it was, and would rant over the injustices of the world, but the thing was he couldn't take care of himself and needed help mainly to make runs to the store.

He started out getting George to take him and somehow George palmed him off on me. Pat would call me up and offer me a dollar or two to make a run for him. If I went myself it wasn't too bad, but frequently he would insist on going along, to pick something out or something, and that was the hassle. First I would have to help him get dressed, help him on with his clothes, buckle his belt, here grab hold of that, etc., cigars and gin bottles around; he once spent a day and a half on the floor till he got to a phone and called for help, living off of grapes that had fallen too. I would try to go to the store by myself whenever possible but sometimes he had to go and went through a whole ritual of warming up before he could and then I would have to help him into the car; one time I had to pick him up and put him in and it would have been faster if I could have done that all the time but he wouldn't have let me—his head bloody but unbowed—and I'd help him out when we got to the shopping center, but then the real horror began.

He had one of those frames with wheels that he hobbled along on and everyone would turn around and stare. I would shrink behind pretending I didn't know him, just showing up in time to open doors etc. Sometimes we would go to several places, Southland Plaza I believe was one, and it took quite a while. It wasn't worth it for the "gas money." I just did it because I'm softhearted and can't say no and he had these stories about how impossible it was to do it otherwise, how much taxis cost, and there was someone else who wouldn't do it for less than $5. I just got roped into it. When he called, I would try to make excuses but would always agree in the end. I kinda dug the old guy and admired his tenacity but it required imposing on other people.

I suggested an old folks home once which ticked him off. He had to go to Harbor General Hospital once in a while. I took him there once and he had me smuggle in a bottle of booze. He used to drink some kind of gin, I think it was called Old Miners, 90 proof, for $3.69 a quart at Thrifty. At the hospital, there was a guy with his jaw wired together and another one walking along with an injection-solution bottle connected to his arm which was carried by an orderly who walked along with him. Which reminds me that one time Pat had a catheter after he got out of the hospital, and I had to watch him adjust it preliminary to one of our outings. It was almost like a plot designed to see how much I would put up with. Another time I was there, I had to have a drink or so before or after our outing, to even the tally and make the ordeal more endurable, when a marshal came by and served him with a court order. It seemed that he had been involved in a traffic accident. Apparently, he had been driving his own car until a short time before I met him and had finally had a wreck, got his license suspended, and was being sued by the other party. He snarled, after the marshal left, "You can't squeeze blood out of a turnip." An apothegm that took on peculiar piquancy when applied to his person. What was amazing was that he had got by for that long, or had ever been licensed to drive. He must have deteriorated rapidly. No one in the world would have given him a driver's license in his condition. And that's how I inherited him—Pat would have run right out and tried to drive if he'd had a car.

I finally moved away and I'm sure I'll never know what became of him.

RETURN TO SANTA BARBARA: DESOLATION AT HOWARD'S AND THE PISSING PROBLEM

When I got back to Santa Barbara I went by Suzie's who wasn't home, then Jeanine's who was and gave me tea, and then to Nan and Ray's where I needed to piss. They live in a loft sort of thing and use the john next door. Their explanation of where it was, was rather vague and perhaps evasive so I went to Howard's which is just a block away. When I got there a scene of stark horror greeted my eyes. While I had been gone all the trees, except the two tall palms, had been cut down and the garden, which was like a small park, was in ruins. I had planned to piss in the trees. So, I went into the john in back. I knew the toilet didn't work but turned on the cold water tap and it worked so I thought what the hell I'll piss in the sink, they don't use it anyway. So, I started pissing but heard a noise and found the trap was out and it was all just running into a bucket under the sink. So, I cut off the water and went into the house, no one was there, and used one of the inside johns. I had been looking forward to a little to pissing in the woods—back to nature and a feeling of getting away with something.

It turned out that the owner, name of Krieg, was clearing the place in preparation for building apartments and was working on tearing the place apart. Dumpy says he's the working'est son of a bitch he's ever seen. I call him Blitz Krieg. The way he went through this place. Jungle Gym.

AT THE BIRD CAGE

Soon after I got to Santa Barbara Dumpy took me out to Isla Vista to a place where Gordy was living with these two chicks, Joanie and Terry. They are some far-out chicks and many funny things happened that night but the funniest thing I ever did see was what happened when we went to the Bird Cage. This is a rock and roll dance hall beer joint out there. "It's the only place to go," Terry told me, not meaning it was THE place to go but that there was nowhere else to go.

We were in there for a while and Joanie, a tall blatant blonde, asked me if I wanted to go out and smoke a number with her. We went looking for a deserted parking lot but when we got behind a truck there were these people in it so we went back to my car and smoked it there. I had her blow the smoke into my mouth which she didn't mind doing, and after a few routines we started heading back to the place. We were just crossing the street when we saw these two young chicks standing on the opposite curb. They didn't look quite 21, both were short and dark, and looked similar, so maybe they were twins. They sure came on the same way. One of them said to the other, "Shall we?" Apparently, they decided to, because one of them ran up to Joanie and went "Bleaugh!" in her face; sort of a semi-epileptic scream and grimace, then ran across the street to their car, a Volvo, and rolled the window down. I said, "Why did you do that?" and they both laughed hysterically, their heads banging back against the seat, and then they did it again, and we realized they were just flat flipped out and went back to the Bird Cage.

THE SANTA ANA CONDITION

A few weeks ago a strong Santa Ana wind blew up, or what they call the Santa Ana condition up here, since it's not really from the Santa Ana Mountains like in LA, just an onshore wind, and it split off half of a big eucalyptus tree, over 100 feet tall, along the road, dead point on the top, tall and straight and thin and pale; turned out it was on state property, highway right of way I guess, and Knowles called the state and had them haul it off. It had torn off part of an oak tree on the way down. They bucked it up and we hauled some of it off for firewood. It struck me as sort of a death knell for the elder Knowles, like the old stories of a dog howling at midnight before someone dies; old Ed is a lot like that tree, tall and erect and white, 77 years and still works out every day. When the sewer line clogged he was out there digging feverishly and Suzy begged me to go out and do the digging because he had already had two or three heart attacks and I went out and it was all I could do to out-dig him, and I'm a diggin' sonofabitch and he still wouldn't stop.

Suzy introduced me to him with a note, since he's supposed to be deaf, though at times he seemed to understand what we were saying, so couldn't tell if it's a con or what. There's a pair of his old army dress pants in my closet and American flags in several closets and even corners, like behind the piano, and all the woodwork in the house is dry and brittle and creaks every time you make a move or a ghost sighs. Which they do every time you move. And so it's sort of like the final playing of the Battle Hymn of the Republic, with old Ed at attention saluting as he keels over, finally too stiff and too strong to bend, and so he falls, as he would want it, busting his way out of life; "Let's shoot our way to freedom," as Bill Gaines used to say, every joint in the old house popping like a spasm and the old flags unfurling blue as the color of his eyes. Maybe I'm just an old sentimentalist but I try to give a man his due when I can find one.

THE HIGHWAY DEPT. THROWS A CURVE

There's a curve in the road just before you get to Knowles' place where I'm staying and a stone wall around the entrance which cars keep hitting because of its delectable location. Just can't pass it by over a certain speed. One day when I was working for Bob Easton, he drove me home and the road was blocked by flagmen and flares just before the place. We went around and there was a Highway Patrolman stopping traffic at the other end. We finally got through and there was a crew with a loader and a dump truck and several men sweeping up the debris and other crap and finishing off the cement work on the wall. Bob talked to one of the men; he knew him because he's in the construction business and it turns out that the truck that hit the wall was a cement truck, so the cement company just sent its own men out and repaired the wall itself. So no bills, though there were a couple of white-shirted guys down the road measuring, insurance on the truck I suppose. A good case of doing the wrong thing in the right place and time. If only everything could work out that way. Or better. Which is dreaming.

ZUMA

Got back to Zuma about 9:30 this morning. Stewart answered the door because no one was up but him and Sandy who was on the patio in the Bawa chair coming down with a sunburn. It turned out that everyone had stayed up till about 5 that morning so the arrangements we had made for me to get there early so that Suzy could get up to Montecito and come back the same day were now by the wayside since they wouldn't get up till 12 or 1. So Stuart, 4 years old, whom I met a couple of days earlier and he had asked me what my sign was, and we find we're both Gemini's, latches on to me and we go into a field trip discussion alternating between the more or less usual kid questions about how things work, plants, and animals, etc. which I fielded as best I could, finding I could do it better than I used to, partly because he asked better questions, and he's asking me, "You wanna know something?" and then gives me his view on things. I learned that there are 614,000 orchards to a tree and that the lizards come inside if you leave the doors open and drink the wine, and when they're drunk they eat beads. Anteaters, on the other hand, when drunk swell up to an enormous size. Sort of like one of those 16th-century travelogues about the fabulous creatures on dark continents but hot off the subconscious press. Whenever he got to something he didn't know he would improvise freely. He told me that some people when they get drunk shear the feet off ants and eat them. He couldn't explain why they shear the feet off. In addition, some crazies take off in planes and crash them on purpose.

We got into a discussion about human skin pigmentation. I told him it was a mixture of several colors; he asked about red, white, and blue, I said no but then realized that all those colors do enter into skin color, so he went into a trip about how I could have stars on my head and stripes down my body; I told him they occur only in mixture, not serially, but he persisted until I called him a red, white, and blue headache, which he took up as a slogan, not knowing till I told him what it meant when someone calls you a headache. He was half-sitting on me, I was half dozing and answering his questions and digging his answers off the top of my head while he occasionally got so tripped out it was too much, a mood sort of like Mexico City, languorous and frenetic with volcanic electricity at the same time. The patio was surrounded by citrus trees and orange blossoms were in the air. Stuart had a bunch of clay toys he had made on the table which he said when all put together would be the world of fun.

The discourse got around to grapefruit. I told him it was hard to find a sweet one and we decided that you had to get one that was so sweet it fell asleep and catch it when it was asleep so it couldn't bite, but before it died and went rotten.

I've switched to an Olympia typewriter with French, German, and Spanish diacritical marks which I couldn't think of anything to do with till I realized my middle name is really spelled with an umlaut but I've always spelled it Baetjer since English typewriters don't have umlauts, so now I can write it right for the first time in my life, Alan Bätjer Russo. There. A spectrum spray of lines of descent, English-German (or Dutch)-Italian dusk to dawn the jetstream of time outracing the sun. Joanie Lewis loaned me the typewriter, a fantastic machine with intermediate spacing between the lines! I drove around LA two days with it in the station wagon locking it at every stop, $500 or so machine, intending to hook it up at Montecito but since I can't get back up there till tomorrow I have set it up in the study at Lebrun's, a fantastic house of cast concrete ingrained by the boards used for molds; funny cause I had just been thinking of building a house that way, but maybe with plywood molds. I have to write now to keep from talking myself into a sore throat, every night I get drunk and talk till I wake up with a sore throat; if there's no one around or no one will listen I talk to myself, turning into a compulsive talker, rapafatrat, passed a furniture store in LA called Rapport.

The last few days have been dominated by *Nashville Skyline*. Everywhere I go there's a copy of it people have been playing steadily since it came out. "Lay Lady Lay" seems to be the universal favorite, side 2 band 1; on Mikes Garrard AT60 you can start in there without the top arm on and it will restart.

The latest news flash is Stuart came in and said, "There's a human in the house, what shall we do?" I asked who it was, and he said, "The one with the baby." I said, "Your mother?" and he said, "No, my mother's shadow is the human."

He kept trying to get my beer I told him it's for humans so he went into the kitchen demanding human beer.

At Zuma night before last we got to making up songs. David's wife was stoned so George asked her if she wanted to go to bed and I made up a song that went:
"Talking to a head/about goin' to bed
is like asking an accident what it thinks about the dead."
Then I made one that went:
"Someday from way up beyond the stars
we'll see the light that threw the shadows from our bars
Lord, won't we feel funny then
we'll just sit around spittin' on the old pigpen
Lord, won't we feel funny then."

Turns out his wife is Tamara, or used to be, and changed her name to Helena, accent on the second syllable. As soon as I saw her I thought she looked familiar and she said my name sounded familiar, but her pseudonym threw me. Over the next couple of days I couldn't remember her name and whenever I heard David call her HelEna it jarred, I could tell that wasn't her name. I finally asked her what name she used to go by and she told me she was a junky I knew back in old post-beatnik San Francisco days, went straight and got a new name from Bapak.

Sandy Bull was there the first night when I went to Topanga with George and Suzy and we went to the Ash Grove to hear him play. He was so zonked he could hardly find the strings and had his amplifier hooked up backwards. I asked him if he was doing stuff, he said no, just a little speed. But he is digging a track on his left forearm unlike any I've ever seen; working from the crook toward his hand, the vein gets smaller so it's harder to hit, so each shot takes more hits, with the result that the downstream end is like an open trench, still fresh from the last assault.

Just ate lunch at a Mexican-American restaurant with tangible hyphenation. The menu said ask us about our few daily specials, and had barbecued lamb heads on it. I asked the waitress for it, she called the cook over in Spanish, he said, "What?" I pointed it out on the menu, thinking that would help, but he suddenly became very nearsighted, squinted and said he couldn't see it, so I said it again. I wanted to find out what it was, an adventure in low cuisine, but it was also the cheapest thing on the menu. I was kinda embarrassed to say it again; the guy down the counter got up and sat at a table, the cook smiled apologetically and said he had just sold the last one. I couldn't tell if it was for Chicanos only or if he didn't want to admit they didn't keep a full menu or what. Wonder how much trouble it would have been to ask about the specials—probably would have to draw an Aztec hieroglyph on a napkin.

Strange planes are going over. They're twin-engined, sound like gas, square-tipped wings, dark nacelles and tail, no insignia, fixed landing gear. Didn't know they made 'em like that anymore. Maybe for landing in rough terrain, an Airmobile job? In Topanga the other day an Air Force radar plane, twin-engine, came in low, lower than the limit, and circled the hills. Last few days I've had the feeling they've been around everywhere I go. Like if I kept my eyes on the sky instead of the road, I'd see them. Or they might be just over the horizon, beamed in, you couldn't tell.

Reminds me of the time I went to Baker Beach with Lauren Owen. There was an Army pickup in the parking lot and three guys in civvies and smocks standing around on the beach, like they were waiting for something. In a few minutes two planes come in over the Golden Gate, a C-135 and a four-engine turboprop, both equipped with special electronics gear. They came in as low and slow as they could, heading straight for the beach. Then we saw a parachute open, not a regular one but with a lot of little cup-like chutes, and a roll of silk which unrolled as it fell, attached to the chutes and turning into a long streamer. If there hadn't been any wind it would have fallen right at our feet. But the wind carried it into the trees up the hill. The guys watched it, then got in the pickup and drove off.

The planes circled around for a long time afterward.

FISH IT OUT, MOTHERFUCKER

The other night Dave and I went to a bar-cafe in Summerland to get a hamburger, and for some reason, I can't figure out why, I was carrying my piece and after we ordered I went into the john to chamber a round. Which seems to indicate that the action anticipated which might call for the piece was forthcoming rather than bygone, and I pull it out and pull the slide back but much to my surprise there was already one in the chamber and it ejects up and falls right into the can. The one damn can in the place and it lands in it. Well, I was standing right next to it and now I only have five rounds left but I don't want to lose one so I "screw up my courage" as they used to say, and stick my hand down into the toilet stool for it. Being heavy it had settled clear down to the bottom and I had to stick my arm up to the hilt in this cold contaminated water—disgusting when you think about it. I dried the round off with toilet paper and put it back in, none for the worse. But I just can't figure out why I was packing at the time, can't think of any reason. Maybe it was down at the bottom of the toilet . . .

DOES PLASTIC GROW HERE?

The Strange has been flying so thick and fast lately I can't keep track of it or distinguish what's worth writing down and what isn't. But today something strange happened. It was in a laundromat in Hawthorne, and how I came to be there is a long story, but needn't concern us here. I noticed something sticking out from my arm. My right forearm it was. When I looked I saw that there was a small patch of peeling skin, sunburned or something, and this thing was sticking almost straight out from the area. It was about a third of an inch long and looked like wax, or plastic—wax was the first thing I thought of. I touched it and it felt slick, like wax or plastic. Then I pulled it off, thinking it must be just stuck to my skin, but it peeled like dead skin would. I rolled it between my fingers, and it melted and soaked into my skin, like lotion. Wax doesn't do that, or skin either. Maybe some kind of plastic? The only explanation I can think of is that just before then I had been drinking from a paper cup that must have been coated with wax or plastic, and maybe it somehow got on my arm—pretty unlikely, I admit. It was a strange drink, called an Icee with a choice of Cola or Pink Champagne flavor. I got the Pink Champagne since it wasn't any more, eleven cents, and you get a paper cup full, piled up in fact like a Dairy Queen cone with a sort of ice that comes out of a machine. I asked what kind of drink is this, and was told it's a slush, a very soft ice, and you get a plastic straw and slurp it up in a semi-liquid state. It says on the cup, "The coldest drink in town." There also is a place on the cup where it says to cut it out and save it, but doesn't say what will happen if you do, or if anything will. But the ice was strange; it didn't melt but if you let it sit long enough it would turn to a froth and then evaporate. Plastic ice. Tasted sort of like the red liquid you used to get in wax candies, like rockets, took me way back.

HALF-DRUNK MEANDERINGS

You see in all these TV commercial and billboards where they are trying to get the corn silk, you know, the highlights in the girl's hair, the real Rita McCoy, to shine through the plastic cocoon they've woven to hatch this creature, in a laugh, mostly silent in the ones where the girl is running across fields to embrace her lover, but their ideal is to get it audible, a husky laugh, to break through the husk of corn, which has to be used for the fiber content, dontcha know, but once that laugh has established the aura of hay and hey and hehe, the connection will have been made, husk husky through the silk silky into the milk drink, 100% Class A, won't you try some today, forget about your tired old chromosomes and try Elusive Miracle today! To get it to where you couldn't tell the difference between the real thing and the imitation, and to present it in such terms that you couldn't question it without calling into question the premises on which your concept of reality was based—and come to think of it, what were they? Oh I know, but would it show up on a TV screen just because it was real? No, it has to surface in a spray of electromagnetic rays that can be recorded, right or wrong, you got it on tape "and you know what that's worth." Like trying to get a wad of come to talk about right and wrong. Anyway to get a reflective (and around the hair and eyes, refractive) thing to translate into light waves that can be converted into electromagnetic signals that will be registered in the subject brains as—well, corn silk and honey, milk and the dream gleaming through the teeth, and the beam seeming through the hair, and the morning glory shimmering through the eyes, to get the Affect of meaning without putting in the logically requisite preconditions, as long as the Effect has been recorded, like the idea of collage of film and animation, as long as it comes out with the desired image, who cares where it came from? It's there, and no one can deny it . . . I just looked into the cup from which I have been drinking wine and noticed stains in a pattern like marbled paper with a blonde hair sticking out, probably the cup I used for Supercoffee this morning, the gelatin catching the resins, or vice versa, random sworls spun straight off the matrix where meanings are determined, our minds are like an alley of a city collapsing to the sky . . .

DARK THIRTY

We were going to the motorcycle races in Ventura only for some reason there weren't any and we arrived late and there was no one there except a drunk, fortyish Okie couple. The man says he knows where the races are and recognizing his accent, I asked him what part of Oklahoma you from and he mentioned some towns and I showed them my license plate, delighting the old lady, "Look honeybun, they're from Oklahoma too!" And their story was they were almost out of gas which didn't seem to cover it so I said why don't you go into town, you can't get anything out here, and he said, "We're just waiting till 'dark-thirty', you know what I mean?" Well I didn't and still don't quite; Dave Bearden's brother James says he's heard it lots of times but he works with Okie-types, so guess it's a down-home kind of expression, meaning, at least in that context, late enough to do something that you couldn't do earlier, which apparently was to siphon gas out of someone's tank. I've asked a number of people but none of them except James has ever heard it. Like "copacetic"; when I checked around I found about half the people I asked had heard it and the other half doubted that there was such a word.

AT MONTECITO

This morning I woke up with a sunburn from putting in the garden the day before and a sore throat from talking so much last night. I asked Suzy for some lotion and she said she'd go to the store for some Solarcaine. Meanwhile, she went about fixing breakfast, finally burning the toast, while Jeanine, who turns out to be the old lady of the designer who is building a "spec" house comes in. She volunteers some baby lotion which I finally take her up on after a few rounds with Suzy about Solarcaine, breakfast, and going to the store. Suzy is rubbing the lotion on my back when it develops that the lotion, as well as the bottle, is pink. Suzy says, "Do they make a blue lotion for blue babies?" In the fun that followed it turned out she meant boys—'cause they get blue things instead of pink. But no blue lotion this time, Suzy and no blue babies, please.

Later Suzy and Jeanine went outside to play tennis. I went and watched and tried to play a little. After we were done playing, I noticed a book Jeanine had and found out she is interested in mysticism from somewhat the same angle as me, and we got to talking, soon very seriously, about capital letter words. I almost spelled it 'works'. Later inside we and George and Suzy talked, still more seriously, about and about It. J. was on a good trip and didn't think anything else mattered while I played devil's advocate like on Haight Street, trying to interject some alternate possibilities, sure I was right but hoping against hope she was—we both remained unchanged, but I cannot say I was unswayed. She grabbed me by the arm and said, "We've got to get him out of San Francisco" I told her I was out. But as for the rest—I have a different set of facts to face. Let's face it. But maybe we can each face our own together? Where is Montecito, anyway? And how come I thought today was Wednesday when it's Friday?

As for how I got that sore throat last night, part of what we rapped about was dreams. I recounted several of mine, but the one that cracked us up (keep it light for now)—have you ever written a book on a desk with two cans of Edgeworth Ready-Rubbed tobacco on it?—was about the suit of armor in the night.

I dreamed I was in the Haight Ashbury in 1961—and I was—and

ran into a suit of armor, brass or bronze except around the eyeholes, which were star-shaped, and other trim, which was dark blue or black (color adjustment in my dreams is vague). Actually, I couldn't see inside the armor, but, you know, in dreams you can tell, and I could tell there wasn't anyone much in it. It hit me on the shoulder with the flat of its sword, and I hit it with mine, in some sort of ritual salutation. Then it said, "My father is Dad, and my only brother is Marlboro." I said, half-joking, "Yeah? And who's your grandmother?" and he said, "Huckleberry Finn." How much joking I don't know. Then he told me he was looking for his father and I told him I had just seen a similar suit of armor at Marian Bunnell's place, and maybe that was him. He asked how to get there and I showed him the bus stop. I had to help him get on—guess he'd never ridden a bus before and maybe rusty in the joints—it was quite a hassle and I had to apologize to the driver—a spade—the whole thing was kind of embarrassing with everyone on the bus looking. Marian never said he came by.

JOYCE CHEN AND THE CHICKEN SEEDS

There is a Chinese woman named Joyce Chen, only she pronounces it as in "Chin," who has a cooking program on the educational TV channel. She grew up in the old country and speaks English in the stereotype of the Chinese accent, substituting r's and l's. "Dis hunnaht yir olt ache haf velly strenj fravor, maybe not evellyone rike." Sometimes she catches herself mixing an r and an l and corrects herself—maybe they flash a sign at her. Tonight she showed how to cook some chicken dish, first going into how the Buddhists in China would have to pray— pronounced "play"— to the chicken to absolve themselves of sin, but that we could buy it already killed and not have to worry about it. Then she showed how to cut up a pepper and remove the seeds and white stuff inside. She apparently was trying to make an analogy between removing the white from the pepper and gristle from the chicken and got carried away with the mostly unstated analogy and referred to the seeds as "chicken" seeds.

DON'T-FORGET-A-THING DEPARTMENT

I was reading THE PETER PRINCIPLE and it reminded me of a couple of things. He mentions a trash service that comes by and picks up the contents of locked wastebaskets and grinds them to a pulp. I worked for a while in an office at a defense plant in LA where they had two wastebaskets—one for plain trash, and one for pieces of classified material, so that you had classified trash and unclassified trash.

Later in the book, explaining how to avoid promotions, he suggests leaving desk drawers open, which he says may be sufficient for clerical employees. This reminded me of the time I was working in an office, the first regular job I ever had, and at the end of the day the person who sat in front of me left the carriage of the typewriter off to one side, and the office manager saw it and centered it. The girl who left it off-center wasn't trying to avoid promotion though. She got the job through me and other friends who worked there, but she couldn't type. She just hunted the letters up, painfully slowly, and I would type fast, bang the carriage, talk loudly, frantically trying to drown out that pathetic pecking. The manager, who was a nice guy (she was a cute girl, also) took to giving her work to do which just required handwriting.

SANTA CRUZ AND WHY NOT

Oh, listen I'm drunk but this really did happen and it just serves as a justification for undeserved paranoia but this is how it happened. Me, Dave Bearden, and Judith had gone to the hippy place in Santa Cruz and wanted to make a phone call and they didn't have a pay phone. So we were walking down the street and came to a bar. That is, the sign said it was a bar, and I went in and asked, "Do you have a payphone?" And was told something to the effect of no. Well apparently, they didn't and I left expecting nothing more because it was a middle-class neighborhood bar. But when we got out to the car we heard clicking and scrapings and it was clear the place was being closed for the night. This place was so straight and uptight that I freaked them out so bad just by asking if they had a payphone that they locked the door. They didn't have any reason to think I'd be back. Were they afraid another freak would come in and ask if they had a payphone? I guess that would just be too much for one night so they were calling it quits. I didn't realize.

WIDE-RANGING SPECULATIONS

I was sitting looking out the window at the grey morning mountains wondering what to do, too late to go back to bed, too early to get the paper, late delivery up here, and I thought, I'll write! That's what it's come to, that's where it's always been, I just wrote poetry when my anguish got to where I couldn't work it off any other way but now I'm to that almost all the time, so I'm writing a book, working full time now instead of joypoppin', like I was thinking yesterday after I stopped at a park in the valley and did 47 pushups, new mark for me, just one teenager watching, which helped a little but it was mainly for myself, about pushing myself to the limits, and beyond if possible, which everyone is doing these days one way or another, so that this way, instead of being flabby of spirit and mind, with a vague grey area where you might be capable or might not, you know exactly where your limits are—they're right around your skin, at the next tick of the clock, the next step forward or back. So that THERE becomes HERE— the here and now people like to talk about; it can get a little shitty down at the nitty-gritty but that's life, not a dream anymore and not all a nightmare either—the fear of which is partly what kept people out of this terra incognita, then they got overconfident and took the step you can't retrace, and now they're up against it, literally, do or die, sink or swim, now or never. It's hard. There have been many casualties already and there'll be more. Maybe me. And that's why I'm writing this, partly to write some of what happened and partly to turn this pressure into something else—words on paper in this case, to effect a change of state, which seems to be the name of the game, which phrase was flying thick and fast early 1969 or late 1968, and a possible title that has occurred to me is State-line, U.S.A. The revolutionary state of mind, to bring about a change of state or State, has become standard equipment among the young, spread like a virus through the hippies and the spades. I notice that in Southern Cal. a lot of cars have American flag stickers on their windows, like everyone over 30 or 35 or everyone who works in aerospace industries. In North Dakota, the kids would fly them but not here. The lines are being drawn and crossed, every bluff is being called and every challenge met. Maybe it's going to be, do and die. Everybody has become an absolutist, a fanatic. There's no more room for accommodation, compromise, and a sacrifice of one value for another for the greater good of the majority, it's everything all at once or nothing at all. If they knew what it was like, to have to face the truth, the whole truth, and nothing but the truth, so help you god, 24 hours a day 365 days a year for all eternity they might have second thoughts, but you have to start out with first thoughts before you get seconds. And by then you've chosen up. A one-way world, unless you can unravel the time tapes, and then you just know more, a mixed blessing under some circumstances an outright curse, blessings generally come mixed; as Richard White said, "A little of the devil in every god-made thing."

Pandora's Box has finally been opened, the magnum opus of all history, and now they are finding out they can't get it to shut again. Shoulda read the book but no one listens; we're different, outlaws, renegades from cosmic law, larval superheroes born shot from gun in a sea of napalm, grasping the grail at last and finding it burns, and you can never let it go, you'd have to cut yourself off, at a price greater than death, total LOSS, the work and agony triumph, which we can feel down to our atoms, of the entire life process and more, that it took to get us here, flowing through our hands, focused on now, this our only chance, 5 billion years of groundwork, culminating in us, poor little us suddenly turning into great big us, just how poor or little or great or big remaining open. Partly like this responsibility fell upon us and partly we demanded it, seized it, driven by some demonic or divine force-depending on point of view. Hard to tell the players without a score card. It's hard to get the enemy into a rifle sight.

But Pandora's Box is more than a metaphor, 2000 gallons a day more, flowing into the Santa Barbara Channel from that busted well, and they can't get it to stop. Forces have a way of becoming objectified in some way like that when they are at work. The same thing is happening in people's minds, and everywhere. All concatenating. Everything that seemed impossible before now seeming inescapable. Like going down an Up escalator instead up a Down one. I was always afraid it would never happen and now I'm afraid it will. Feast or famine. I was always afraid I didn't have a circuit breaker and now I'm afraid I do. But it's more or less identical to me. I'll break when it breaks. Trying to push myself to the breaking point physically, maybe because that seems distinct and knowable, while I'm afraid of that other stuff, maybe I can get it to where they meet, typical American and human approach. Probably very effective and very dangerous.

I suppose the next step will be an underground nuclear test that will break the earth's mantle and the molten core will come out. If they can't handle a little oil . . . then it'd be like the Beatles song, "Your insides are out, your outsides are in."

Curiosity killed the cat, they say, man HAD to find out what was in that big black box, that's part of the process, and it had to happen here and now. It's been relatively easy up till now, now the hard part begins, controlling these forces being released, or being destroyed by them. Within and without. So this is why we were called together here . . .

Human life, both from the aspect of the earth and the aspect of the universe, regarding both as organisms desiring continued life, must have some of the characteristics of cancer. Uncontrolled, limitless and pointless (in terms of the superorganism) reproduction, destruction of other organs, i.e. life forms, injection of toxins, chemical and atomic, into the system, etc. If anybody is overseeing this show, I should think they would want to shut it down. But maybe for them too it's a Pandora's Box; once they created man the fat was in the fire, like the horror shows where a robot runs amok, man may be like that in the universe, the earth like a searing sore, capable of blowing the whole thing and they can't figure out how to turn it off because it's radioactive. If the earth blew, the solar system might, and then maybe a chain reaction throughout the galaxy and on—is the freed atom Antichrist risen? Is that how we're going to go out, through the roof? Is the Phoenix going to rise from the ashes of all creation? Is that what we came here for, to arrange our own cremation, to triumph over an existence that directly? People have been trying to be so subtle till now, no one thought of the direct approach. "Let's shoot our way to freedom," as Bill Gaines said. Phew. Things sure are getting heavy, as they say, an increasingly relevant and inescapable word, much as I hate the snobbery I associate with it. Is this a heavy book? I can't worry about things like that, not expecting there to be any posterity to judge. There may be some advanced models among the young that could handle such a situation, but the elders are trying to wrap it up before the kids get their hands on it. Time element. Wires getting pulled, tighter and tighter. By whom? Friend or foe? Are we using or being used? Both inextricably at once? If the Gnostic theory is correct, the force impelling us to destruct is benign, desiring to free us from our prison and return to our heavenly home. Otherwise, the whole thing might be a big mistake . . . well que sera, sera. Ha ha.

AT JEAN'S

The neighbor kid just knocked on the door, ostensibly to ask if Nicole was home, but really to find out if they had moved or who I was, or what. Too many neighbors around here, you can hear them walking overhead, like cockroaches, scraping against the walls. Like cockroaches going down the courtyard between this building and the one facing it about 15 feet away. Living in a house spoils you so apartments make you feel like you're living on the bottom of a three-tier sheep truck. The sheep on the top are clean, the ones in the middle are pretty funky, and the ones on the bottom are barely recognizable.

Anyway, this kid reminded me of the time I was here on Halloween and some neighbor kids came in to go trick or treating with Nicole, and one was just budding, 11 or so, and she saw George with his beard and said, "I'm going to be a hippie when I grow up." I figured she was wearing a training bra and said, "Hippies don't wear bras, nya nya." She consulted in whispers with one of the other girls and told me, "They do too, and anyway it's none of your business." Later she said Jean didn't have to go with them because they had two mothers already, and I said, "That's probably what they tell all the mothers." She said, "Aw, he's crazy, let's go."

This was shortly after my mind-breaking acid trip at Topanga. I had just recovered from it enough to get out of the house. I got on a manic trip and was rolling around giggling and making remarks such as, "You know Einstein said he couldn't believe God played dice with the cosmos, well actually the cosmos plays God with dice." I'd gone sort of a neo-gnostic on the take, where the God of the Bible, or Jehovah anyway, is only the Demiurge and in some ways the devil. Judging by the Book of Job, God and the devil collaborated on some experiments. It's a toss-up who won that one. I guess everybody got theirs.

NEW WORLD BLUES

A couple of days ago with everything getting so uptight at Montecito, I conceived a nationwide plan of split-second precision that would get me out of it so neatly. Mike and Joannie were coming up Saturday and going back Sunday. My parents were going to drive from Tulsa to Rochester, leaving Monday. So I was going to go back with Mike and Joannie, and drop the typewriter off at Topanga (this is Jean's), go to the LA airport with Mike, (he works right across the road from it), fly to Tulsa, and go east with the folks. Joan might be in Buffalo, which is right near Rochester; or I might just stay in Tulsa, with the whole house to myself for a change. Anyway, I wouldn't have to get onto Suzie's food trips. Anyway, it's free of course, but you have to pay for everything somehow, like sometimes you have a choice between paying with time or money, like at a bar you get service while at a wine tasting room you can't be too demanding; same with restaurants and breadlines. You pay at a breadline by standing in line. It seems like to get anything I have to beg or impose myself or do something distasteful. Lately, I've had to keep apologizing for myself and I'm pretty sick of it. That's about all I want money for, so I can live without doing that shit.

Well, I got to Topanga but couldn't make up my mind about leaving, and would have had to call my folks then, so I ended up doing what I always do when I can't decide, which is nothing. I went down to the little store in Topanga and there was a notice on the wall that went: "$50 reward for my lost memory, 4 years of my life notes lost." Some poor freak had lost his poetry/notebook at the Renaissance Fair and was advertising to get it back. It ended with a desperate plea like "Have a heart."

Saw an ad today for Contempo Space Ranges, that's what they call stoves these days. Got those New World Blues.

THE TEA BAG FIASCO

In some ways, my whole life the last ten years seems to be divided into chapters which each begin with going to San Francisco and end with leaving it. Like the tide, or sunrise and sunset. One time I went back after being gone for a long time, came in on the Bay Bridge, my favorite way of entering San Francisco, because it all looms up in front of you at once, the fabled hills, the wretched fog, the electric sign saying 54 degrees, etc. I was hungry and went to the Lucky Grill, a Chinese hash house on 66th Street in skid row. It's the cheapest restaurant in town. I'm something of an expert on cheap San Francisco restaurants.

I went in, prices had gone up a nickel, and there was this "denizen" there who was claiming that the waiter had poured coffee on his tea bag. He wouldn't shut up about it; he was drunkenly indignant and seemed to be demanding justice from above, or maybe only that this injustice be registered. "Look there, he put coffee on my tea bag." The waiter told him to shut up but he wouldn't and finally, the waiter pulled out a billy club-like thing from behind the counter and rapped him on the hand with it. Chinese waiters in skid row joints are ready for trouble. It was sort of like a schoolteacher disciplining an unruly kid, but maybe he thought it was bad for business to have someone putting down the service like that, and maybe it outraged his professional pride. Of course, I don't know whether he really did pour coffee on his tea bag or not.

HAUNTED HOUSE

Suzy just said, "Put that in your book and smoke it!" They just switched typewriters on me, turns out the electric was Bob Easton's; don't know if I can keep up with myself on this manual, the automatic key came in handy cause I make so many mistakes and changes.

This house is alive in several worlds at once. Houses come to life backwards, starting out dead and gradually coming alive; for instance, termites, cockroaches, and ants begin to live in them and eat them, but the house is eating them at the same time, a change of state, transformation of matter into energy, dead matter into living, but both going both directions—forwards and backwards at the same time. Coming to life backwards and dying forwards and vice versa. And in four dimensions too at least, living color you bet, as the house acquires a personality and gets imprinted astrally by its occupants; this one is obviously haunted, noises on the stairs and that sort of thing, but they're harmless ghosts that have long since made peace with their world. They mind their own business and you mind yours.

ZOOFAGOUS PAINT

I just found this picture in a copy of Mahan's *Civil Engineering*. It was in the section on "Timber." The book was published in 1884 by John Wiley and Sons, 15 Astor Place, New York, a new edition of a work originally published in 1873. It apparently was very up-to-date at the time, with the results of the latest experiments on the strength of steel, etc. The last item in the index is "Zoofagous paint," p. 102, which term was coined by Mr. Mallet to describe a kind of paint to "preserve zincked iron both from corrosion and fouling in sea water." The directions for making it are: "To 100 lbs. of a mixture of drying linseed oil, red lead, sulphate of barytes, and a little spirits of turpentine, add 20 lbs. of the oxychloride of copper and 3 lbs. of yellow soap and common rosin, in equal proportions, with a little water." The purpose of Zoofagous paint is to keep marine plants and animals from attaching themselves to a metal surface, on account of its poisonous qualities.

This book at one time belonged to J.A. Floyd, mining engineer, Trinidad, Colorado.

BURNT POLAROID

Meanwhile, back at the ranch: Suzy just threw a Rouault in the fireplace. She was taking Polaroid pictures in the living room, George and Bob Easton were there. I walked into the room and leaned against the doorway and snap, she had taken our picture before I realized it. It came out very dark, but George looked like a Rouault crucifixion; it had a somber brooding magic to it but she thought it was ruined. I was just starting to exclaim how great it was when the phone rang and she went to answer it. I left the room and when I came back asked her where it was and she said she had just thrown it into the fireplace. I pulled it out—it was just singed and faded at one end, but it was the top, with George's face gone. If it had landed the other way around it still could have been saved, but we lost it by a quarter-inch too little and a second too late. There is a big book of Rouault on the table in that room that got on the film but we were out of synch—that's how the picture came in, and that's how it went out. Easy come easy go in this world the same as the next.

I told her I was putting it in the book so Suzy came in and said (it's the day before Easter): "Are you gonna be rabid? You gonna be a basket case?" Gettin' in her licks.

RUMINATIONS ABOUT ACID AND ALL THAT

One thing that acid conclusively proved, as far as I'm concerned anyway, is that the jewel is in the lotus, but you can't get there from here. Which I suppose is some kind of advance in the state of abstract knowledge, since there had been some disagreement about the point, but it didn't make me feel any better.

"Feel any better" isn't a very good reason to take acid. It might backfire.

I finally reached the goal I was seeking, taking acid and other things. But it didn't work out the way I expected. I was seeking the essence of human life—some mystical, spiritual element that set it above everything, the supernal. I always took it for granted that it existed, and that it was just a matter of finding out what it was. But my investigations concluded that there wasn't any such thing, which had never even occurred to me as a possibility. The last time I took acid, it was "revealed" to me that all human processes, including the highest, like Joy, followed natural laws, which were basically the same as those that governed all other processes, that they were all reducible to formulas of Chemistry and Physics. I'm not so sure now, but at the time (the last time I took acid) I could see it right down to the atomic level, like watching a movie through an electron microscope, so many milligrams per molecule per millisecond equaling so much love, god, truth, etc. I was convinced. Needless to say, this wasn't the show I had come to see, not at all. Sort of like Congress appointing a committee to investigate pornography and they spend a lot of time and money, and when they produce the report, Congress doesn't like the way it comes out and screams their heads off.

Now every acid trip is partial and consequently distorted to some extent. This is the basic flaw of acid. You just see on each trip, one thing, or one side or aspect of things, but in such a way that it appears to be the whole thing, or so important that other things don't matter. Even the experience of unity is partial and one-sided, because unity isn't the whole thing, either—things aren't one unified, harmonious whole. Harmony is a universal principle, but so is discord and strife. Everything has an equal opposite, which makes a truth, by itself, an untruth. Of course, you can drop acid again and see another side of things, but it never adds up to the whole thing. I finally realized why you can't see the whole thing at once: because it doesn't exist!

Man has to complete the circle. Reality is incomplete. It lacks something which it is our job to provide. The reason we can't see this is that we're standing in the place we are looking for. I lost my youth, my health, my friends, my lovers, everything, just finding out that I hadn't even got started; that I'd been barking up the wrong tree all my life; that what is needed isn't to see, or find, or know something that already exists, but to do and be something that doesn't exist yet. What this would entail is so vast, and difficult, and terrifying, that I don't have the strength or courage to even contemplate just what it would be. I'm tired and scared. I guess someone else will have to carry the ball. If my experiences could be of some use to someone else, I guess it wouldn't have all been wasted, but people don't like my revelations and the conclusions I draw from them and I can see why. I don't care much for them myself. They're hard and hard to take. I'm just stuck with them.

As for the long-term picture, I can't offer much hope. Not if you're looking for a pot of gold at the end of the rainbow. The reason there isn't a pot of gold is that there isn't any end of the rainbow. There isn't any end of anything. If you did get to the summit of this level of existence and transcended it, you wouldn't find yourself on cloud nine. You would be in another world, higher than this one, but governed by the same basic laws, just translated to another level. The same cosmic principles would be at war there too, and you would have to choose up sides and start fighting all over again, only the enemy would be much more powerful. While the rewards would be greater, so would be the pain. And so on, through all the levels of existence. Not much to look forward to if you're looking for eternal rest. Maybe they give you a breather between worlds, or maybe the new one is a pleasant change, at first.

So I conclude that mysticism is a trap, a trick to get us to keep playing the game by offering an illusory reward. So the Buddhists, who were a jump ahead of the westerners, tried to cop out into non-being. I learned from Amanita muscaria that there is a world of non-being, but it's a whole lot worse than any level of existence. It's sort of a negative universe where you would be a bit out of place, and I don't think there's any way out: no exit. I just don't know what to tell you, folks. In the words of the Preacher, "In much 'wisdom' is much grief," and "He that increaseth knowledge increaseth sorrow."

Still, as long as we're here, I guess we might as well give it one more try. Maybe something will turn up . . .

MIDNIGHT OIL

So here I am burning the midnight oil. 1:10 oil burning habit if you know the time lapse pardon the typos not called on trade oil burning habit burning the candle at both ends middle top see what happens when they meet you see this typewriter's had extra banks of keys psyche you out place your fingers wrong kace abd every letter comes out wrong I guess I'm giving you a running demonstration of what I mean decipher this you're ready for NSA cryptography psychic training courses they say Hitler had lip readers deaf folks in Istambul through telescopes pathetic pre-radar which the Germans scorned and lost the war blew it had it won and overreached well I'm so blotto I cant type write I mean right haven't been at it for days you can see how many sore throats I've written my way out of, off that manic trip, some days couldn't even get hardly my chin off my chest these errors are partly having my fingers on the wrong bank of keys extended keyboard you see start wrong and you end wrong

So Suzy rolled her car at point Mugu hauled to Port Hueneme only deep water port between LA and SF didn't need that deep a channel for the VW of course went down to see if I should buy it two bills is all they are offering plus 58 $ tow and storage goes up two a day would have got it but the windshield looks intractable that afternoon after so much hassle to borrow a car went down and couldn't decide, then that night Suzy says the boys at Vista VW offered her 5 bills could have resold it for a profit which I sorely need, just one to many times behind Night before last Dumpy left here and got so drunk it was when we killed that qt of vodka etc. he passed out alongside the freeway got hauled in and snowed them with his badge had to drink coffee and function lady nihht working it off in the squad room in SB.

Suzy and I got outrageous saw the Beatles on the Glen Campbell show doo get back fought and spat all night Italian style for jollies Jeanine didn't pick up on it got bugged like they tried to quiet Bob and me during the show and I told S. "don't shush me" and raised my hand in a mock slap-cocked position, hillbilly joke, J. was quiet, S. says its her mood three days a week, she's always seemed so larky before, guess I freaked her, there you see, it was too good to be true, she genteel and would never understand deep down-home dirt, S and I finally came to shouts, I'm too drunk to write all that's piled up, start the day drinking to get up and taper off on beer till I'm flush with the deck and this is what comes out. Back to the drawing room gents, more brandy and cigars and sweep the girls under the carpet. Lush fucks me up too much now and my gums are rotting, got so pissed off the other night because Dumpy and me brought a chick here and she balled him thot it was arranged with me, got falling down drunk on beer, something wrong.

```
        So hsere I em here bu;rningin the midnight oil  1;10 pxxnszpm oil burning
                                     Time
habit k ag if you know the txxxxxxxxxxx lapse pardppn the typos not calleed
tj t om tje trade d oil burninng habit  burning the candle st both ends middle
x tpp see wdt jappens  when they meet you see this typewritere had extra
banks of keys psycbe you out place your fibgers urobg  kace abd every letter
comes out wrong  I guess I'm giving you a runninng demonstration of what I
mean decipher this youre ready for NSA cryptograohy d psychic training course
they say Hitler had lip readers sixx deaf folks in Istambul through telescopes
pathetic pre-radar which the Germans scorned and lost the war blew it had it
won and overreached well I'm so blotto I cant type write I mean right havent
been at it for days you can see how many sore throats I've writtem my way out
of, off that manic trip, some days couldnt even get hardly my chin offmy
chest these errors are partly having my fingers on the wrong bank of keys
extended keyboard you see start wrgng abd you end wrong

    Oo Duzy rolled her car at point Mugu hauled to Port Hueneme only deep water
port between LA and SF didnt need that deep a channel for the vw of course
went down to see Idf I should buy it 2 bills is all they are offering plus 58
$ tow and storage goes up 2$a day would have got it but the windshield looks
intractable that afternoon after much hassle to borrow a car went down and
couldnt decide, then that night Suzy says the boys at Vista VV offered her
5 bills could have resold it for a profit which I sorely need, just one to many
i times behind Night before last Dumpy left here and got so drunk it was when
we killed that qt of vodka etc he passed out alongside the freeway got hauled in
and snowed them with his badge had to drink coffee and functbon lady nihht
working it off in the squad room in SB.
suzy and I got outragious say the Beatles on the Glen Campbell show doo get
bacl fought and spat all night Italian style for jollies Jeanine didnt pick
up on it got bugged like they tried to quiet Bob and me during the show and I
told S. "dont shush me"and raised my hand in a mock slap-cocked position, hill
billy joke, J. was quiet, S. says its her mood 3 days a week, she always seemed
do lsrky before, guess I freaked her, there you see, it was  too good to be
true, shes genteel and would never understand deep down home dirt, S and I
finallly came to shouts,I'm too drunk to  write all thats piled up, start the
day drinking coffee to get up and taper off on beer till I'm flush with the
deck and this is what comes out. Back to the drawing room gents, more brandy and
cigars and sweep the girls under the carpet. Lush fucks me up too much now
and my gums are rotting, got so pissed off the other night because Dumpy and
me brought a chick here and she balled him thot it was arranged with me, got fLLING
down drunk on beer, somtehing wrong.
```

Midnight Oil original typescript

Alan Russo and Jean Meyer, 1965

LOVE
LETTERS

—

"Savage as nightmare
the climax rhythms climb and glide
teeth of landslide, might of moving paw
octopus vise twisting the continent into focus
the lion faces the unicorn"

— ALAN RUSSO, "BOARDMAN STREET POEM"

ALAN'S INCARNATED MUSE
TO JEAN MEYER, FROM DION WRIGHT

"It takes courage to be a poet."

— ANDREI CORDESCU

Dear Jean,

One of the benefits of age is the clarifying of the past. I wonder if you have ever apprehended yourself as a Muse? It seems to me that you were desired by many men, particularly artists, and that all these men defined themselves by the way in which they related to you. I doubt that many of them ever saw it that way, but I have to suppose that you did. Your nature, and how men responded to it, were equivalent to registering their characters in a mirror, in which an accurate reflection was reflected back at those who had wits to see it.

This can't have been a very congenial karma for you to own, and must have propelled you into a mode of consciousness in which you wondered if any one of the suitors saw you for yourself. I guess Alan did.

I'm struck by the metaphor of him playing Odysseus to your Penelope, something of a stretch for the lack of heroic circumstances, maybe, but it has its point: he the wanderer in strange lands while you maintained at the hearth, and dealt with the suitors. Alan, too, seemed to be a quasi-mythological creature, and I'm certain that his projected symbol, something like a collision of Adonis and the Minotaur, were as difficult for him to emerge from behind as yours as Juno must have been.

Life, and having it, are the prime mystery, I suppose, and right behind that one comes the mystery of personal incarnation, as in who am I, and why am I as I am? Eventually the blessed, or at least the insightful and fortunate, will imagine an idea about it. In my experience, seeing who one is does not change anything, except in some cases to make the native in question decide to improve, as well as possible, the raw materials found within.

This is hard work, and by no means a sure success when beginning. Even toward the end, most persons who have set to work to anneal their characters will achieve only partial success, except for an occasional saint, maybe. All of this is what leads me to think that reincarnation, however it works, is likely. Cause and effect rule everywhere in the perceived Universe, and it's only ignorance or arrogance or both that can suppose a human being might be exempt from the basic operating rules of the entire Cosmos.

It's treacherous ground to get onto, describing perceptions and how correct they might be, especially when the persuasions of gender come into it. At first sight I saw you as a living version of the iconic Botticelli woman in his painting, *The Birth of Venus*. You had had a prosaic birth and childhood, but they were private within you. You burst onto the counter-cultural Art scene without preamble, as this fully-formed Thalia, knocking every man coo-coo by the force of your beauty. You were a mirror from which men had their characters reflected back at them, but your part was to remain surprised at the impact of your image. Your inner reality was beside the point to all these smitten men, except Alan, and they only related to you as an ethereal image they wanted to ravish. That must have been frustrating and boring.

I'm glad that you found whatever you found with Alan, and he with you. I presume that your transactions were riddled with compromise, Alan being who he was, so glued into that spiritual tar pit. You probably extricated him from that more than he might otherwise ever have been.

You both worked off a lot of karma. I hope for another chapter for you in another world, the better world you both deserved.

— Dion Wright

FRAGMENTS OF LOVE LETTERS
TO JEAN, FROM ALAN

Dear Jean,

Too much too early, too little too late. Looking back over what I've written it's too late to retract anything. I've been meaning to write you, but, well, I guess it's what they call circumstances—in other words I didn't do it.

I love you so much that it's like a disease I can't control.

Jean I mean that my love for you is such that if it was an arrow aimed for your heart I would release it even though I knew it would kill you because we needed it—Well, that ain't lovin' you, baby. No. I want you alive. I swear I love you like it was a plague—something from a previous lifetime. Jean, I'm drunk and I guess crazy, but *in vino veritas*. O what a bunch of shit. I'm trying to say something.

Let W. B. Yeats say it...

How many loved you with love false or true
But one man loved the pilgrim soul in you
And murmur, a little sadly, how love fled
And paced among the mountains overhead
And hid his head amongst a cloud of stars.

I want to put where I am where you are. If I come to California it would just be to see you, dearie.

Incidentally, bitch, I pronounced "amulette" right, it's not "ahmulette." You threw that right in when I was trying to say something important and difficult—but maybe I was embarrassing you. As for "amenities," my dictionary is strangely silent. Mixmatch of whatever incongruent strains, I love you. Even the bitch has her strangely perfumed appeal. I would rather kiss your ass than hold Jane Fonda's hand. I think, Christ, maybe we deserve each other. Well, godspeed the force within you and without you. Don't die and quit correcting my pronunciation.

End, but not of love.
A man of no fortune,
but with a name to come.

— Alan

EPITAPH
TO ALAN, FROM JEAN

Memories of you.

I'm not sure how these personal bits could inform your work, and I can hear one of your pithy comments about an ex-girlfriend/ recovering alcoholic as a reliable source. I wish I knew your version.

In January 1960 I met Mike and Jane Lewis in San Francisco, and a short time later I moved into Oak Street and met you. Mike is the only one left with a good memory. He could write *The Oak Street Quartet* for all of us. I remember you on the couch in the living room—there when we went to work—there when we came home—there in the evenings—there most of the weekends. When did you write? You did bestir yourself to collect codeine cough syrup for us all, and you were a great peyote preparer. What a chef! It's a wonder one of us didn't fall out the window. We'd get high and hang over the sill and try to catch sight of one of Dion's iguanas he left down in the garden. What innocent pastimes. Those first few years we were all over the City, Big Sur, up and down the coast—visiting, crashing, actually moving in somewhere, whatever—you and I always kept in touch.

By 1964 George, Nicole, and I were living in Redondo Beach, where you roomed with us. This was probably your most domestic couple of years. George was usually off chasing skirts and being ever so busy 'being an artist'; too busy for the mundane running of a household—that he left to you and me. You and me day in and day out doing the very ordinary stuff of life, fixing Nicole's toys, painting her room, gardening, and re-doing the living room for me, and bickering, bickering—you could be such a nag! But since you did everything for me, and were on the whole such an interesting company, and funny, even in your foul humor—it was wonderful to put up with you. You and Mike, earlier in Santa Barbara, were the real househusbands—in all ways but in my bed. And when did you write? Up in your attic room? Then George announced that he was leaving me to go live with Suzie somebody. You told me that your turn had come and that

I would feel so much better if I slept with you. I was too much of a mess to start something, and you could see how distressed I was. So you gallantly bundled me into your car and drove us to Ojai. We spent the day in the Oak Grove listening to Krishnamurti. I remember a full moon and crying on your shoulder all the way home. What a waste of moonlight. You helped me pack up, Nicole and I went up to Victoria to stay with Sheila Steele, and you went back to San Francisco. I saw you a few times before I went to Europe, and a year or so later, when I came back, we finally had our little love affair.

We were both living in the Haight then, just a few blocks apart. We kept our separate flats, and you would come and spend the night. Your body was like a Greek statue in those days, but I never saw you work out—nor did I ever see you write, ever. You were a good lover, passionate and attentive, but no cuddler. In the mornings you were up and dressed and out the door. I felt that you were embarrassed that you had been so naked and vulnerable, and you needed to recollect yourself. Or you had to go score. Probably both. After a few months, I got a job and moved to Santa Monica. I'm not sure how long you stayed before going back to Tulsa. We wrote; we always kept in touch.

It was a long time before we saw each other again, about 1975. I was living in Santa Barbara with my second husband, and you came to town with Sue and Howard Crawford and Dumpy, and stayed for a while. I also remember visiting you in a scruffy downtown hotel. This was some time after you'd lived with Mike and Joan in San Diego, and Thea had died. The Blue Meanies were really getting to you. You could still sparkle and spout some of your pithy one-liners, but you were bending under the weight of your deep, entangled angst. Also, the Doors-of Perception-Drug-Days were almost over. Too expensive, for one thing. Now you were just medicating with cheap wine. Sue and I were both spoken for—so once again you could profess your unrequited loves. I think that you made a career out of your lost Lenore's. By the time I was divorced and was free again, you were too deep in the bottle to see beyond it. Somehow you made it back to Tulsa, and there were letters, and you took to those late, late-night calls. Always we kept in touch.

Too bad I didn't keep all your letters. Forty years' worth would make a book by themselves. I've just come across two in which you are professing your love for me in such a YOU way that I can hear your voice . . . How many could call me a bitch as a term of endearment? Only you. Reading them again made me laugh out loud—and sigh a little, too. A year later I got sober—hospital, AA, therapy—and typical of the newly converted, I tried to enlist you, too. It worked—on and off. Here's a small pile of notes from you telling me of some of your battles—wins and defeats—flirting with getting cleaned up. Life was always so hard for you, and we always kept in touch.

You came out to see me for the last time around 1985. You were sober the whole time, but having a hard go. You were put out that I wouldn't go to bed with you, but really Alan, you were going about the house unbathed, unshaven, slogging along in a Thorazine shuffle imitation, doing everything you could to be unappealing. You were never like that, What were you playing at? One day after the mailman came you started yelling at me that I was getting it on with him. Poor dear, I'd had enough, and asked you to leave. You had always been in my life. I never thought for a moment that I would never see you again. So you were back in Tulsa, and even though we were miffed with each other, we always kept in touch.

You went through an aliens-among-us-UFO-sightings period. Those calls were hard. You'd get mad if I didn't agree with you, and I didn't. You were getting more and more negative about everything. I was having my own struggles keeping my head above water and didn't have the strength to swim for us both. The letters turned into postcards, and the calls were months and months apart. Sometimes when Mike came to visit we'd call you—those difficult years when you took care first of your father, and then your mother, as they ailed and finally died. Then, later on, we'd call your sister, and get your latest number. It became harder and harder to track you down, but we always stayed in touch.

And then we didn't. How did that happen? It was getting to be like talking to a black hole when I did get you—so I started putting it off. And you—was it too hard to talk to sunny California when you were in such a dark space? I'd think of you now and then, and wonder how you were but didn't contact you right then. You'd always be there, right? And time went by, and by and by someone told me you had died. "Oh." That's all I could say. A lifetime with you, and poof, you're gone. And now the sadness sets in. And great remorse that I wasn't a better friend; that I didn't continue to try to cheer you up—at least let you know that somebody cared about you.

So this is my last letter to you, and all I can come up with is a sketchy chronology. I wish I could sing you a grand eulogy. If I had your way with words I could tell you how much I admired your intellect, your profundity, your reverence for beauty—how I grieved for your soul-agony, your entrenched sadness, your loneliness— how I was touched by your strength, your gentleness, your many kindnesses—how I enjoyed your wit, your unique slant on things, even your nagging me.

Alan, you delighted me. You made me laugh. But you were never mean to me. You never made me cry. Until now.

Goodbye, my dear Eeyore.

Love, Jean

Alan Russo, Lompoc, California, 1977
Photograph by James Bearden

ABOUT THE AUTHOR

Alan Bätjer Russo was born May 25, 1938 in Auburn, New York. His parents were Salvatore and Erna Bätjer Russo, and he had an older sister named Terry. In 1942 the family relocated to Hamilton Square, New Jersey and in 1948 moved to Wichita, Kansas.

Something of a prodigy, Alan graduated from high school early and enrolled at Wichita University, where he took classes taught by Professor William Nelson, who encouraged his interest in the literary arts. He published several of his poems and a notable translation from Latin of *Pervigilium Veneris* (The Vigil of Venus) in campus literary magazines. While at WU, he befriended members of the local literary and artistic scene—including fellow students Glenn Todd, Justin Hein, Charles Plymell, Roxie Powell, and Robert Branaman.

In 1955 he edited an anthology published by Plymell called *Poet's Corner*. *Poet's Corner #2* followed in 1959. In 1960, Plymell published a sheaf of Alan's poems with the title *The Locked Man*. That same year Alan moved to San Francisco to be followed by several of his Wichita cohorts. He subsequently published poems in a number of literary magazines and chapbooks created by Plymell, Bob Branaman, and David Omer Bearden. Alan spent the next two decades primarily in California but with stints in the mid-west and New York. He had a variety of jobs including staff-member at the *San Francisco Oracle* in 1967-1968. He also began working sub-rosa on a sequence of prose writings that would comprise an "autobiographical novel" he called *State Line*.

By the 1980's he was living full-time in Tulsa, Oklahoma where Salvatore and Erna Russo had moved to in 1964. He supported himself by driving a cab, then eventually became his parents' full-time caregiver. His friend Justin Hein visited him in Tulsa on three separate occasions, and in 1991 Alan traveled to Wichita to be reunited with Charles Plymell and Bob Branaman for an event at the Wichita Art Museum. After his parents passed away in 1998 and 1999, he fell ill himself in 2002 and spent his final six months in a Tulsa nursing home.

He passed on May 24, 2003. On his death certificate, his occupation read "Poet and Cab Driver."

DR BEAUCHAMP
CREDIT DENTIST
FEATURING
SODIUM
PENTOTHAL

Now if it was nitrous oxide I'd go for it...

BOOKS BROUGHT OUT BY
ROSACE PUBLICATIONS

ANTHOLOGIES

SMOKING MIRROR (1974) Chapbook

LE FEU DU CIEL (1965) Chapbook

BY DAVID OMER BEARDEN

THE THING IN PACKY INNARD'S PLACE (2019) Novel

THE MENTAL TRAVELER (2018) Poetry Book

REDRESS (1983) Chapbook

THE ROSACE IN A STAR CHAMBER (1981) Chapbook

SO LONG AT THE FAIR & DOWN AT THE PALOMINO CLUB
& OTHER POEMS (1976) Chapbook

BY ALAN BÄTJER RUSSO

STATE LINE (2021) Collected Poems and Other Writings

DOMINION AND OTHER POEMS (1977) Chapbook

BY DION WRIGHT

ZIP AREA (Forthcoming) Correspondence Book

TEMPUS FUGITIVE (2016) Memoir of the 60s

LEARN MORE AT
WWW.ROSACEPUBLICATIONS.COM

Made in the USA
Columbia, SC
07 June 2022

61440534R00174